In recognition of those who suffered
from the tragedies of September 11, 2001,
this document is dedicated to all who
have given their lives in an effort
to make this world a safer place.

NFPA 25

Standard for the

Inspection, Testing, and Maintenance of Water-Based Fire Protection Systems

2002 Edition

This edition of NFPA 25, *Standard for the Inspection, Testing, and Maintenance of Water-Based Fire Protection Systems,* was prepared by the Technical Committee on Inspection, Testing, and Maintenance of Water-Based Systems and acted on by NFPA at its November Association Technical Meeting held November 10–14, 2001, in Dallas, TX. It was issued by the Standards Council on January 11, 2002, with an effective date of January 31, 2002, and supersedes all previous editions.

This edition of NFPA 25 was approved as an American National Standard on January 31, 2002.

Origin and Development of NFPA 25

The first edition of NFPA 25 was a collection of inspection, testing, and maintenance provisions that helped ensure the successful operation of water-based fire protection systems. NFPA 25 was developed as an extension of existing documents such as NFPA 13A, *Recommended Practice for the Inspection, Testing, and Maintenance of Sprinkler Systems,* and NFPA 14A, *Recommended Practice for the Inspection, Testing, and Maintenance of Standpipe and Hose Systems,* which have successfully assisted authorities having jurisdiction and building owners with routine inspections of sprinkler systems and standpipes. These documents have since been withdrawn from the NFPA standards system. NFPA 25 became the main document governing sprinkler systems as well as related systems, including underground piping, fire pumps, storage tanks, water spray systems, and foam-water sprinkler systems.

This document provides instruction on how to conduct inspection, testing, and maintenance activities. It also stipulates how often such activities are required to be completed. Requirements are provided for impairment procedures, notification processes, and system restoration. This type of information, where incorporated into a building maintenance program, enhances the demonstrated favorable experience of all water-based fire protection systems.

The second edition incorporated several improvements that reflected the initial experience with the standard. A new chapter was added that addresses obstructions in pipe as well as appropriate corrective actions.

The third edition refined testing requirements and frequencies and provided additional guidance for preplanned impairment programs. The document scope was expanded to include marine systems.

This fourth edition continues to refine testing frequencies for water-flow devices and evaluation of the annual fire pump test data. This edition also includes additional information regarding evaluation and test methods for microbiologically influenced corrosion (MIC).

Technical Committee on Inspection, Testing, and Maintenance of Water-Based Systems

Kenneth W. Linder, *Chair*
Industrial Risk Insurers, CT [I]

Clement J. Adams, Chubb Group of Insurance Companies, PA [I]

Gary S. Andress, LMG Property Engineering, WI [I]

Michael J. Bosma, The Viking Corporation, MI [M]
Rep. National Fire Sprinkler Association

John K. Bouchard, Palmer & Cay, Inc., MA [I]

Eugene A. Cable, U.S. Department of Veterans Affairs, NY [U]

Walter A. Damon, Schirmer Engineering Corporation, IL [SE]
Rep. TC on Fire Pumps

Manuel J. DeLerno, S-P-D Industries Inc., IL [M]
Rep. Illinois Fire Prevention Association

James M. Fantauzzi, North East Fire Protection Systems Inc., NY [IM]
Rep. American Fire Sprinkler Association, Inc.

James M. Feld, Feld Engineering, CA [SE]

Patricia J. Fisher, Boston Properties, MA [U]

Gary Gagnon, Alcan, Inc., Canada [U]

John K. Gillette, III, Denton Fire Department, TX [E]
Rep. International Fire Code Institute

Christopher M. Goddard, AstraZeneca Inc., DE [U]

Jon T. Harris, National Foam, Inc., PA [M]

William C. Harris, Fairbanks Morse Pump, KS [M]

Stephen R. Hoover, Stephen R. Hoover Associates, IL [SE]

Larry Keeping, Vipond Fire Protection, Canada [IM]
Rep. Canadian Automatic Sprinkler Association

John Lake, Marion County Fire/Rescue, FL [E]

George E. Laverick, Underwriters Laboratories Inc., IL [RT]

Russell B. Leavitt, TVA, Fire & Life Safety, Inc., CA [U]
Rep. The Home Depot

Carl A. Maurice, Fairfax County Fire/Rescue Department, VA [E]

Frank L. Moore, Moore Pump and Equipment, Inc., MS [IM]

John D. Munno, Constellation Energy Group, MD [U]
Rep. Edison Electric Institute

M. G. Myers, Myers Risk Services, Inc., PA [SE]

Richard Oliver, Oliver Sprinkler Company, Inc., PA [IM]
Rep. National Fire Sprinkler Association

Eric Packard, Local 669 JATC Education Fund, MD [L]
Rep. United Association of Journeymen and Apprentices of the Plumbing and Pipe Fitting Industry of the United States and Canada

John F. Saidi, University of California, CA [U]

J. William Sheppard, General Motors Corporation, MI [U]
Rep. NFPA Industrial Fire Protection Section

Terry L. Victor, Tyco/Grinnell Fire Protection, MD [M]

William E. Wilcox, FM Global, MA [I]

Alternates

Kerry M. Bell, Underwriters Laboratories Inc., IL [RT]
(Alt. to G. E. Laverick)

John A. Beukema, Reliable Automatic Sprinkler Company, NY [M]
(Alt. to M. J. Bosma)

Russell P. Fleming, National Fire Sprinkler Association, NY [IM]
(Alt. to R. Oliver)

Larry J. Fronczak, Canadian Automatic Sprinkler Association, Canada [IM]
(Alt. to L. Keeping)

Joseph B. Hankins, Jr., FM Global, MA [I]
(Alt. to W. E. Wilcox)

Ronald J. Huggins, American Fire Sprinkler Association, Inc., TX [IM]
(Alt. to J. M. Fantauzzi)

Peter A. Larrimer, U.S. Department of Veterans Affairs, PA [U]
(Alt. to E. A. Cable)

Robert J. Pearce, Jr., Industrial Risk Insurers, CA [I]
(Alt. to K. W. Linder)

Gayle Pennel, Schirmer Engineering Corporation, IL [SE]
(Alt. to W. A. Damon)

Ronald Rispoli, Entergy Corporation, AR [U]
(Alt. to J. D. Munno)

Peter W. Thomas, Tyco Fire Products, RI [M]
(Alt. to T. L. Victor)

Ralph Tiede, LMG Property Engineering, NY [I]
(Alt. to G. S. Andress)

Donald Walton, TVA, Fire & Life Safety, Inc., CA [U]
(Alt. to R. B. Leavitt)

Barry J. Waterman, Acme Sprinkler Service Co., IL [M]
(Alt. to M. J. DeLerno)

Robert A. Woodard, CIGNA Loss Control, PA [I]
(Vot. Alt. to American Insurance Services Group Rep.)

Nonvoting

Rohit Khanna, U.S. Consumer Product Safety Commission, MD [C]

Thomas F. Norton, Norel Service Company, Inc., MA
Rep. National Fire Alarm Code Committee

David R. Hague, NFPA Staff Liaison

Committee Scope: This Committee shall have primary responsibility for documents on inspection, testing, and maintenance of systems utilizing water as a method of extinguishment. These include sprinkler systems, standpipe and hose systems, fire service piping and appurtenances, fire pumps, water storage tanks, fixed water spray systems, foam-water systems, valves, and allied equipment. This Committee shall also develop procedures for the conduct and reporting of routine system impairments.

This list represents the membership at the time the Committee was balloted on the final text of this edition. Since that time, changes in the membership may have occurred. A key to classifications is found at the back of the document.

NOTE: Membership on a committee shall not in and of itself constitute an endorsement of the Association or any document developed by the committee on which the member serves.

Contents

NFPA 25

Standard for the

Inspection, Testing, and Maintenance of Water-Based Fire Protection Systems

2002 Edition

NOTICE: An asterisk (*) following the number or letter designating a paragraph indicates that explanatory material on the paragraph can be found in Annex A.

Changes other than editorial are indicated by a vertical rule beside the paragraph, table, or figure in which the change occurred. These rules are included as an aid to the user in identifying changes from the previous edition. Where one or more complete paragraphs have been deleted, the deletion is indicated by a bullet between the paragraphs that remain.

A reference in brackets [ ] following a section or paragraph indicates material that has been extracted from another NFPA document. As an aid to the user, Annex D lists the complete title and edition of the source documents for both mandatory and nonmandatory extracts. Editorial changes to extracted material consist of revising references to an appropriate division in this document or the inclusion of the document number with the division number when the reference is to the original document. Requests for interpretations or revisions of extracted text shall be sent to the appropriate technical committee.

Information on referenced publications can be found in Chapter 2 and Annex D.

Chapter 1   Administration

1.1 Scope. This document establishes the minimum requirements for the periodic inspection, testing, and maintenance of water-based fire protection systems, including land-based and marine applications. The types of systems addressed by this standard include, but are not limited to, sprinkler, standpipe and hose, fixed water spray, and foam water. Included are the water supplies that are part of these systems, such as private fire service mains and appurtenances, fire pumps and water storage tanks, and valves that control system flow. The document also addresses impairment handling and reporting. This standard applies to fire protection systems that have been properly installed in accordance with generally accepted practices. Where a system has not been installed in accordance with generally accepted practices, the corrective action is beyond the scope of this standard. The corrective action to ensure that the system performs in a satisfactory manner shall be in accordance with the appropriate installation standard.

1.1.1 This standard shall not apply to sprinkler systems designed and installed in accordance with NFPA 13D, *Standard for the Installation of Sprinkler Systems in One- and Two-Family Dwellings and Manufactured Homes.*

1.2* Purpose. The purpose of this document is to provide requirements that ensure a reasonable degree of protection for life and property from fire through minimum inspection, testing, and maintenance methods for water-based fire protection systems. In those cases where it is determined that an

existing situation involves a distinct hazard to life or property, the authority having jurisdiction shall be permitted to require inspection, testing, and maintenance methods in excess of those required by the standard.

1.3* Application. It is not the intent of this document to limit or restrict the use of other inspection, testing, or maintenance programs that provide an equivalent level of system integrity and performance to that detailed in this document. The authority having jurisdiction shall be consulted and approval obtained for such alternative programs.

1.4* Units. Metric units of measurement in this standard are in accordance with the modernized metric system known as the International System of Units (SI).

1.4.1 If a value for measurement as given in this standard is followed by an equivalent value in other units, the first stated shall be regarded as the requirement. A given equivalent value shall be considered to be approximate.

1.4.2 SI units have been converted by multiplying the quantity by the conversion factor and then rounding the result to the appropriate number of significant digits. Where nominal or trade sizes exist, the nominal dimension has been recognized in each unit.

Chapter 2   Referenced Publications

2.1 General. The documents or portions thereof listed in this chapter are referenced within this standard and shall be considered part of the requirements of this document.

2.2 NFPA Publications. National Fire Protection Association, 1 Batterymarch Park, P.O. Box 9101, Quincy, MA 02269-9101.

NFPA 11, *Standard for Low-Expansion Foam*, 1998 edition.
NFPA 13, *Standard for the Installation of Sprinkler Systems*, 1999 edition.
NFPA 13D, *Standard for the Installation of Sprinkler Systems in One- and Two-Family Dwellings and Manufactured Homes*, 1999 edition.
NFPA 15, *Standard for Water Spray Fixed Systems for Fire Protection*, 2001 edition.
NFPA 16, *Standard for the Installation of Foam-Water Sprinkler and Foam-Water Spray Systems*, 1999 edition.
NFPA 20, *Standard for the Installation of Stationary Pumps for Fire Protection*, 1999 edition.
NFPA 22, *Standard for Water Tanks for Private Fire Protection*, 1998 edition.
NFPA 72®, *National Fire Alarm Code®*, 1999 edition.
NFPA 110, *Standard for Emergency and Standby Power Systems*, 2002 edition.
NFPA 307, *Standard for the Construction and Fire Protection of Marine Terminals, Piers, and Wharves*, 2000 edition.
NFPA 409, *Standard on Aircraft Hangars*, 2001 edition.
NFPA 1962, *Standard for the Care, Use, and Service Testing of Fire Hose Including Couplings and Nozzles*, 1998 edition.

2.3 Other Publications.

2.3.1 ASTM Publication. American Society for Testing and Materials, 100 Barr Harbor Drive, West Conshohocken, PA 19428-2959.

ASTM D 3359, *Standard Test Methods for Measuring Adhesion by Tape Test*, 1997.

Chapter 3 Definitions

3.1 General. The definitions contained in this chapter shall apply to the terms used in this standard. Where terms are not included, common usage of the terms shall apply.

3.2 NFPA Official Definitions.

3.2.1* Approved. Acceptable to the authority having jurisdiction.

3.2.2* Authority Having Jurisdiction (AHJ). The organization, office, or individual responsible for approving equipment, materials, an installation, or a procedure.

3.2.3* Listed. Equipment, materials, or services included in a list published by an organization that is acceptable to the authority having jurisdiction and concerned with evaluation of products or services, that maintains periodic inspection of production of listed equipment or materials or periodic evaluation of services, and whose listing states that either the equipment, material, or service meets appropriate designated standards or has been tested and found suitable for a specified purpose.

3.2.4 Shall. Indicates a mandatory requirement.

3.2.5 Should. Indicates a recommendation or that which is advised but not required.

3.2.6 Standard. A document, the main text of which contains only mandatory provisions using the word "shall" to indicate requirements and which is in a form generally suitable for mandatory reference by another standard or code or for adoption into law. Nonmandatory provisions shall be located in an appendix or annex, footnote, or fine-print note and are not to be considered a part of the requirements of a standard.

3.3 General Definitions.

3.3.1 Alarm Receiving Facility. The place where alarm or supervisory signals are received. This can include proprietary or remote locations, central station, or fire departments.

3.3.2* Automatic Detection Equipment. Equipment that automatically detects heat, flame, products of combustion, flammable gases, or other conditions likely to produce fire or explosion and cause other automatic actuation of alarm and protection equipment.

3.3.3 Automatic Fire Detector. A device that detects abnormally high temperature, rate of temperature rise, visible or invisible particles, infrared or visible radiation, or gases produced by a fire.

3.3.4 Automatic Operation. Operation without human intervention. This operation includes, but is not limited to, heat, rate of heat rise, smoke, or pressure change.

3.3.5 Class of Service. Standpipe systems are grouped into three general classes of service for intended use in the extinguishment of fire.

3.3.5.1 Class I. A Class I standpipe system provides 65-mm (2½-in.) hose connections or 65-mm (2½-in.) hose stations supplied from a standpipe or combined riser in order to supply water for use by fire departments and those trained in handling heavy fire streams. No hose is provided.

3.3.5.2 Class II. A Class II standpipe system that provides 40-mm (1½-in.) hose stations to supply water for use primarily by the building occupants or by the fire department during initial response.

3.3.5.3 Class III. A Class III standpipe system that provides 40-mm (1½-in.) and 65-mm (2½-in.) hose connections or 40-mm (1½-in.) and 65-mm (2½-in.) hose stations supplied from a standpipe or combination riser in order to supply water for use by building occupants and a larger volume of water for use by fire departments and those trained in handling heavy fire streams.

3.3.6 Discharge Device. A device designed to discharge water or foam-water solution in a predetermined, fixed, or adjustable pattern. Examples include, but are not limited to, sprinklers, spray nozzles, and hose nozzles.

3.3.7 Double Check Valve Assembly (DCVA). This assembly consists of two internally loaded check valves, either spring-loaded or internally weighted, installed as a unit between two tightly closing resilient-seated shutoff valves as an assembly, and fittings with properly located resilient-seated test cocks.

3.3.8 Drain.

3.3.8.1 Main Drain. The primary drain connection located on the system riser and also utilized as a flow test connection.

3.3.8.2 Sectional Drain. A drain located beyond a sectional control valve that drains only a portion of the system (e.g., a drain located beyond a floor control valve on a multi-story building).

3.3.9 Fire Department Connection. A connection through which the fire department can pump supplemental water into the sprinkler system, standpipe, or other system furnishing water for fire extinguishment to supplement existing water supplies.

3.3.10* Fire Hydrant. A valved connection on a water main for the purpose of supplying water to fire hose or other fire protection apparatus. [1141:2.1]

3.3.10.1* Dry Barrel Hydrant (Frostproof Hydrant). This is the most common type of hydrant; it has a control valve below the frost line between the footpiece and the barrel. A drain is located at the bottom of the barrel above the control valve seat for proper drainage after operation.

3.3.10.2* Monitor Nozzle Hydrant. A hydrant equipped with a monitor nozzle capable of delivering more than 946 L/min (250 gpm).

3.3.10.3* Wall Hydrant. A hydrant mounted on the outside of a wall of a building, fed from interior piping, and equipped with control valves located inside the building that normally are key-operated from the building's exterior.

3.3.10.4* Wet Barrel Hydrant. A type of hydrant that sometimes is used where there is no danger of freezing weather. Each outlet on a wet barrel hydrant is provided with a valved outlet threaded for fire hose.

3.3.11 Foam Concentrate. A liquid that is stored in a containment vessel and is metered into a flowing water stream at a specified concentration by the proportioning system.

3.3.12 Foam Discharge Device. Any device that, when fed with a foam-water solution, produces foam. These devices shall be permitted to be non-air-aspirating (e.g., sprinklers, water nozzles) or air-aspirating (e.g., foam-water sprinklers, directional foam-water nozzles, foam nozzles). All discharge devices have a special pattern of distribution peculiar to the particular device.

3.3.13 Hose Connection. A combination of equipment provided for connection of a hose to the standpipe system that includes a hose valve with a threaded outlet. [**14**:1.4]

3.3.14* Hose House. An enclosure located over or adjacent to a hydrant or other water supply designed to contain the necessary hose nozzles, hose wrenches, gaskets, and spanners to be used in fire fighting in conjunction with and to provide aid to the local fire department.

3.3.15 Hose Nozzle. A device intended for discharging water for manual suppression or extinguishment of a fire.

3.3.16 Hose Station. A combination of a hose rack, hose nozzle, hose, and hose connection. [**14**:1.4]

3.3.17 Hose Storage Devices.

3.3.17.1* Conventional Pin Rack. A hose rack where the hose is folded vertically and attached over the pins.

3.3.17.2* Horizontal Rack. A hose rack where the hose is connected to the valve, then stack-folded horizontally to the top of the rack.

3.3.17.3* Hose Reel. A circular device used to store hose.

3.3.17.4* Semiautomatic Hose Rack Assembly. The same as a "conventional" pin rack or hose reel except that, after the valve is opened, a retaining device holds the hose and water until the last few feet are removed.

3.3.18 Impairment. A shutdown of a system or portion thereof.

3.3.18.1 Emergency Impairment. A condition where a water-based fire protection system or portion thereof is out of order due to an unexpected occurrence, such as a ruptured pipe, an operated sprinkler, or an interruption of the water supply to the system.

3.3.18.2 Preplanned Impairment. A condition where a water-based fire protection system or a portion thereof is out of service due to work that has been planned in advance, such as revisions to the water supply or sprinkler system piping.

3.3.19 Inspection. A visual examination of a system or portion thereof to verify that it appears to be in operating condition and is free of physical damage. [**820**:1.5]

3.3.20 Inspection, Testing, and Maintenance Service. A service program provided by a qualified contractor or qualified owner's representative in which all components unique to the property's systems are inspected and tested at the required times and necessary maintenance is provided. This program includes logging and retention of relevant records.

3.3.21 Interior Cabinet. A cabinet that contains hose rack assemblies; Class I, II, or III fire department valves; fire extinguishers; or various combinations of these.

3.3.22 Maintenance. Work performed to keep equipment operable or to make repairs.

3.3.23 Manual Operation. Operation of a system or its components through human action.

3.3.24 Nozzles.

3.3.24.1* Monitor Nozzle. A device specifically designed with large, clear waterways to provide a powerful, far-reaching stream for the protection of large amounts of combustible materials, aircraft, tank farms, and any other special hazard locations where large amounts of water need to be instantly available without the delay of laying hose lines. The nozzle is normally fitted with one of three interchangeable tips that measure 40 mm, 45 mm, and 50 mm (1½ in., 1¾ in., and 2 in.) in diameter.

3.3.24.2* Water Spray Nozzle. An open or automatic water discharge device that, when discharging water under pressure, will distribute the water in a specific, directional pattern. [**15**:1.4]

3.3.25 Orifice Plate Proportioning. This system utilizes an orifice plate(s) through which passes a specific amount of foam concentrate at a specific pressure drop across the orifice plate(s).

3.3.26 Pressure Regulating Device. A device designed for the purpose of reducing, regulating, controlling, or restricting water pressure. Examples include pressure reducing valves, pressure control valves, and pressure restricting devices. [**14**:1.4]

3.3.27 Pressure Restricting Device. A valve or device designed for the purpose of reducing the downstream water pressure under flowing (residual) conditions only. [**14**:1.4]

3.3.28* Pressure Vacuum Vent. A venting device mounted on atmospheric foam concentrate storage vessels to allow for concentrate expansion and contraction and for tank breathing during concentrate discharge or filling. At rest (static condition), this device is closed to prevent free breathing of the foam concentrate storage tank.

3.3.29* Proportioners.

3.3.29.1* Bladder Tank Proportioner. This system is similar to a standard pressure proportioner, except the foam concentrate is contained inside a diaphragm bag that is contained inside a pressure vessel. Operation is the same as a standard pressure proportioner, except that, because of the separation of the foam concentrate and water, this system can be used with all foam concentrates, regardless of specific gravity.

3.3.29.2* In-Line Balanced Pressure Proportioner. This system is similar to a standard balanced pressure system, except the pumped concentrate pressure is maintained at a fixed preset value. Balancing of water and liquid takes place at individual proportioners located in the system riser or in segments of multiple systems.

3.3.29.3* Line Proportioner. This system uses a venturi pickup-type device where water passing through the unit creates a vacuum, thereby allowing foam concentrate to be picked up from an atmospheric storage container.

3.3.29.4* Standard Balanced Pressure Proportioner. This system utilizes a foam concentrate pump. Foam concentrate is drawn from an atmospheric storage tank, is pressurized by the pump, and passes back through a diaphragm balancing valve to the storage tank. Water- and foam concentrate-sensing lines are directed to the balancing valve and maintain the foam liquid at a pressure equal to that of the water pressure. The two equal pressures are fed to the proportioner proper and are mixed at a predetermined rate.

3.3.29.5* Standard Pressure Proportioner. This system uses a pressure vessel containing foam concentrate. Water is supplied to the proportioner, which directs an amount of the supply downward onto the contained concentrate, thereby pressurizing the tank. Pressurized concentrate then is forced through an orifice back into the flowing water stream. This type of system is applicable for use with foam concentrates having a specific gravity substantially higher than water. It is not applicable for use with foam concentrates with a specific gravity at or near that of water.

3.3.30 Qualified. Having knowledge of the installation, construction, or operation of apparatus and the hazards involved.

3.3.31 Reduced-Pressure Principle Backflow Prevention Assembly (RPBA). Two independently acting check valves together with a hydraulically operating, mechanically independent pressure differential relief valve located between the check valves and below the first check valve. These units are located between two tightly closed resilient-seated shutoff valves, as an assembly, and are equipped with properly located resilient-seated test cocks.

3.3.32 Sprinklers.

3.3.32.1 Concealed Sprinkler. A recessed sprinkler with cover plates. [**13**:1.4]

3.3.32.2 Corrosion-Resistant Sprinkler. A sprinkler fabricated with corrosion-resistant material, or with special coatings or platings, to be used in an atmosphere that would normally corrode sprinklers. [**13**:1.4]

3.3.32.3 Dry Sprinkler. A sprinkler secured in an extension nipple that has a seal at the inlet end to prevent water from entering the nipple until the sprinkler operates. [**13**:1.4]

3.3.32.4 Early Suppression Fast-Response (ESFR) Sprinkler. A type of fast-response sprinkler that meets the criteria of 1.4.5.1(a)(1) of NFPA 13-1999 and is listed for its capability to provide fire suppression of specific high-challenge fire hazards. [**13**:1.4]

3.3.32.5 Extended Coverage Sprinkler. A type of spray sprinkler with maximum coverage areas as specified in Sections 5.8 and 5.9 of NFPA 13-1999. [**13**:1.4]

3.3.32.6 Flush Sprinkler. A sprinkler in which all or part of the body, including the shank thread, is mounted above the lower plane of the ceiling. [**13**:1.4]

3.3.32.7 Intermediate Level Sprinkler/Rack Storage Sprinkler. A sprinkler equipped with integral shields to protect its operating elements from the discharge of sprinklers installed at higher elevations. [**13**:1.4]

3.3.32.8 Large Drop Sprinkler. A type of sprinkler that is capable of producing characteristic large water droplets and that is listed for its capability to provide fire control of specific high-challenge fire hazards. [**13**:1.4]

3.3.32.9 Nozzles. A device for use in applications requiring special water discharge patterns, directional spray, or other unusual discharge characteristics. [**13**:1.4]

3.3.32.10 Old-Style/Conventional Sprinkler. A sprinkler that directs from 40 percent to 60 percent of the total water initially in a downward direction and that is designed to be installed with the deflector either upright or pendent. [**13**:1.4]

3.3.32.11 Open Sprinkler. A sprinkler that does not have actuators or heat-responsive elements. [**13**:1.4]

3.3.32.12 Ornamental/Decorative Sprinkler. A sprinkler that has been painted or plated by the manufacturer. [**13**:1.4]

3.3.32.13 Pendent Sprinkler. A sprinkler designed to be installed in such a way that the water stream is directed downward against the deflector. [**13**:1.4]

3.3.32.14 Quick-Response Early Suppression (QRES) Sprinkler. A type of quick-response sprinkler that meets the criteria of 1.4.5.1(a)(1) of NFPA 13-1999 and is listed for its capability to provide fire suppression of specific fire hazards. [**13**:1.4]

3.3.32.15 Quick-Response Extended Coverage Sprinkler. A type of quick-response sprinkler that meets the criteria of 1.4.5.1(a)(1) of NFPA 13-1999 and complies with the extended protection areas defined in Chapter 5 of NFPA 13-1999. [**13**:1.4]

3.3.32.16 Quick-Response (QR) Sprinkler. A type of spray sprinkler that meets the criteria of 1.4.5.1(a)(1) of NFPA 13-1999 and is listed as a quick-response sprinkler for its intended use. [**13**:1.4]

3.3.32.17 Recessed Sprinkler. A sprinkler in which all or part of the body, other than the shank thread, is mounted within a recessed housing. [**13**:1.4]

3.3.32.18 Residential Sprinkler. A type of fast-response sprinkler that meets the criteria of 1.4.5.1(a)(1) of NFPA 13-1999 that has been specifically investigated for its ability to enhance survivability in the room of fire origin and is listed for use in the protection of dwelling units. [**13**:1.4]

3.3.32.19 Sidewall Sprinkler. A sprinkler having special deflectors that are designed to discharge most of the water away from the nearby wall in a pattern resembling one-quarter of a sphere, with a small portion of the discharge directed at the wall behind the sprinkler. [**13**:1.4]

3.3.32.20 Special Sprinkler. A sprinkler that has been tested and listed as prescribed in 5.4.9 of NFPA 13-1999. [**13**:1.4]

3.3.32.21 Spray Sprinkler. A type of sprinkler listed for its capability to provide fire control for a wide range of fire hazards. [**13**:1.4]

3.3.32.22 Standard Spray Sprinkler. A spray sprinkler with maximum coverage areas as specified in Sections 5.6 and 5.7 of NFPA 13-1999. [**13**:1.4]

3.3.32.23 Upright Sprinkler. A sprinkler designed to be installed in such a way that the water spray is directed upwards against the deflector. [**13**:1.4]

3.3.33 Standpipe System.

3.3.33.1 Standpipe System. An arrangement of piping, valves, hose connections, and allied equipment installed in a building or structure, with the hose connections located in such a manner that water can be discharged in streams or spray patterns through attached hose and nozzles, for the purpose of extinguishing a fire, thereby protecting a building or structure and its contents in addition to protecting the occupants. This is accomplished by means of connections to water supply systems or by means of pumps, tanks, and other equipment necessary to provide an adequate supply of water to the hose connections. [**14**:1.4]

3.3.33.2 Dry Standpipe System. A system that shall be arranged as follows: (1) includes devices to admit water to the system automatically by opening a hose valve; (2) admits water to the system through manual operation of remote control devices located at each hose station; (3) has no permanent water supply (a filled standpipe having a small water supply connection to keep the piping filled by requiring water to be pumped into the system shall be considered to be a dry standpipe). [**14**:1.4]

3.3.33.3 Wet Standpipe. A standpipe system having piping containing water at all times. [**14**:1.4]

3.3.34* Strainer. A device capable of removing from the water all solids of sufficient size that are obstructing water spray nozzles.

3.3.35 Supervision. A means of monitoring system status and indicating abnormal conditions.

3.3.36 Testing. A procedure used to determine the status of a system as intended by conducting periodic physical checks on water-based fire protection systems such as water-flow tests, fire pump tests, alarm tests, and trip tests of dry pipe, deluge, or preaction valves. These tests follow up on the original acceptance test at intervals specified in the appropriate chapter of this standard.

3.3.37 Water Spray. The use of water in a form having a predetermined pattern, particle size, velocity, and density discharged from specially designed nozzles or devices. Water spray fixed systems are usually applied to special fire protection problems, since the protection can be specifically designed to provide for fire control, extinguishment, or exposure protection. Water spray fixed systems shall be permitted to be independent of, or supplementary to, other forms of protection.

3.3.38 Water Supply. A source of water that provides the flows (L/min) and pressures (bar) required by the water-based fire protection system.

3.4 Deluge Foam-Water Sprinkler and Foam-Water Spray Systems Definitions.

3.4.1 Foam-Water Spray System. A special system that is pipe-connected to a source of foam concentrate and to a water supply. The system is equipped with foam-water spray nozzles for extinguishing agent discharge (foam followed by water or in reverse order) and for distribution over the area to be protected. System operation arrangements parallel those for foam-water sprinkler systems as described in the definition of Foam-Water Sprinkler System. [**16**:1.3]

3.4.2 Foam-Water Sprinkler System. A special system pipe connected to a source of foam concentrate and to a water supply and equipped with appropriate discharge devices for fire protection agent discharge and for distribution over the area to be protected. The piping system is connected to the water supply through a control valve that usually is actuated by operation of automatic detection equipment installed in the same areas as the sprinklers. When this valve opens, water flows into the piping system and foam concentrate is injected into the water. The resulting foam solution discharging through the discharge devices generates and distributes foam. Upon exhaustion of the foam concentrate supply, water discharge follows and continues until shut off manually. Systems also can be used for discharge of water first, followed by discharge of foam for a specific period, and then followed by water until manually shut off. Existing deluge sprinkler systems that have been converted to the use of aqueous film-forming foam are classed as foam-water sprinkler systems. [**16**:1.3]

3.5 Valve Definitions.

3.5.1* Control Valve. A valve controlling flow to water-based fire protection systems. Control valves do not include hose valves, inspector's test valves, drain valves, trim valves for dry pipe, preaction and deluge valves, check valves, or relief valves.

3.5.2 Deluge Valve. A water supply control valve intended to be operated by actuation of an automatic detection system that is installed in the same area as the water spray nozzles. Each control valve also shall be capable of manual operation.

3.5.3 Hose Valve. The control valve to an individual hose connection. [**14**:1.4]

3.5.4 Pressure Control Valve. A pilot-operated pressure reducing valve designed for the purpose of reducing the downstream water pressure to a specific value under both flowing (residual) and nonflowing (static) conditions. [**14**:1.4]

3.5.5 Pressure Reducing Valve. A valve designed for the purpose of reducing the downstream water pressure under both flowing (residual) and nonflowing (static) conditions.

3.6 Water-Based Fire Protection System Definitions.

3.6.1 Combined Standpipe and Sprinkler System. A system where the water piping services both 65-mm (2½-in.) outlets for fire department use and outlets for automatic sprinklers.

3.6.2 Fire Pump. A pump supplying water at the flow and pressure required by water-based fire protection systems.

3.6.3 Private Fire Service Main. The pipe and its appurtenances located on private property between a source of water and the base of the riser (i.e., the flange, the flange and spigot piece, or the base tee) for automatic sprinkler systems, open sprinkler systems, water spray fixed systems, standpipe systems, inlets to foam-making systems, or the base elbow of private hydrants or monitor nozzles. Where connected to a public water system, the private service main begins at a point designated by the public water utility, usually at a manually operated valve near the property line. Where connected to fire pumps, the main begins at the fire-protection-system side of the pump discharge valve. Where connected to a gravity or pressure tank, the main begins at the inlet side of the tank's check valve. Private fire service mains can include supply and distribution piping installed above ground, in trenches, and inside or outside of buildings. The provisions of this definition also apply to pipeline strainers. [**13**:1.4]

3.6.4* Sprinkler System. For fire protection purposes, an integrated system of underground and overhead piping designed in accordance with fire protection engineering standards. The installation includes one or more automatic water supplies. The portion of the sprinkler system aboveground is a network of specially sized or hydraulically designed piping installed in a building, structure, or area, generally overhead, and to which sprinklers are attached in a systematic pattern. The valve controlling each system riser is located in the system riser or its supply piping. Each sprinkler system riser includes a device for actuating an alarm when the system is in operation. The system is usually activated by heat from a fire and discharges water over the fire area. [**13**:1.4]

3.6.4.1 Antifreeze Sprinkler System. A wet pipe sprinkler system employing automatic sprinklers that are attached to a piping system that contains an antifreeze solution and that are connected to a water supply. The antifreeze solution is discharged, followed by water, immediately upon operation of sprinklers opened by heat from a fire. [**13**:1.4]

3.6.4.2 Combined Dry Pipe–Preaction System. A sprinkler system employing automatic sprinklers attached to a piping system containing air under pressure, with a supplemental detection system installed in the same areas as the sprinklers. Operation of the detection system actuates tripping devices that open dry pipe valves simultaneously and without loss of air pressure in the system. Operation of the detection system also opens listed air exhaust valves at the end of the feed main, which usually precedes the opening of sprinklers. The detection system also serves as an automatic fire alarm system. [**13**:1.4]

3.6.4.3 Deluge Sprinkler System. A sprinkler system employing open sprinklers that are attached to a piping system that is connected to a water supply through a valve that is opened by the operation of a detection system installed in the same areas as the sprinklers. When this valve opens, water flows into the piping system and discharges from all sprinklers attached thereto. [**13**:1.4]

3.6.4.4 Dry Pipe Sprinkler System. A sprinkler system employing automatic sprinklers that are attached to a piping system containing air or nitrogen under pressure, the release of which (as from the opening of a sprinkler) permits the water pressure to open a valve known as a dry pipe valve, and the water then flows into the piping system and out the opened sprinklers. [**13**:1.4]

3.6.4.5 Preaction Sprinkler System. A sprinkler system employing automatic sprinklers attached to a piping system that contains air that might or might not be under pressure, with a supplemental detection system installed in the same areas as the sprinklers. [**13**:1.4]

3.6.4.6* Wet Pipe Sprinkler System. A sprinkler system employing automatic sprinklers attached to a piping system containing water and connected to a water supply so that water discharges immediately from sprinklers opened by heat from a fire. [**13**:1.4]

3.6.5 Water Spray Fixed System. A special fixed pipe system connected to a reliable fire protection water supply and equipped with water spray nozzles for specific water discharge and distribution over the surface or area to be protected. The piping system is connected to the water supply through an automatically or manually actuated valve that initiates the flow of water. An automatic valve is actuated by operation of automatic detection equipment installed in the same areas as the water spray nozzles. (In special cases, the automatic detection system also is located in another area.)

3.6.6 Water Tank. A tank supplying water for water-based fire protection systems.

Chapter 4   General Requirements

4.1 Responsibility of the Owner or Occupant.

4.1.1* The owner or occupant shall provide ready accessibility to components of water-based fire protection systems that require inspection, testing, or maintenance.

4.1.2* The responsibility for properly maintaining a water-based fire protection system shall be that of the owner of the property.

4.1.2.1 By means of periodic inspections, tests, and maintenance, the equipment shall be shown to be in good operating condition, or any defects or impairments shall be revealed.

4.1.2.2 Inspection, testing, and maintenance shall be implemented in accordance with procedures meeting or exceeding those established in this document and in accordance with the manufacturer's instructions.

4.1.2.3 These tasks shall be performed by personnel who have developed competence through training and experience.

4.1.2.4 Where the owner is not the occupant, the owner shall be permitted to pass on the authority for inspecting, testing, and maintaining the fire protection systems to the occupant, management firm, or managing individual through specific provisions in the lease, written use agreement, or management contract.

4.1.3 The owner or occupant shall notify the authority having jurisdiction, the fire department, if required, and the alarm-receiving facility before testing or shutting down a system or its supply.

4.1.3.1 The notification shall include the purpose for the shutdown, the system or component involved, and the estimated time of shutdown.

4.1.3.2 The authority having jurisdiction, the fire department, and the alarm-receiving facility shall be notified when the system, supply, or component is returned to service.

4.1.3.3 Where an occupant, management firm, or managing individual has received the authority for inspection, testing, and maintenance in accordance with 4.1.2.4, the occupant, management firm, or managing individual shall comply with 4.1.3.

4.1.4* The owner or occupant shall promptly correct or repair deficiencies, damaged parts, or impairments found while performing the inspection, test, and maintenance requirements of this standard.

4.1.4.1 Corrections and repairs shall be performed by qualified maintenance personnel or a qualified contractor.

4.1.4.2 Where an occupant, management firm, or managing individual has received the authority for inspection, testing, and maintenance in accordance with 4.1.2.4, the occupant, management firm, or managing individual shall comply with 4.1.4.

4.1.5* The building owner or occupant shall not make changes in the occupancy, the use or process, or the materials used or stored in the building without evaluation of the fire protection systems for their capability to protect the new occupancy, use, or materials.

4.1.5.1 The evaluation shall consider factors that include, but are not limited to, the following:

(1) Occupancy changes such as converting office or production space into warehousing
(2) Process or material changes such as metal stamping of molded plastics
(3) Building revisions such as relocated walls, added mezzanines, and ceilings added below sprinklers
(4) Removal of heating systems in spaces with piping subject to freezing

4.1.5.2 Where an occupant, management firm, or managing individual has received the authority for inspection, testing, and maintenance in accordance with 4.1.2.4, the occupant, management firm, or managing individual shall comply with 4.1.5.

4.1.6 Where changes in the occupancy, hazard, water supply, storage commodity, storage arrangement, building modification, or other condition that affects the installation criteria of the system are identified, the owner or occupant shall promptly take steps, such as contacting a qualified contractor, consultant, or engineer, to evaluate the adequacy of the installed system in order to protect the building or hazard in question.

4.1.6.1 Where the evaluation reveals a deficiency causing a threat to life or property, the owner shall make appropriate corrections. All requirements of the authority having jurisdiction shall be followed.

4.1.6.2 Where an occupant, management firm, or managing individual has received the authority for inspection, testing, and maintenance in accordance with 4.1.2.4, the occupant, management firm, or managing individual shall comply with 4.1.6.

4.1.7 Where a water-based fire protection system is returned to service following an impairment, the system shall be verified to be working properly.

4.2 Impairments. Where an impairment to a water-based fire protection system occurs, the procedures outlined in Chapter 13 of this standard shall be followed, including the attachment of a tag to the impaired system.

4.3 Records.

4.3.1* Records of inspections, tests, and maintenance of the system and its components shall be made available to the authority having jurisdiction upon request.

4.3.2 Records shall indicate the procedure performed (e.g., inspection, test, or maintenance), the organization that performed the work, the results, and the date.

4.3.3 Records shall be maintained by the owner.

4.3.4 Original records shall be retained for the life of the system.

4.3.5 Subsequent records shall be retained for a period of 1 year after the next inspection, test, or maintenance required by the standard.

4.4* Inspection. System components shall be inspected at intervals specified in the appropriate chapters.

4.5 Testing.

4.5.1 All components and systems shall be tested to verify that they function as intended.

4.5.1.1 The frequency of tests shall be in accordance with this standard.

4.5.1.2 Fire protection system components shall be restored to full operational condition following testing including reinstallation of plugs and caps for auxiliary drains and test valves.

4.5.2 During all testing and maintenance, water supplies including fire pumps shall remain in service unless all impairment procedures contained in Chapter 13 are followed.

4.5.3 Test results shall be compared with those of the original acceptance test (if available) and with the most recent test results.

4.5.4 The types of tests required for each protection system and its components are detailed in the appropriate chapter.

4.5.5 Specialized equipment required for testing is defined in the appropriate chapter.

4.5.6* When a major component or subsystem is rebuilt or replaced, the subsystem shall be tested in accordance with the original acceptance test required for that subsystem.

4.5.6.1 Sprinkler systems in accordance with 5.4.3 shall be tested.

4.6* Maintenance. Maintenance shall be performed to keep the system equipment operable or to make repairs.

4.6.1 As-built system installation drawings, original acceptance test records, and device manufacturer's maintenance bulletins shall be retained to assist in the proper care of the system and its components.

4.7 Safety. Inspection, testing, and maintenance activities shall be conducted in a safe manner.

4.7.1 Confined Spaces. Legally required precautions shall be taken prior to entering confined spaces such as tanks, valve pits, or trenches.

4.7.2 Fall Protection. Legally required equipment shall be worn or used to prevent injury from falls to personnel.

4.7.3 Special Hazards. Precautions shall be taken to address any special hazards, such as protection against drowning where working on the top of a filled embankment or a supported, rubberized fabric tank, or over open water or other liquids.

4.7.4* Hazardous Materials.

4.7.4.1 Legally required equipment shall be used where working in an environment with hazardous materials present.

4.7.4.2 The owner shall advise anyone performing inspection, testing, and maintenance on any system under the scope of this document, with regard to hazardous materials stored on the premises.

4.8* Electrical Safety. Legally required precautions shall be taken when testing or maintaining electric controllers for motor-driven fire pumps.

4.9 Corrective Action. Manufacturers shall be permitted to make modifications to their own listed product in the field with listed devices that restore the original performance as intended by the listing, where acceptable to the authority having jurisdiction.

Chapter 5   Sprinkler Systems

5.1 General. This chapter shall provide the minimum requirements for the routine inspection, testing, and maintenance of sprinkler systems. Table 5.1 shall be used to determine the minimum required frequencies for inspection, testing, and maintenance.

Table 5.1 Summary of Sprinkler System Inspection, Testing, and Maintenance

Item	Activity	Frequency	Reference
Gauges (dry, preaction, and deluge systems)	Inspection	Weekly/monthly	5.2.4.2, 5.2.4.3
Control valves	Inspection	Weekly/monthly	Table 12.1
Alarm devices	Inspection	Quarterly	5.2.6
Gauges (wet pipe systems)	Inspection	Monthly	5.2.4.1
Hydraulic nameplate	Inspection	Quarterly	5.2.7
Buildings	Inspection	Annually (prior to freezing weather)	5.2.5
Hanger/seismic bracing	Inspection	Annually	5.2.3
Pipe and fittings	Inspection	Annually	5.2.2
Sprinklers	Inspection	Annually	5.2.1
Spare sprinklers	Inspection	Annually	5.2.1.3
Fire department connections	Inspection	Quarterly	Table 12.1
Valves (all types)	Inspection		Table 12.1
Alarm devices	Test	Quarterly/semiannually	5.3.3
Main drain	Test	Annually	Table 12.1
Antifreeze solution	Test	Annually	5.3.4
Gauges	Test	5 years	5.3.2
Sprinklers — extra-high temperature	Test	5 years	5.3.1.1.1.3
Sprinklers — fast response	Test	At 20 years and every 10 years thereafter	5.3.1.1.1.2
Sprinklers	Test	At 50 years and every 10 years thereafter	5.3.1.1.1
Valves (all types)	Maintenance	Annually or as needed	Table 12.1
Obstruction investigation	Maintenance	5 years or as needed	10.2.1, 10.2.2
Low point drains (dry pipe system)	Maintenance	Annually prior to freezing and as needed	12.4.4.3.3

5.1.1 Valves and Connections. Valves and fire department connections shall be inspected, tested, and maintained in accordance with Chapter 12.

5.1.2 Impairments. The procedures outlined in Chapter 14 shall be followed where an impairment to protection occurs.

5.1.3 Notification to Supervisory Service. To avoid false alarms where a supervisory service is provided, the alarm receiving facility shall be notified by the owner or designated representative as follows:

(1) Before conducting any test or procedure that could result in the activation of an alarm
(2) After such tests or procedures are concluded

5.1.4 Records. Records shall be maintained in accordance with Section 4.3.

5.2* Inspection.

5.2.1 Sprinklers.

5.2.1.1* Sprinklers shall be inspected from the floor level annually.

5.2.1.1.1 Sprinklers shall not show signs of leakage; shall be free of corrosion, foreign materials, paint, and physical damage; and shall be installed in the proper orientation (e.g., upright, pendent, or sidewall).

5.2.1.1.2 Any sprinkler shall be replaced that has signs of leakage; is painted, corroded, damaged, or loaded; or in the improper orientation.

5.2.1.1.3 Glass bulb sprinklers shall be replaced if the bulbs have emptied.

5.2.1.1.4* Sprinklers installed in concealed spaces such as above suspended ceilings shall not require inspection.

5.2.1.1.5 Sprinklers installed in areas that are inaccessible for safety considerations due to process operations shall be inspected during each scheduled shutdown.

5.2.1.2* Unacceptable obstructions to spray patterns shall be corrected.

5.2.1.3 The supply of spare sprinklers shall be inspected annually for the following:

(1) The proper number and type of sprinklers
(2) A sprinkler wrench for each type of sprinkler

5.2.2* Pipe and Fittings. Sprinkler pipe and fittings shall be inspected annually from the floor level.

5.2.2.1 Pipe and fittings shall be in good condition and free of mechanical damage, leakage, corrosion, and misalignment.

5.2.2.2 Sprinkler piping shall not be subjected to external loads by materials either resting on the pipe or hung from the pipe.

5.2.2.3* Pipe and fittings installed in concealed spaces such as above suspended ceilings shall not require inspection.

5.2.2.4 Pipe installed in areas that are inaccessible for safety considerations due to process operations shall be inspected during each scheduled shutdown.

5.2.3* Hangers and Seismic Braces. Sprinkler pipe hangers and seismic braces shall be inspected annually from the floor level.

5.2.3.1 Hangers and seismic braces shall not be damaged or loose.

5.2.3.2 Hangers and seismic braces that are damaged or loose shall be replaced or refastened.

5.2.3.3* Hangers and seismic braces installed in concealed spaces such as above suspended ceilings shall not require inspection.

5.2.3.4 Hangers installed in areas that are inaccessible for safety considerations due to process operations shall be inspected during each scheduled shutdown.

5.2.4 Gauges.

5.2.4.1* Gauges on wet pipe sprinkler systems shall be inspected monthly to ensure that they are in good condition and that normal water supply pressure is being maintained.

5.2.4.2 Gauges on dry, preaction, and deluge systems shall be inspected weekly to ensure that normal air and water pressures are being maintained.

5.2.4.3 Where air pressure supervision is connected to a constantly attended location, gauges shall be inspected monthly.

5.2.4.4* For dry pipe or preaction systems protecting freezers, in accordance with Figure A.5.2.4.4 the air pressure gauge near the compressor shall be compared weekly to the pressure gauge above the dry pipe or preaction valve. When the gauge near the compressor is reading higher than the gauge near the dry pipe valve, the air line in service shall be taken out of service, and the alternate air line opened to equalize the pressure. The air line taken out of service shall be internally inspected, have all ice blockage removed, and shall be reassembled for use as a future alternate air line.

5.2.5 Buildings. Annually, prior to the onset of freezing weather, buildings with wet pipe systems shall be inspected to verify that windows, skylights, doors, ventilators, other openings and closures, blind spaces, unused attics, stair towers, roof houses, and low spaces under buildings do not expose water-filled sprinkler piping to freezing and to verify that adequate heat [minimum 4.4°C (40°F)] is available.

5.2.6 Alarm Devices. Alarm devices shall be inspected quarterly to verify that they are free of physical damage.

5.2.7* Hydraulic Nameplate. The hydraulic nameplate for hydraulically designed systems shall be inspected quarterly to verify that it is attached securely to the sprinkler riser and is legible.

5.2.8 Hose Connections. Hose connections and hose shall be inspected in accordance with the requirements of Chapter 6 and Chapter 12.

5.3 Testing.

5.3.1* Sprinklers.

5.3.1.1* Where required by this section, sample sprinklers shall be submitted to a recognized testing laboratory acceptable to the authority having jurisdiction for field service testing.

5.3.1.1.1 Where sprinklers have been in service for 50 years, they shall be replaced or representative samples from one or more sample areas shall be tested. Test procedures shall be repeated at 10-year intervals.

5.3.1.1.1.1 Sprinklers manufactured prior to 1920 shall be replaced.

5.3.1.1.1.2 Sprinklers manufactured using fast-response elements that have been in service for 20 years shall be tested. They shall be retested at 10-year intervals.

5.3.1.1.1.3* Representative samples of solder-type sprinklers with a temperature classification of extra high 163°C (325°F) or greater that are exposed to semicontinuous to continuous maximum allowable ambient temperature conditions shall be tested at 5-year intervals.

5.3.1.1.1.4 Where sprinklers have been in service for 75 years, they shall be replaced or representative samples from one or more sample areas shall be submitted to a recognized testing laboratory acceptable to the authority having jurisdiction for field service testing. Test procedures shall be repeated at 5-year intervals.

5.3.1.1.1.5 Dry sprinklers that have been in service for 10 years shall be tested or replaced. If maintained and serviced, they shall be retested at 10-year intervals.

5.3.1.1.2* Where sprinklers are subjected to harsh environments, including corrosive atmospheres and corrosive water supplies, on a 5-year basis, sprinklers shall either be replaced or representative sprinkler samples shall be tested.

5.3.1.1.3 Where historical data indicates, longer intervals between testing shall be permitted.

5.3.1.2* A representative sample of sprinklers for testing per 5.3.1.1.1 shall consist of a minimum of not less than 4 sprinklers or 1 percent of the number of sprinklers per individual sprinkler sample, whichever is greater.

5.3.1.3 Where one sprinkler within a representative sample fails to meet the test requirement, all sprinklers represented by that sample shall be replaced.

5.3.1.3.1 Manufacturers shall be permitted to make modifications to their own sprinklers in the field with listed devices that restore the original performance as intended by the listing, where acceptable to the authority having jurisdiction.

5.3.2* Gauges. Gauges shall be replaced every 5 years or tested every 5 years by comparison with a calibrated gauge. Gauges not accurate to within 3 percent of the full scale shall be recalibrated or replaced.

5.3.3* Alarm Devices.

5.3.3.1 Water-flow devices including, but not limited to, mechanical water motor gongs and pressure switch type shall be tested quarterly.

5.3.3.2* Vane-type waterflow devices shall be tested semiannually.

5.3.3.3* Testing the water-flow alarms on wet pipe systems shall be accomplished by opening the inspector's test connection.

5.3.3.3.1 Where freezing weather conditions or other circumstances prohibit use of the inspector's test connection, the bypass connection shall be permitted to be used.

5.3.3.4 Fire pumps shall not be turned off during testing unless all impairment procedures contained in Chapter 14 are followed.

5.3.3.5* Testing the water-flow alarm on dry pipe, preaction, or deluge systems shall be accomplished by using the bypass connection.

5.3.4* Antifreeze Systems. The freezing point of solutions in antifreeze shall be tested annually by measuring the specific gravity with a hydrometer or refractometer and adjusting the solutions if necessary.

5.3.4.1 Solutions shall be in accordance with Table 5.3.4.1(a) and Table 5.3.4.1(b).

5.3.4.2 The use of antifreeze solutions shall be in accordance with any state or local health regulations.

5.3.5 Hose Connections. Hose connections and hose shall be tested in accordance with the requirements of Chapter 6 and Chapter 12.

5.4 Maintenance.

5.4.1 Sprinklers.

5.4.1.1 Replacement sprinklers shall have the proper characteristics for the application intended. These shall include the following:

(1) Style

(2) Orifice size and *K*-factor
(3) Temperature rating
(4) Coating, if any
(5) Deflector type (e.g., upright, pendent, sidewall)
(6) Design requirements

5.4.1.1.1* Spray sprinklers shall be permitted to replace old-style sprinklers.

5.4.1.1.2 Replacement sprinklers for piers and wharves shall comply with NFPA 307, *Standard for the Construction and Fire Protection of Marine Terminals, Piers, and Wharves.*

5.4.1.2 Only new, listed sprinklers shall be used to replace existing sprinklers.

5.4.1.3* Special and quick-response sprinklers as defined by NFPA 13, *Standard for the Installation of Sprinkler Systems*, shall be replaced with sprinklers of the same make, model, orifice, size, temperature range and thermal response characteristics, and *K*-factor.

5.4.1.3.1 If the special or quick-response sprinkler is no longer manufactured, a special or quick-response sprinkler with comparable performance characteristics shall be installed.

5.4.1.4* A supply of spare sprinklers (never fewer than six) shall be maintained on the premises so that any sprinklers that have operated or been damaged in any way can be promptly replaced.

Table 5.3.4.1(a) Antifreeze Solutions to Be Used If Nonpotable Water Is Connected to Sprinklers

Material	Solution (by volume)	Specific Gravity at 60°F (15.6°C)	Freezing Point (°C)	Freezing Point (°F)
Glycerine*				
Diethylene glycol	50% water	1.078	−25.0	−13
	45% water	1.081	−32.8	−27
	40% water	1.086	−41.1	−42
	Hydrometer scale 1.000 to 1.120 (subdivisions 0.002)			
Ethylene glycol	61% water	1.056	−23.3	−10
	56% water	1.063	−28.9	−20
	51% water	1.069	−34.4	−30
	47% water	1.073	−40.0	−40
	Hydrometer scale 1.000 to 1.120 (subdivisions 0.002)			
Propylene glycol*				
Calcium chloride 80% "flake"	lb CaCl$_2$/gal of water			
Fire protection grade**				
Add corrosion	2.83	1.183	−17.8	0
inhibitor of sodium	3.38	1.212	−23.3	−10
bichromate	3.89	1.237	−28.9	−20
¾ oz/gal water	4.37	1.258	−34.4	−30
	4.73	1.274	−40.0	−40
	4.93	1.283	−45.6	−50

*If used, see Table 5.3.4.1(b).

**Free from magnesium chloride and other impurities.

Table 5.3.4.1(b) Antifreeze Solutions to Be Used If Potable Water Is Connected to Sprinklers

Material	Solution (by volume)	Specific Gravity at 60°F (15.6°C)	Freezing Point	
			(°C)	(°F)
Glycerine C.P. or U.S.P. grade*	50% water	1.133	−26.1	−15
	40% water	1.151	−30.0	−22
	30% water	1.165	−40.0	−40
	Hydrometer scale 1.000 to 1.200			
Propylene glycol	70% water	1.027	−12.8	+9
	60% water	1.034	−21.1	−6
	50% water	1.041	−32.2	−26
	40% water	1.045	−51.1	−60
	Hydrometer scale 1.000 to 1.200			

*C.P. = Chemically pure; U.S.P. = United States Pharmacopoeia 96.9%.

5.4.1.4.1 The sprinklers shall correspond to the types and temperature ratings of the sprinklers in the property.

5.4.1.4.2 The sprinklers shall be kept in a cabinet located where the temperature in which they are subjected will at no time exceed 38°C (100°F).

5.4.1.4.2.1 Where dry sprinklers of different lengths are installed, spare dry sprinklers shall not be required, provided that a means of returning the system to service is furnished.

5.4.1.5 The stock of spare sprinklers shall include all types and ratings installed and shall be as follows:

(1) For protected facilities having under 300 sprinklers — no fewer than 6 sprinklers
(2) For protected facilities having 300 to 1000 sprinklers — no fewer than 12 sprinklers
(3) For protected facilities having over 1000 sprinklers — no fewer than 24 sprinklers

5.4.1.6* A special sprinkler wrench shall be provided and kept in the cabinet to be used in the removal and installation of sprinklers. One sprinkler wrench shall be provided for each type of sprinkler installed.

5.4.1.7 Sprinklers protecting spray coating areas shall be protected against overspray residue.

5.4.1.7.1 Sprinklers subject to overspray accumulations shall be protected using plastic bags having a maximum thickness of 0.076 mm (0.003 in.) or shall be protected with small paper bags.

5.4.1.7.2 Coverings shall be replaced when deposits or residue accumulate.

5.4.1.8* Sprinklers shall not be altered in any respect or have any type of ornamentation, paint, or coatings applied after shipment from the place of manufacture.

5.4.1.9 Sprinklers and automatic spray nozzles used for protecting commercial-type cooking equipment and ventilating systems shall be replaced annually.

5.4.1.9.1 Where automatic bulb-type sprinklers or spray nozzles are used and annual examination shows no buildup of grease or other material on the sprinklers or spray nozzles, such sprinklers and spray nozzles shall not be required to be replaced.

5.4.2* Dry Pipe Systems. Dry pipe systems shall be kept dry at all times.

5.4.2.1 During nonfreezing weather, a dry pipe system shall be permitted to be left wet if the only other option is to remove the system from service while waiting for parts or during repair activities.

5.4.2.2 Air driers shall be maintained in accordance with the manufacturer's instructions.

5.4.2.3 Compressors used in conjunction with dry pipe sprinkler systems shall be maintained in accordance with the manufacturer's instructions.

5.4.3* Installation and Acceptance Testing. Where maintenance or repair requires the replacement of sprinkler system components affecting more than 20 sprinklers, those components shall be installed and tested in accordance with NFPA 13, *Standard for the Installation of Sprinkler Systems.*

5.4.4* Marine Systems. Sprinkler systems that are normally maintained using fresh water as a source shall be drained and refilled, then drained and refilled again with fresh water following the introduction of raw water into the system.

Chapter 6   Standpipe and Hose Systems

6.1 General. This chapter shall provide the minimum requirements for the routine inspection, testing, and maintenance of standpipe and hose systems. Table 6.1 shall be used to determine the minimum required frequencies for inspection, testing, and maintenance.

6.1.1 Valves and Connections. Valves and fire department connections shall be inspected, tested, and maintained in accordance with Chapter 12.

6.1.2 Impairments. Where the inspection, testing, and maintenance of standpipe and hose systems results or involves a system that is out of service, the procedures outlined in Chapter 14 shall be followed.

Table 6.1 Summary of Standpipe and Hose Systems Inspection, Testing, and Maintenance

Item	Activity	Frequency	Reference
Control valves	Inspection	Weekly/monthly	Table 12.1
Pressure regulating devices	Inspection	Quarterly	Table 12.1
Piping	Inspection	Quarterly	6.2.1
Hose connections	Inspection	Quarterly	Table 12.1
Cabinet	Inspection	Annually	NFPA 1962
Hose	Inspection	Annually	NFPA 1962
Hose storage device	Inspection	Annually	NFPA 1962
Alarm device	Test	Quarterly	Table 12.1
Hose nozzle	Test	Annually	NFPA 1962
Hose storage device	Test	Annually	NFPA 1962
Hose	Test	5 years/3 years	NFPA 1962
Pressure control valve	Test	5 years	Table 12.1
Pressure reducing valve	Test	5 years	Table 12.1
Hydrostatic test	Test	5 years	6.3.2
Flow test	Test	5 years	6.3.1
Main drain test	Test	Annually	Table 12.1
Hose connections	Maintenance	Annually	Table 6.2.2
Valves (all types)	Maintenance	Annually/as needed	Table 12.1

6.2 Inspection.

6.2.1 Components of standpipe and hose systems shall be visually inspected quarterly or as specified in Table 6.1.

6.2.2 Table 6.2.2 shall be used for the inspection, testing, and maintenance of all classes of standpipe and hose systems.

6.2.3 Checkpoints and corrective actions outlined in Table 6.2.2 shall be followed to determine that components are free of corrosion, foreign material, physical damage, tampering, or other conditions that adversely affect system operation.

6.3 Testing. The tests shall be conducted by a qualified person. Where water damage is a possibility, an air test shall be conducted on the system at 1.7 bar (25 psi) prior to introducing water to the system.

6.3.1 Flow Tests.

6.3.1.1* A flow test shall be conducted every 5 years at the hydraulically most remote hose connection of each zone of an automatic standpipe system to verify the water supply still provides the design pressure at the required flow.

6.3.1.2 Where a flow test of the hydraulically most remote outlet(s) is not practical, the authority having jurisdiction shall be consulted for the appropriate location for the test.

6.3.1.3 All systems shall be flow tested and pressure tested at the requirements in effect at the time of the installation.

6.3.1.3.1 The actual test method(s) and performance criteria shall be discussed in advance with the authority having jurisdiction.

6.3.1.4 Standpipes, sprinkler connections to standpipes, or hose stations equipped with pressure reducing valves or pressure regulating valves shall have these valves inspected, tested, and maintained in accordance with the requirements of Chapter 12.

6.3.1.5 A main drain test shall be performed on all standpipe systems with automatic water supplies in accordance with the requirements of Chapter 12.

6.3.1.5.1 The test shall be performed at the low point drain for each standpipe or the main drain test connection where the supply main enters the building (when provided).

6.3.1.5.2 Pressure gauges shall be provided for the test and shall be maintained in accordance with 5.3.2.

6.3.2 Hydrostatic Tests.

6.3.2.1 Hydrostatic tests at not less than 13.8-bar (200-psi) pressure for 2 hours, or at 3.4 bar (50 psi) in excess of the maximum pressure, where maximum pressure is in excess of 10.3 bar (150 psi), shall be conducted every 5 years on dry standpipe systems and dry portions of wet standpipe systems.

6.3.2.2* Hydrostatic tests shall be conducted in manual standpipe systems in accordance with 6.3.2.1 or on any system that has been modified or repaired.

6.3.2.2.1 Manual wet standpipes that are part of a combined sprinkler/standpipe system shall not be required to be tested in accordance with 6.3.2.2.

6.3.2.3 The hydrostatic test pressure shall be measured at the low elevation point of the individual system or zone being tested. The inside standpipe piping shall show no leakage.

6.3.3 Alarm Devices. Where provided, waterflow alarm and supervisory devices shall be tested on a quarterly basis.

6.3.3.1 Where freezing conditions necessitate a delay in testing, tests shall be performed as soon as weather allows.

6.4 Maintenance. Maintenance and repairs shall be in accordance with 6.2.3 and Table 6.2.2.

6.4.1 Hose Connections. After each use, all hose connected to sprinkler systems shall be cleaned, drained, and thoroughly dried before being placed in service. Hose that has been exposed to hazardous materials shall be disposed of in an approved manner or shall be decontaminated by a method approved for the contaminant and by the hose manufacturer's recommendation. Equipment that does not pass the inspection requirements of 5.2.8 or the testing requirements of 5.3.5 shall be repaired and tested again or replaced.

6.5 Records. Records shall be maintained in accordance with Section 4.3.

Table 6.2.2 Standpipe and Hose Systems

Component/Checkpoint	Corrective Action
Hose Connections	
Cap missing	Replace
Fire hose connection damaged	Repair
Valve handles missing	Replace
Cap gaskets missing or deteriorated	Replace
Valve leaking	Close or repair
Visible obstructions	Remove
Restricting device missing	Replace
Manual, semiautomatic, or dry standpipe — valve does not operate smoothly	Lubricate or repair
Piping	
Damaged piping	Repair
Control valves damaged	Repair or replace
Missing or damaged pipe support device	Repair or replace
Damaged supervisory devices	Repair or replace
Hose	
Inspect	Remove and inspect the hose, including gaskets, and rerack or rereel at intervals in accordance with NFPA 1962, *Standard for the Care, Use, and Service Testing of Fire Hose Including Couplings and Nozzles*
Mildew, cuts, abrasions, and deterioration evident	Replace with listed, lined, jacketed hose
Coupling damaged	Replace or repair
Gaskets missing or deteriorated	Replace
Incompatible threads on coupling	Replace or provide thread adapter
Hose not connected to hose rack nipple or valve	Connect
Hose test outdated	Retest or replace in accordance with NFPA 1962, *Standard for the Care, Use, and Service Testing of Fire Hose Including Couplings and Nozzles*
Hose Nozzle	
Hose nozzle missing	Replace with listed nozzle
Gasket missing or deteriorated	Replace
Obstructions	Remove
Nozzle does not operate smoothly	Repair or replace
Hose Storage Device	
Difficult to operate	Repair or replace
Damaged	Repair or replace
Obstruction	Remove
Hose improperly racked or rolled	Remove
Nozzle clip in place and nozzle correctly contained?	Replace if necessary
If enclosed in cabinet, will hose rack swing out at least 90 degrees?	Repair or remove any obstructions
Cabinet	
Check overall condition for corroded or damaged parts	Repair or replace parts; replace entire cabinet if necessary
Difficult to open	Repair
Cabinet door will not open fully	Repair or move obstructions
Door glazing cracked or broken	Replace
If cabinet is break-glass type, is lock functioning properly?	Repair or replace
Glass break device missing or not attached	Replace or attach
Not properly identified as containing fire equipment	Provide identification
Visible obstructions	Remove
All valves, hose, nozzles, fire extinguisher, etc., easily accessible	Remove any material not related

Chapter 7 Private Fire Service Mains

7.1 General. This chapter shall provide the minimum requirements for the routine inspection, testing, and maintenance of private fire service mains and their appurtenances.

Table 7.1 shall be used to determine the minimum required frequencies for inspection, testing, and maintenance.

7.1.1 These functions shall be permitted to be carried out simultaneously.

Table 7.1 Summary of Private Fire Service Main Inspection, Testing, and Maintenance

Item	Activity	Frequency	Reference
Hose houses	Inspection	Quarterly	7.2.2.7
Hydrants (dry barrel and wall)	Inspection	Annually and after each operation	7.2.2.4
Monitor nozzles	Inspection	Semiannually	7.2.2.6
Hydrants (wet barrel)	Inspection	Annually and after each operation	7.2.2.5
Mainline strainers	Inspection	Annually and after each significant flow	7.2.2.3
Piping (exposed)	Inspection	Annually	7.2.2.1
Piping (underground)	Inspection	See 7.2.2.2	7.2.2.2
Monitor nozzles	Test	Flow annually (range and operation)	7.3.3
Hydrants	Test	Flow annually	7.3.2
Piping (exposed and underground)	Flow test	5 years	7.3.1
Mainline strainers	Maintenance	Annually and after each operation	7.4.2
Hose houses	Maintenance	Annually	7.4.5
Hydrants	Maintenance	Annually	7.4.3
Monitor nozzles	Maintenance	Annually	7.4.4

7.1.2 Valves and Connections. Valves and fire department connections shall be inspected, tested, and maintained in accordance with Chapter 12.

7.1.3 Fire Hose. Fire hose shall be maintained in accordance with NFPA 1962, *Standard for the Care, Use, and Service Testing of Fire Hose Including Couplings and Nozzles.*

7.1.4 Impairments. The procedures outlined in Chapter 14 shall be followed wherever such an impairment to protection occurs.

7.1.5 Notification to Supervisory Service. To avoid false alarms where a supervisory service is provided, the alarm receiving facilities always shall be notified by the owner or designated representative as follows:

(1) Before conducting any test or procedure that could result in the activation of an alarm
(2) After such tests or procedures are concluded

7.2 Inspection.

7.2.1 General. Private fire service mains and their appurtenances shall be inspected at the intervals specified in Table 7.1.

7.2.2* Procedures. All procedures shall be carried out in accordance with the manufacturer's instructions, where applicable.

7.2.2.1 Exposed Piping.

7.2.2.1.1 Exposed piping shall be inspected annually.

7.2.2.1.2 Piping shall be inspected, and the necessary corrective action shall be taken as shown in Table 7.2.2.1.2.

7.2.2.1.3 Piping installed in areas that are inaccessible for safety considerations due to process operations shall be inspected during each scheduled shutdown.

7.2.2.2 Underground Piping. Generally, underground piping cannot be inspected on a routine basis. However, flow testing

Table 7.2.2.1.2 Exposed Piping

Condition	Corrective Action
Leaks	Repair
Physical damage	Repair or replace
Corrosion	Clean or replace and coat with corrosion protection
Restraint methods	Repair or replace

can reveal the condition of underground piping and shall be conducted in accordance with Section 7.3.

7.2.2.3* Mainline Strainers. Mainline strainers shall be inspected and cleaned after each system flow exceeding that of a nominal 50-mm (2-in.) orifice and shall be removed and inspected annually for failing, damaged, and corroded parts with the necessary corrective action taken as shown in Table 7.2.2.3.

Table 7.2.2.3 Mainline Strainers

Condition	Corrective Action
Plugging or fouling	Clean
Corrosion	Replace or repair

7.2.2.4 Dry Barrel and Wall Hydrants. Dry barrel and wall hydrants shall be inspected annually and after each operation with the necessary corrective action taken as shown in Table 7.2.2.4.

7.2.2.5 Wet Barrel Hydrants. Wet barrel hydrants shall be inspected annually and after each operation with the necessary corrective action taken as shown in Table 7.2.2.5.

Table 7.2.2.4 Dry Barrel and Wall Hydrants

Condition	Corrective Action
Inaccessible	Make accessible
Barrel contains water or ice (presence of water or ice could indicate a faulty drain, a leaky hydrant valve, or high groundwater table)	Repair and drain; for high groundwater it could be necessary to plug the drain and pump out the barrel after each use
Improper drainage from barrel	Repair drain
Leaks in outlets or at top of hydrant	Repair or replace gaskets, packing, or parts as necessary
Cracks in hydrant barrel	Repair or replace
Tightness of outlets	Lubricate if necessary; tighten if necessary
Worn nozzle threads	Repair or replace
Worn hydrant operating nut	Repair or replace
Availability of operating wrench	Make sure wrench is available

Table 7.2.2.5 Wet Barrel Hydrants

Condition	Corrective Action
Inaccessible	Make accessible
Leaks in outlets or at top of hydrant	Repair or replace gaskets, packing, or parts as necessary
Cracks in hydrant barrel	Repair or replace
Tightness of outlets	Lubricate if necessary; tighten if necessary
Worn nozzle threads	Repair or replace
Worn hydrant operating nut	Repair or replace
Availability of operating wrench	Make sure wrench is available

7.2.2.6 Monitor Nozzles. Monitor nozzles shall be inspected semiannually with the necessary corrective action taken as shown in Table 7.2.2.6.

Table 7.2.2.6 Monitor Nozzles

Condition	Corrective Action
Leakage	Repair
Physical damage	Repair or replace
Corrosion	Clean or replace, and lubricate or protect as necessary

7.2.2.7 Hose Houses. Hose houses shall be inspected quarterly with the necessary corrective action taken as shown in Table 7.2.2.7.

7.3 Testing.

7.3.1* Underground and Exposed Piping Flow Tests. Underground and exposed piping shall be flow tested to de-

Table 7.2.2.7 Hose Houses

Condition	Corrective Action
Inaccessible	Make accessible
Physical damage	Repair or replace
Missing equipment	Replace equipment

termine the internal condition of the piping at minimum 5-year intervals.

7.3.1.1 Flow tests shall be made at flows representative of those expected during a fire for the purpose of comparing the friction loss characteristics of the pipe with those expected for the particular type of pipe involved, with due consideration given to the age of the pipe and to the results of previous flow tests.

7.3.1.2 Any flow test results that indicate deterioration of available water flow and pressure shall be investigated to the complete satisfaction of the authority having jurisdiction to ensure that the required flow and pressure are available for fire protection.

7.3.1.3 Where underground piping supplies individual fire sprinkler, standpipe, water spray, or foam-water sprinkler systems and there are no means to conduct full flow tests, tests generating the maximum available flows shall be permitted.

7.3.2 Hydrants. Hydrants shall be tested annually to ensure proper functioning.

7.3.2.1 Each hydrant shall be opened fully and waterflowed until all foreign material has cleared.

7.3.2.2 Flow shall be maintained for not less than 1 minute.

7.3.2.3 After operation, dry barrel and wall hydrants shall be observed for proper drainage from the barrel.

7.3.2.4 Full drainage shall take no longer than 60 minutes.

7.3.2.5 Where soil conditions or other factors are such that the hydrant barrel does not drain within 60 minutes, or where the groundwater level is above that of the hydrant drain, the hydrant drain shall be plugged and the water in the barrel shall be pumped out.

7.3.2.6 Dry barrel hydrants that are located in areas subject to freezing weather and that have plugged drains shall be identified clearly as needing pumping after operation.

7.3.3 Monitor Nozzles.

7.3.3.1 Monitor nozzles that are mounted on hydrants shall be tested as specified in 7.3.2.

7.3.3.2 All monitor nozzles shall be oscillated and moved throughout their full range annually to ensure proper operability.

7.3.4 Hose Houses. All fire hose shall be tested in accordance with NFPA 1962, *Standard for the Care, Use, and Service Testing of Fire Hose Including Couplings and Nozzles.*

7.4 Maintenance.

7.4.1 General. All equipment shall be maintained in proper working condition, consistent with the manufacturer's recommendations.

7.4.2 Mainline Strainers. Mainline strainers shall be cleaned annually and after each operation.

7.4.3 Hydrants.

7.4.3.1 Hydrants shall be lubricated annually to ensure that all stems, caps, plugs, and threads are in proper operating condition.

7.4.3.2* Hydrants shall be kept free of snow, ice, or other materials and protected against mechanical damage so that free access is ensured.

7.4.4 Monitor Nozzles. Monitor nozzles shall be lubricated annually to ensure proper operating condition.

7.4.5 Hose Houses. Hose houses shall be maintained annually in a condition to ensure that all fire hose and required components are in usable condition.

7.5 Records. Records shall be maintained in accordance with Section 4.3.

Chapter 8   Fire Pumps

8.1* General. This chapter shall provide the minimum requirements for the routine inspection, testing, and maintenance of fire pump assemblies. Table 8.1 shall be used to determine the minimum required frequencies for inspection, testing, and maintenance.

8.1.1 Valves and Connections. Valves and fire department connections shall be inspected, tested, and maintained in accordance with Chapter 12.

8.1.2* Auxiliary Equipment. The pump assembly auxiliary equipment shall include the following:

(1) Pump accessories as follows:
   (a) Pump shaft coupling
   (b) Automatic air release valve
   (c) Pressure gauges
   (d) Circulation relief valve (not used in conjunction with diesel engine drive with heat exchanger)
(2) Pump test device(s)

(3) Pump relief valve and piping (where maximum pump discharge pressure exceeds the rating of the system components or the driver is of variable speed)
(4) Alarm sensors and indicators
(5) Right-angle gear sets (for engine-driven vertical shaft turbine pumps)
(6) Pressure maintenance (jockey) pump and accessories

8.1.3 Water Supply to Pump Suction. The suction supply for the fire pump shall provide the required flow at a gauge pressure of zero (0) bar [zero (0) psi] or higher at the pump suction flange to meet the system demand.

8.1.3.1 Those installations for which NFPA 20, *Standard for the Installation of Stationary Pumps for Fire Protection*, permitted negative suction gauge pressures at the time of pump installation, where the system demand still can be met by the pump and water supply, shall be considered to be in compliance with 8.1.3.

8.1.4 Energy Source. The energy sources for the pump driver shall supply the necessary brake horsepower of the driver so that the pump meets system demand.

8.1.5 Driver. The pump driver shall not overload beyond its rating (including any service factor allowance) when delivering the necessary brake horsepower.

8.1.6* Controller. Automatic and manual controllers for applying the energy source to the driver shall be capable of providing this operation for the type of pump used.

8.1.7 Impairments. The procedures outlined in Chapter 14 shall be followed where an impairment to protection occurs.

8.1.8 Notification to Supervisory Service. To avoid false alarms where a supervisory service is provided, the alarm receiving facility always shall be notified by the owner or designated representative as follows:

(1) Before conducting any test or procedure that could result in the activation of an alarm
(2) After such tests or procedures are concluded

8.2 Inspection.

8.2.1 The purpose of inspection shall be to verify that the pump assembly appears to be in operating condition and is free from physical damage.

Table 8.1 Summary of Fire Pump Inspection, Testing, and Maintenance

Item	Activity	Frequency	Reference
Pump house, heating ventilating louvers	Inspection	Weekly	8.2.2(1)
Fire pump system	Inspection	Weekly	8.2.2(2)
Pump operation			
No-flow condition	Test	Weekly	8.3.1
Flow condition	Test	Annually	8.3.3.1
Hydraulic	Maintenance	Annually	8.5
Mechanical transmission	Maintenance	Annually	8.5
Electrical system	Maintenance	Varies	8.5
Controller, various components	Maintenance	Varies	8.5
Motor	Maintenance	Annually	8.5
Diesel engine system, various components	Maintenance	Varies	8.5

8.2.2* The pertinent visual observations specified in the following checklists shall be performed weekly:

(1) Pump house conditions:

   (a) Heat is adequate, not less than 4.4°C (40°F) [21°C (70°F) for pump room with diesel pumps without engine heaters].

   (b) Ventilating louvers are free to operate.

(2) Pump system conditions:

   (a) Pump suction and discharge and bypass valves are fully open.

   (b) Piping is free of leaks.

   (c) Suction line pressure gauge reading is normal.

   (d) System line pressure gauge reading is normal.

   (e) Suction reservoir is full.

   (f) Wet pit suction screens are unobstructed and in place.

(3) Electrical system conditions:

   (a) Controller pilot light (power on) is illuminated.

   (b) Transfer switch normal pilot light is illuminated.

   (c) Isolating switch is closed — standby (emergency) source.

   (d) Reverse phase alarm pilot light is off or normal phase rotation pilot light is on.

   (e) Oil level in vertical motor sight glass is normal.

(4) Diesel engine system conditions:

   (a) Fuel tank is two-thirds full.

   (b) Controller selector switch is in auto position.

   (c) Batteries' (2) voltage readings are normal.

   (d) Batteries' (2) charging current readings are normal.

   (e) Batteries' (2) pilot lights are on or battery failure (2) pilot lights are off.

   (f) All alarm pilot lights are off.

   (g) Engine running time meter is reading.

   (h) Oil level in right angle gear drive is normal.

   (i) Crankcase oil level is normal.

   (j) Cooling water level is normal.

   (k) Electrolyte level in batteries is normal.

   (l) Battery terminals are free from corrosion.

   (m) Water-jacket heater is operating.

(5)*Steam system conditions: Steam pressure gauge reading is normal.

8.3* Testing.

8.3.1 A weekly test of fire pump assemblies shall be conducted without flowing water.

8.3.1.1 This test shall be conducted by starting the pump automatically.

8.3.1.2 The electric pump shall run a minimum of 10 minutes.

8.3.1.3 The diesel pump shall run a minimum of 30 minutes.

8.3.1.4 A valve installed to open as a safety feature shall be permitted to discharge water.

8.3.1.5 The automatic weekly test timer shall be permitted to be substituted for the starting procedure.

8.3.2 Weekly Tests.

8.3.2.1* Qualified operating personnel shall be in attendance during the weekly pump operation.

8.3.2.2 The pertinent visual observations or adjustments specified in the following checklists shall be conducted while the pump is running:

(1) Pump system procedure:

   (a) Record the system suction and discharge pressure gauge readings

   (b) Check the pump packing glands for slight discharge

   (c) Adjust gland nuts if necessary

   (d) Check for unusual noise or vibration

   (e) Check packing boxes, bearings, or pump casing for overheating

   (f) Record the pump starting pressure

(2) Electrical system procedure:

   (a) Observe the time for motor to accelerate to full speed

   (b) Record the time controller is on first step (for reduced voltage or reduced current starting)

   (c) Record the time pump runs after starting (for automatic stop controllers)

(3) Diesel engine system procedure:

   (a) Observe the time for engine to crank

   (b) Observe the time for engine to reach running speed

   (c) Observe the engine oil pressure gauge, speed indicator, water, and oil temperature indicators periodically while engine is running

   (d) Record any abnormalities

   (e) Check the heat exchanger for cooling water flow

(4) Steam system procedure:

   (a) Record the steam pressure gauge reading

   (b) Observe the time for turbine to reach running speed

8.3.3 Annual Tests.

8.3.3.1 An annual test of each pump assembly shall be conducted under minimum, rated, and peak flows of the fire pump by controlling the quantity of water discharged through approved test devices.

8.3.3.1.1* If available suction supplies do not allow flowing of 150 percent of the rated pump capacity, the fire pump shall be permitted to operate at maximum allowable discharge.

8.3.3.1.2* This test shall be conducted as described in 8.3.3.1.2.1, 8.3.3.1.2.2, or 8.3.3.1.2.3.

8.3.3.1.2.1 Use of the Pump Discharge Via the Hose Streams. Pump suction and discharge pressures and the flow measurements of each hose stream shall determine the total pump output. Care shall be taken to prevent water damage by verifying there is adequate drainage for the high-pressure water discharge from hoses.

8.3.3.1.2.2 Use of the Pump Discharge Via the Bypass Flowmeter to Drain or Suction the Reservoir. Pump suction and discharge pressures and the flowmeter measurements shall determine the total pump output.

8.3.3.1.2.3 Use of the Pump Discharge Via the Bypass Flowmeter to Pump Suction (Closed-Loop Metering). Pump suction and discharge pressures and the flowmeter measurements shall determine the total pump output.

8.3.3.1.3 Where the annual test is conducted periodically in accordance with 8.3.3.1.2.3, a test shall be conducted every 3 years in accordance with 8.3.3.1.2.1 or 8.3.3.1.2.2 in lieu of the method described in 8.3.3.1.2.3.

8.3.3.1.4 Where 8.3.3.1.2.2 or 8.3.3.1.2.3 is used, the flow meter shall be adjusted immediately prior to conducting the test in accordance with the manufacturer's instructions. If the test results are not consistent with the previous annual test, 8.3.3.1.2.1 shall be used. If testing in accordance with

8.3.3.1.2.1 is not possible, a flowmeter calibration shall be performed and the test shall be repeated.

8.3.3.2 The pertinent visual observations, measurements, and adjustments specified in the following checklists shall be conducted annually while the pump is running and flowing water under the specified output condition:

(1) At no-flow condition (churn):
   (a) Check the circulation relief valve for operation to discharge water
   (b) Check the pressure relief valve (if installed) for proper operation
   (c) Continue the test for ½ hour
(2) At each flow condition:
   (a) Record the electric motor voltage and current (all lines)
   (b) Record the pump speed in rpm
   (c) Record the simultaneous (approximately) readings of pump suction and discharge pressures and pump discharge flow

8.3.3.3* For installations having a pressure relief valve, the operation of the relief valve shall be closely observed during each flow condition to determine if the pump discharge pressure exceeds the normal operating pressure of the system components.

8.3.3.3.1 The pressure relief valve shall also be observed during each flow condition to determine if the pressure relief valve closes at the proper pressure.

8.3.3.3.2 A pressure relief valve that is open during a flow condition will affect test results.

8.3.3.3.3 The pressure relief valve shall be closed during flow conditions if necessary to achieve minimum rated characteristics for the pump and reset to normal position at the conclusion of the pump test.

8.3.3.4 For installations having an automatic transfer switch, the following test shall be performed to ensure that the overcurrent protective devices (i.e., fuses or circuit breakers) do not open:

(1) Simulate a power failure condition while the pump is operating at peak load
(2) Verify that the transfer switch transfers power to the alternate power source
(3) Verify that the pump continues to perform at peak load
(4) Remove the power failure condition and verify that after a time delay, the pump is reconnected to the normal power source

8.3.3.5 Alarm conditions shall be simulated by activating alarm circuits at alarm sensor locations, and all such local or remote alarm indicating devices (visual and audible) shall be observed for operation.

8.3.3.6 Safety. Section 4.7 shall be followed for safety requirements while working near electric motor-driven fire pumps.

8.3.3.7* Suction Screens. After the water-flow portions of the annual test or fire protection system activations, the suction screens shall be inspected and cleared of any debris or obstructions.

8.3.4 Other Tests.

8.3.4.1 Engine generator sets supplying emergency or standby power to fire pump assemblies shall be tested routinely in accordance with NFPA 110, *Standard for Emergency and Standby Power Systems.*

8.3.4.2 Automatic transfer switches shall be tested routinely and exercised in accordance with NFPA 110, *Standard for Emergency and Standby Power Systems.*

8.3.4.3 Tests of appropriate environmental pump room space conditions (e.g., heating, ventilation, illumination) shall be made to ensure proper manual or automatic operation of the associated equipment.

8.3.4.4* Parallel and angular alignment of the pump and driver shall be checked during the annual test. Any misalignment shall be corrected.

8.3.5 Test Results and Evaluation.

8.3.5.1* Interpretation.

8.3.5.1.1 The interpretation of the test results shall be the basis of determination of performance of the pump assembly.

8.3.5.1.2 Qualified individuals shall make interpretation of the test results.

8.3.5.2 Engine Speed.

8.3.5.2.1 Theoretical factors for correction to the rated speed shall not be applied where determining the compliance of the pump per the test.

8.3.5.2.2 Increasing the engine speed beyond the rated speed of the pump at rated condition is not an acceptable method for meeting the rated pump performance.

8.3.5.3 The fire pump assembly shall be considered acceptable if either of the following conditions is shown during the test:

(1)*The test matches the initial unadjusted field acceptance test curve.
(2) The fire pump matches the performance characteristics as indicated on the pump nameplate.

8.3.5.4* Degradation in excess of 5 percent of the pressure of the initial unadjusted acceptance test curve or nameplate shall require an investigation to reveal the cause of degraded performance.

8.3.5.5 Current and voltage readings whose product does not exceed the product of the rated voltage and rated full-load current multiplied by the permitted motor service factor shall be considered acceptable. Voltage readings at the motor within 5 percent below or 10 percent above the rated (i.e., nameplate) voltage shall be considered acceptable.

8.4 Reports.

8.4.1 Any abnormality observed during inspection or testing shall be reported promptly to the person responsible for correcting the abnormality.

8.4.2* Test results shall be recorded and retained for comparison purposes in accordance with Section 4.3.

8.4.2.1 All time delay intervals associated with the pump's starting, stopping, and energy source transfer shall be recorded.

8.5 Maintenance.

8.5.1* A preventive maintenance program shall be established on all components of the pump assembly in accordance with the manufacturer's recommendations.

8.5.2 Records shall be maintained on all work performed on the pump, driver, controller, and auxiliary equipment.

8.5.3 In the absence of manufacturer's recommendations for preventive maintenance, Table 8.5.3 shall be used for alternative requirements.

Table 8.5.3 Summary of Fire Pump Inspection, Testing, and Maintenance

Complete as Applicable	Visual Inspection	Check	Change	Clean	Test	Frequency
A. Pump System						
1. Lubricate pump bearings			X			Annually
2. Check pump shaft end play		X				Annually
3. Check accuracy of pressure gauges and sensors		X	X			Annually (change or recalibrate when 5% out of calibration)
4. Check pump coupling alignment		X				Annually
5. Wet pit suction screens		X		X		After each pump operation
B. Mechanical Transmission						
1. Lubricate coupling			X			Annually
2. Lubricate right-angle gear drive			X			Annually
C. Electrical System						
1. Exercise isolating switch and circuit breaker					X	Monthly
2. Trip circuit breaker (if mechanism provided)					X	Annually
3. Operate manual starting means (electrical)					X	Semiannually
4. Inspect and operate emergency manual starting means (without power)	X				X	Annually
5. Tighten electrical connections as necessary		X				Annually
6. Lubricate mechanical moving parts (excluding starters and relays)		X				Annually
7. Calibrate pressure switch settings		X				Annually
8. Grease motor bearings			X			Annually
D. Diesel Engine System						
1. Fuel						
(a) Tank level	X	X				Weekly
(b) Tank float switch	X				X	Weekly
(c) Solenoids valve operation	X				X	Weekly
(d) Strainer, filter, or dirt leg, or combination thereof				X		Quarterly
(e) Water and foreign material in tank				X		Annually
(f) Water in system		X		X		Weekly
(g) Flexible hoses and connectors	X					Weekly
(h) Tank vents and overflow piping unobstructed		X			X	Annually
(i) Piping	X					Annually
2. Lubrication System						
(a) Oil level	X	X				Weekly
(b) Oil change			X			50 hours or annually
(c) Oil filter(s)			X			50 hours or annually
(d) Lube oil heater		X				Weekly
(e) Crankcase breather	X		X	X		Quarterly

(continues)

Table 8.5.3 *Continued*

Complete as Applicable	Visual Inspection	Check	Change	Clean	Test	Frequency
3. Cooling System						
(a) Level	X	X				Weekly
(b) Antifreeze protection level					X	Semiannually
(c) Antifreeze			X			Annually
(d) Adequate cooling water to heat exchanger		X				Weekly
(e) Rod out heat exchanger				X		Annually
(f) Water pump(s)	X					Weekly
(g) Condition of flexible hoses and connections	X	X				Weekly
(h) Jacket water heater		X				Weekly
(i) Inspect duct work, clean louvers (combustion air)	X	X	X			Annually
(j) Water strainer				X		Quarterly
4. Exhaust System						
(a) Leakage	X	X				Weekly
(b) Drain condensate trap		X				Weekly
(c) Insulation and fire hazards	X					Quarterly
(d) Excessive back pressure					X	Annually
(e) Exhaust system hangers and supports	X					Annually
(f) Flexible exhaust section	X					Semiannually
5. Battery System						
(a) Electrolyte level		X				Weekly
(b) Terminals clean and tight	X	X				Quarterly
(c) Remove corrosion, case exterior clean and dry	X		X			Monthly
(d) Specific gravity or state of charge					X	Monthly
(e) Charger and charge rate	X					Monthly
(f) Equalize charge		X				Monthly
6. Electrical System						
(a) General inspection	X					Weekly
(b) Tighten control and power wiring connections		X				Annually
(c) Wire chafing where subject to movement	X	X				Quarterly
(d) Operation of safeties and alarms		X			X	Semiannually
(e) Boxes, panels, and cabinets				X		Semiannually
(f) Circuit breakers or fuses	X	X				Monthly
(g) Circuit breakers or fuses			X			Biennially

8.5.4 The preventive maintenance program shall be initiated immediately after the pump assembly has passed acceptance tests.

Chapter 9 Water Storage Tanks

9.1* General. This chapter shall provide the minimum requirements for the routine inspection, testing, and maintenance of water storage tanks. Table 9.1 shall be used to determine the minimum required frequencies for inspection, testing, and maintenance.

9.1.1 Valves and Connections. Valves and fire department connections shall be inspected, tested, and maintained in accordance with Chapter 12.

9.1.2 Impairments. The procedures outlined in Chapter 14 shall be followed where an impairment to protection occurs.

9.1.3* Notification to Supervisory Service. To avoid false alarms where a supervisory service is provided, the alarm receiving facility always shall be notified by the owner or designated representative as follows:

(1) Before conducting any test or procedure that could result in the activation of an alarm

(2) After such tests or procedures are concluded

Table 9.1 Summary of Water Storage Tank Inspection, Testing, and Maintenance

Item	Activity	Frequency	Reference
Condition of water in tank	Inspection	Monthly/quarterly*	9.2.1
Water temperature	Inspection	Daily/weekly*	9.2.4
Heating system	Inspection	Daily/weekly*	9.2.6.6
Control valves	Inspection	Weekly/monthly	Table 12.1
Water — level	Inspection	Monthly/quarterly	9.2.1
Air pressure	Inspection	Monthly/quarterly	9.2.2
Tank — exterior	Inspection	Quarterly	9.2.5.1
Support structure	Inspection	Quarterly	9.2.5.1
Catwalks and ladders	Inspection	Quarterly	9.2.5.1
Surrounding area	Inspection	Quarterly	9.2.5.2
Hoops and grillage	Inspection	Annually	9.2.5.4
Painted/coated surfaces	Inspection	Annually	9.2.5.5
Expansion joints	Inspection	Annually	9.2.5.3
Interior	Inspection	5 years/3 years	9.2.6
Check valves	Inspection	5 years	Table 12.1
Temperature alarms	Test	Monthly*	9.2.4.2, 9.2.4.3
High temperature limit switches	Test	Monthly*	9.3.4
Water level alarms	Test	Semiannually	9.3.5
Level indicators	Test	5 years	9.3.1
Pressure gauges	Test	5 years	9.3.6
Water level	Maintenance	—	9.4.1
Drain silt	Maintenance	Semiannually	9.4.5
Control valves	Maintenance	Annually	Table 12.1
Embankment-supported coated fabric (ESCF)	Maintenance	—	9.4.6
Check valves	Maintenance	—	12.4.2.2

*Cold weather/heating season only.

9.2 Inspection.

9.2.1 Water Level.

9.2.1.1* Tanks equipped with supervised water level alarms that are connected to a constantly attended location shall be inspected quarterly.

9.2.1.2 Tanks not equipped with supervised water level alarms connected to a constantly attended location shall be inspected monthly.

9.2.2 Air Pressure.

9.2.2.1 Pressure tanks that have their air pressure source supervised in accordance with *NFPA 72®*, *National Fire Alarm Code®*, shall be inspected quarterly.

9.2.2.2 The air pressure in pressure tanks with a nonsupervised air pressure source shall be inspected monthly.

9.2.3 Heating System.

9.2.3.1 Tank heating systems installed on tanks equipped with a supervised low water temperature alarm that are connected to a constantly attended location shall be inspected weekly.

9.2.3.2 Tank heating systems without a supervised low temperature alarm connected to a constantly attended location shall be inspected daily during the heating season.

9.2.4 Water Temperature.

9.2.4.1 The temperature of water tanks shall not be less than 4°C (40°F).

9.2.4.2 The temperature of water in tanks with low temperature alarms connected to a constantly attended location shall be inspected and recorded weekly during the heating season.

9.2.4.3 The temperature of water in tanks without low temperature alarms connected to a constantly attended location shall be inspected and recorded daily during the heating season.

9.2.5 Exterior Inspection.

9.2.5.1* The exterior of the tank, supporting structure, vents, foundation, and catwalks or ladders, where provided, shall be inspected quarterly for signs of obvious damage or weakening.

9.2.5.2 The area surrounding the tank and supporting structure, where provided, shall be inspected quarterly to ensure that the following conditions are met:

(1) The area is free of combustible storage, trash, debris, brush, or material that could present a fire exposure hazard.
(2) The area is free of the accumulation of material on or near parts that could result in accelerated corrosion or rot.
(3) The tank and support are free of ice buildup.
(4) The exterior sides and top of embankments supporting coated fabric tanks are free of erosion.

9.2.5.3 Expansion joints, where provided, shall be inspected annually for leaks and cracks.

9.2.5.4 The hoops and grillage of wooden tanks shall be inspected annually.

9.2.5.5 Exterior painted, coated, or insulated surfaces of the tank and supporting structure, where provided, shall be inspected annually for signs of degradation.

9.2.6 Interior Inspection.

9.2.6.1 Frequency.

9.2.6.1.1* The interior of steel tanks without corrosion protection shall be inspected every 3 years.

9.2.6.1.2 The interior of all other types of tanks shall be inspected every 5 years.

9.2.6.2 Where interior inspection is made by means of underwater evaluation, silt shall first be removed from the tank floor.

9.2.6.3 The tank interior shall be inspected for signs of pitting, corrosion, spalling, rot, other forms of deterioration, waste materials and debris, aquatic growth, and local or general failure of interior coating.

9.2.6.4 Steel tanks exhibiting signs of interior pitting, corrosion, or failure of coating shall be tested in accordance with 9.2.7.

9.2.6.5* Tanks on ring-type foundations with sand in the middle shall be inspected for evidence of voids beneath the floor.

9.2.6.6 The heating system and components including piping shall be inspected.

9.2.6.7 The anti-vortex plate shall be inspected for deterioration or blockage.

9.2.7 Interior Inspection. Where a drained interior inspection of a steel tank is conducted in accordance with 9.2.6.4, the following tests shall be conducted:

(1) Evaluation of tank coatings shall be made in accordance with the adhesion test of ASTM D 3359, *Standard Test Methods for Measuring Adhesion by Tape Test*, generally referred to as the "cross-hatch test."
(2) Dry film thickness measurements shall be taken at random locations to determine the overall coating thickness.
(3) Nondestructive ultrasonic readings shall be taken to evaluate the wall thickness where there is evidence of pitting or corrosion.
(4) Interior surfaces shall be spot wet-sponge tested to detect pinholes, cracks, or other compromises in the coating. Special attention shall be given to sharp edges such as ladder rungs, nuts, and bolts.
(5) Tank bottoms shall be tested for metal loss and/or rust on the underside by use of ultrasonic testing where there is evidence of pitting or corrosion. Removal, visual inspection, and replacement of random floor coupons shall be an acceptable alternative to ultrasonic testing.
(6) Tanks with flat bottoms shall be vacuum-box tested at bottom seams in accordance with test procedures found in NFPA 22, *Standard for Water Tanks for Private Fire Protection*.

9.3 Testing.

9.3.1* Level indicators shall be tested every 5 years for accuracy and freedom of movement.

9.3.2 The tank heating system, where provided, shall be tested prior to the heating season to make certain it is in the proper working order.

9.3.3 Low water temperature alarms, where provided, shall be tested monthly (cold weather only).

9.3.4* High water temperature limit switches on tank heating systems, where provided, shall be tested monthly whenever the heating system is in service.

9.3.5* High and low water level alarms shall be tested semiannually.

9.3.6* Pressure gauges shall be tested every 5 years with a calibrated gauge in accordance with the manufacturer's instructions. Gauges not accurate to within 3 percent of the scale of the gauge being tested shall be recalibrated or replaced.

9.4 Maintenance. Voids discovered beneath the floors of tanks shall be filled by pumping in grout or accessing the sand and replenishing.

9.4.1 The tank shall be maintained full or at the designed water level.

9.4.2 The hatch covers in the roofs and the door at the top of the frostproof casing shall always be kept securely fastened with substantial catches as a protection against freezing and windstorm damage.

9.4.3 No waste materials, such as boards, paint cans, trim, or loose material, shall be left in the tank or on the surface of the tank.

9.4.4 The exposed surfaces of embankment-supported coated fabric (ESCF) tanks shall be cleaned and painted every 2 years or in accordance with the manufacturer's instructions.

9.4.5 Silt shall be removed during interior inspections or more frequently as needed to avoid accumulation to the level of the tank outlet.

9.4.6 Maintenance of Embankment-Supported Coated Fabric (ESCF) Suction Tanks. The maintenance of ESCF tanks shall be completed in accordance with this section and the tank manufacturer's instructions.

9.5 Records. Records shall be maintained in accordance with Section 4.3.

Chapter 10   Water Spray Fixed Systems

10.1* General. This chapter shall provide the minimum requirements for the routine inspection, testing, and maintenance of water spray protection from fixed nozzle systems only. Table 10.1 shall be used to determine the minimum required frequencies for inspection, testing, and maintenance.

10.1.1 This chapter shall not cover water spray protection from portable nozzles, sprinkler systems, monitor nozzles, or other means of application.

10.1.2* NFPA 15, *Standard for Water Spray Fixed Systems for Fire Protection*, shall be consulted to determine the requirements for design and installation, including acceptance testing.

10.1.3 Valves and Connections. Valves and fire department connections shall be inspected, tested, and maintained in accordance with Chapter 12.

Table 10.1 Summary of Water Spray Fixed System Inspection, Testing, and Maintenance

Item	Activity	Frequency	Reference
Backflow preventer	Inspection		Chapter 12
Check valves	Inspection		Chapter 12
Control valves	Inspection	Weekly (sealed)	Chapter 12
Control valves	Inspection	Monthly (locked, supervised)	Chapter 12
Deluge valve	Inspection		10.2.2, Chapter 12
Detection systems	Inspection		*NFPA 72*
Detector check valves	Inspection		Chapter 12
Drainage	Inspection	Quarterly	10.2.8
Electric motor	Inspection		10.2.9, Chapter 8
Engine drive	Inspection		10.2.9, Chapter 8
Fire pump	Inspection		10.2.9, Chapter 8
Fittings	Inspection	Quarterly	10.2.4, 10.2.4.1
Fittings (rubber-gasketed)	Inspection	Quarterly	10.2.4.1, A.10.2.4.1
Gravity tanks	Inspection		10.2.10, Chapter 9
Hangers	Inspection	Quarterly	10.2.4.2
Heat (deluge valve house)	Inspection	Daily/weekly	10.2.1.5, Chapter 12
Nozzles	Inspection	Monthly	10.2.1.1, 10.2.1.2, 10.2.1.6, 10.2.5.1, 10.2.5.2
Pipe	Inspection	Quarterly	10.2.1.1, 10.2.1.2, 10.2.4, 10.2.4.1
Pressure tank	Inspection		10.2.10, Chapter 9
Steam driver	Inspection		10.2.9, Chapter 8
Strainers	Inspection	Mfg. instruction	10.2.7
Suction tanks	Inspection		10.2.10, Chapter 9
Supports	Inspection	Quarterly	10.2.1.1, 10.2.1.2, 10.2.4.2
Water supply piping	Inspection		10.2.6.1, 10.2.6.2
UHSWSS — detectors	Inspection	Monthly	10.4.2
UHSWSS — controllers	Inspection	Each shift	10.4.3
UHSWSS — valves	Inspection	Each shift	10.4.4
Backflow preventer	Operational test		Chapter 12
Check valves	Operational test		Chapter 12
Control valves	Operational test	Quarterly	Chapter 12
Deluge valve	Operational test		10.2.2, Chapter 12
Detection systems	Operational test		*NFPA 72*
Detector check valve	Operational test		Chapter 12
Electric motor	Operational test		10.2.9, Chapter 8
Engine drive	Operational test		10.2.9, Chapter 8
Fire pump	Operational test		10.2.9, Chapter 8
Flushing	Operational test	Annually	10.2.1.3, Section 10.3 (flushing of connection to riser, part of annual test)
Gravity tanks	Operational test		10.2.10, Chapter 9
Main drain test	Operational test	Quarterly	Chapter 12
Manual release	Operational test	Annually	10.2.1.3, 10.3.6
Nozzles	Operational test	Annually	10.2.1.3, 10.2.1.6, Section 10.3
Pressure tank	Operational test		Section 10.2, Chapter 9
Steam driver	Operational test		10.2.9, Chapter 8
Strainers	Operational test	Annually	10.2.1.3, 10.2.1.7, 10.2.7
Suction tanks	Operational test		10.2.10, Chapter 9
Water-flow alarm	Operational test	Quarterly	Chapter 5
Water spray system test	Operational test	Annually	Section 10.3, Chapter 12
Water supply flow test	Operational test		7.3.2
UHSWSS	Operational test	Annually	Section 10.4
Backflow preventer	Maintenance		Chapter 12
Check valves	Maintenance		Chapter 12
Control valves	Maintenance	Annually	10.2.1.4, Chapter 12
Deluge valve	Maintenance		10.2.2, Chapter 12
Detection systems	Maintenance		*NFPA 72*
Detector check valve	Maintenance		Chapter 12
Electric motor	Maintenance		10.2.9, Chapter 8

(continues)

Table 10.1 *Continued*

Item	Activity	Frequency	Reference
Engine drive	Maintenance		10.2.9, Chapter 8
Fire pump	Maintenance		10.2.9, Chapter 8
Gravity tanks	Maintenance		10.2.10, Chapter 9
Pressure tank	Maintenance		10.2.6, Chapter 9
Steam driver	Maintenance		10.2.9, Chapter 8
Strainers	Maintenance	Annually	10.2.1.4, 10.2.1.7, 10.2.7
Strainers (baskets/screen)	Maintenance	5 years	10.2.1.4, 10.2.1.8, A.10.2.7
Suction tanks	Maintenance		10.2.10, Chapter 9
Water spray system	Maintenance	Annually	10.2.1.4, Chapter 12

10.1.4* Impairments. The procedures outlined in Chapter 14 and this section shall be followed where an impairment to protection occurs.

10.1.4.1* When a water spray fixed system or any portion thereof is out of service for any reason, notice shall be given to facility management, the local fire department, the on-site fire brigade, and other authorities having jurisdiction, as applicable.

10.1.4.2 A sign shall be posted at each fire department connection or system control valve indicating which portion of the system is out of service.

10.2 Inspection and Maintenance Procedures.

10.2.1 The components described in this section shall be inspected and maintained at the frequency specified in Table 10.1 and in accordance with this standard and the manufacturer's instructions.

10.2.1.1 Items in areas that are inaccessible for safety considerations due to factors such as continuous process operations and energized electrical equipment shall be inspected during each scheduled shutdown but not more than every 18 months.

10.2.1.2 Inspections shall not be required for items in areas with no provision for access and that are not subject to the conditions noted in 10.2.4.1, 10.2.4.2, and 10.2.5.1.

10.2.1.3 Items in areas that are inaccessible for safety considerations shall be tested at longer intervals in accordance with 12.4.3.2.2.2.

10.2.1.4 Other maintenance intervals shall be permitted depending on the results of the visual inspection and operating tests.

10.2.1.5 Deluge valve enclosures shall be inspected in accordance with the provisions of Chapter 12.

10.2.1.6 Nozzle discharge patterns and direction shall be checked during the annual test.

10.2.1.7 Nozzle strainers shall be removed, inspected, and cleaned during the flushing procedure for the mainline strainer.

10.2.1.8 Mainline strainers shall be removed and inspected every 5 years for damaged and corroded parts.

10.2.2 Deluge Valves. Deluge valves shall be inspected, tested, and maintained in accordance with Chapter 12.

10.2.3 Automatic Detection Equipment. Automatic detection equipment shall be inspected, tested, and maintained in ac-

cordance with *NFPA 72, National Fire Alarm Code,* to ensure that the detectors are in place, securely fastened, and protected from corrosion, weather, and mechanical damage and that the communication wiring, control panels, or pneumatic tubing system is functional.

10.2.4* System Piping. System piping, fittings, hangers, and supports shall be inspected and maintained to ensure continuity of water delivery to the spray nozzles at full water-flow and design pressure.

10.2.4.1* System Piping and Fittings. System piping and fittings shall be inspected for the following:

(1) Mechanical damage (e.g., broken piping or cracked fittings)
(2) External conditions (e.g., missing or damaged paint or coatings, rust, and corrosion)
(3) Misalignment or trapped sections
(4) Low point drains (automatic or manual)
(5) Location of rubber-gasketed fittings

10.2.4.2* Hangers and Supports. Hangers and supports shall be inspected for the following and repaired as necessary:

(1) Condition (e.g., missing or damaged paint or coating, rust, and corrosion)
(2) Secure attachment to structural supports and piping
(3) Damaged or missing hangers

10.2.5* Water Spray Nozzles.

10.2.5.1 Water spray nozzles shall be inspected and maintained to ensure that they are in place, continue to be aimed or pointed in the direction intended in the system design, and are free from external loading and corrosion.

10.2.5.2 Where caps or plugs are required, the inspection shall confirm they are in place and free to operate as intended.

10.2.5.3 Misaligned water spray nozzles shall be adjusted (aimed) by visual means, and the discharge patterns shall be checked at the next scheduled flow test.

10.2.6 Water Supply.

10.2.6.1 The dependability of the water supply shall be ensured by regular inspection and maintenance, whether furnished by a municipal source, on-site storage tanks, a fire pump, or private underground piping systems.

10.2.6.2* Water supply piping shall be maintained free of internal obstructions.

10.2.7* Strainers.

10.2.7.1 Mainline strainers (basket or screen) shall be flushed until clear after each operation or flow test.

10.2.7.2 Individual water spray nozzle strainers shall be removed, cleaned, and inspected after each operation or flow test.

10.2.7.3 All strainers shall be inspected and cleaned in accordance with the manufacturer's instructions.

10.2.7.4 Damaged or corroded parts shall be replaced or repaired.

10.2.8 Drainage. The area beneath and surrounding a water spray fixed system shall be inspected visually on a quarterly basis to ensure that drainage facilities, such as trap sumps and drainage trenches, are not blocked and retention embankments or dikes are in good repair.

10.2.9 Fire Pumps. Chapter 8 shall be followed for inspection and maintenance requirements.

10.2.10 Water Tanks (Gravity, Pressure, or Suction Tanks, or Reservoirs). Chapter 9 shall be followed for inspection and maintenance requirements.

10.3 Operational Tests.

10.3.1 Performance. Water spray fixed systems shall require competent and effective care and maintenance to ensure they perform as designed.

10.3.1.1 Frequency of system tests shall be in accordance with Table 10.1.

10.3.1.2 Water spray fixed systems shall be serviced in accordance with this standard and with the manufacturer's instructions.

10.3.2 Notification.

10.3.2.1 To avoid false alarms where a supervisory service is provided, the alarm receiving facility always shall be notified by the owner or designated representative as follows:

(1) Before conducting any test or procedure that could result in the actuation of an alarm
(2) After such tests or procedures are concluded

10.3.2.2 Notify all personnel whose operations could be affected by the system operation.

10.3.2.3 The owner's representative, the authority having jurisdiction, and the fire department or fire brigade shall be notified that testing is to be conducted so they have the opportunity to observe the inspection and testing of the water spray fixed systems.

10.3.3* Test Preparation. Precautions shall be taken to prevent damage to property during the test.

10.3.4 Operational Test Performance. Operational tests shall be conducted to ensure that the water spray fixed systems respond as designed, both automatically and manually.

10.3.4.1* Response Time.

10.3.4.1.1 Under test conditions, the heat detection systems, where exposed to a heat test source, shall operate within 40 seconds.

10.3.4.1.2 Under test conditions, the flammable gas detection system, where exposed to a standard test gas concentration, shall operate within 20 seconds.

10.3.4.1.3 These response times shall be recorded.

10.3.4.2 Discharge Time. The time lapse between operation of detection systems and water delivery time to the protected area shall be recorded.

10.3.4.3* Discharge Patterns.

10.3.4.3.1 The water discharge patterns from all of the spray nozzles shall be observed to ensure that patterns are not impeded by plugged nozzles and to ensure that nozzles are correctly positioned and that obstructions do not prevent discharge patterns from wetting surfaces to be protected.

10.3.4.3.2 Where obstructions occur, the piping and nozzles shall be cleaned and the system retested.

10.3.4.4 Pressure Readings.

10.3.4.4.1 Pressure readings shall be recorded at the hydraulically most remote nozzle to ensure the water flow has not been impeded by partially closed valves or by plugged strainers or piping.

10.3.4.4.2 A second pressure reading shall be recorded at the deluge valve to ensure the water supply is adequate.

10.3.4.4.3 Readings shall be compared to the hydraulic design pressures to ensure the original system design requirements are met and the water supply is adequate to meet the design requirements.

10.3.4.4.3.1 Where the hydraulically most remote nozzle is inaccessible, nozzles shall be permitted to be checked visually without taking a pressure reading on the most remote nozzle.

10.3.4.4.3.2 Where the reading taken at the riser indicates that the water supply has deteriorated, a gauge shall be placed on the hydraulically most remote nozzle and the results compared with the required design pressure.

10.3.5 Multiple Systems. The maximum number of systems expected to operate in case of fire shall be tested simultaneously to check the adequacy of the water supply.

10.3.6 Manual Operation. Manual actuation devices shall be operated annually.

10.3.7 Return to Service. After the full flow test, the water spray system shall be maintained and returned to service in accordance with the manufacturer's instructions.

10.3.7.1 Main Drain Tests.

10.3.7.1.1 Main drain tests shall be conducted at the main riser to determine whether there has been any change in the condition of the water supply piping and controlling valves.

10.3.7.1.2 Static and residual water pressures shall be recorded respectively before, during, and after the operation of the fully opened drain valve.

10.3.7.1.3 Readings shall be compared with those made at the time of the original acceptance tests or with those made at the time of the last test to determine whether there has been any deterioration of the water supply.

10.3.7.2 Low Point Drains.

10.3.7.2.1 To prevent freezing and corrosion, all low point drains in aboveground piping shall be opened, the pipe drained, and the valves closed and plugs replaced.

10.3.7.2.2 Where weep holes are provided in lieu of low point drains, they shall be inspected to ensure they are clear and unobstructed.

10.4 Ultra-High-Speed Water Spray System Operational Tests.

10.4.1 A full operational test, including measurements of response time, shall be conducted at intervals not exceeding 1 year.

10.4.1.1 Systems out of service shall be tested before being placed back in service.

10.4.2 All detectors shall be tested and inspected monthly for physical damage and accumulation of deposits on the lenses of optical detectors.

10.4.3 Controllers shall be inspected for faults at the start of each working shift.

10.4.4 Valves.

10.4.4.1 Valves on the water supply line shall be inspected at the start of each working shift to verify they are open.

10.4.4.2 Valves secured in the open position with a locking device or monitored by a signaling device that will sound a trouble signal at the deluge system control panel or other central location shall not require inspection.

10.4.5 Response Time.

10.4.5.1 The response time shall be verified during the operational test.

10.4.5.2 The response time shall be in accordance with the requirements of the system but not more than 100 milliseconds.

10.5 Records. Section 4.3 shall be followed for recordkeeping and reporting procedures.

Chapter 11   Foam-Water Sprinkler Systems

11.1 General. This chapter shall provide the minimum requirements for the routine inspection, testing, and maintenance of foam-water systems. Table 11.1 shall be used to determine the minimum required frequencies for inspection, testing, and maintenance.

Table 11.1 Summary of Foam-Water Sprinkler System Inspection, Testing, and Maintenance

System/Component	Activity	Frequency	Reference
Discharge device location (sprinkler)	Inspection	Annually	11.2.5
Discharge device location (spray nozzle)	Inspection	Monthly	11.2.5
Discharge device position (sprinkler)	Inspection	Annually	11.2.5
Discharge device position (spray nozzle)	Inspection	Monthly	11.2.5
Foam concentrate strainer(s)	Inspection	Quarterly	11.2.7.2
Drainage in system area	Inspection	Quarterly	11.2.8
Proportioning system(s) — all	Inspection	Monthly	11.2.9
Pipe corrosion	Inspection	Quarterly	11.2.3
Pipe damage	Inspection	Quarterly	11.2.3
Fittings corrosion	Inspection	Quarterly	11.2.3
Fittings damage	Inspection	Quarterly	11.2.3
Hangers/supports	Inspection	Quarterly	11.2.4
Water supply tank(s)	Inspection		Chapter 9
Fire pump(s)	Inspection		Chapter 8
Water supply piping	Inspection		11.2.6.1
Control valve(s)	Inspection	Weekly/monthly	—
Deluge/preaction valve(s)	Inspection		11.2.1, Chapter 12
Detection system	Inspection	See *NFPA 72*	11.2.2
Discharge device location	Test	Annually	11.3.3.6
Discharge device position	Test	Annually	11.3.3.6
Discharge device obstruction	Test	Annually	11.3.3.6
Foam concentrate strainer(s)	Test	Annually	11.2.7.2
Proportioning system(s) — all	Test	Annually	11.2.9
Complete foam-water system(s)	Test	Annually	11.3.3
Foam-water solution	Test	Annually	11.3.6
Manual actuation device(s)	Test	Annually	11.3.5
Backflow preventer(s)	Test	Annually	Chapter 12
Fire pump(s)	Test	See Chapter 8	—
Water supply piping	Test	Annually	Chapter 10
Control valve(s)	Test	See Chapter 12	—
Strainer(s) — mainline	Test	See Chapter 10	11.2.7.1
Deluge/preaction valve(s)	Test	See Chapter 12	11.2.1
Detection system	Test	See *NFPA 72*	11.2.2
Backflow preventer(s)	Test	See Chapter 12	—
Water supply tank(s)	Test	See Chapter 9	—
Water supply flow test	Test	See Chapter 4	11.2.6

Table 11.1 *Continued*

System/Component	Activity	Frequency	Reference
Foam concentrate pump operation	Maintenance	Monthly	11.4.6(A), 11.4.7(A)
Foam concentrate strainer(s)	Maintenance	Quarterly	Section 11.4
Foam concentrate samples	Maintenance	Annually	11.2.10
Proportioning system(s) standard pressure type			
Ball drip (automatic type) drain valves	Maintenance	5 years	11.4.3(A)
Foam concentrate tank — drain and flush	Maintenance	10 years	11.4.3(B)
Corrosion and hydrostatic test	Maintenance	10 years	11.4.3(C)
Bladder tank type			
Sight glass	Maintenance	10 years	11.4.4(A)
Foam concentrate tank — hydrostatic test	Maintenance	10 years	11.4.4(B)
Line type			
Foam concentrate tank — corrosion and pickup pipes	Maintenance	10 years	11.4.5(A)
Foam concentrate tank — drain and flush	Maintenance	10 years	11.4.5(B)
Standard balanced pressure type			
Foam concentrate pump(s)	Maintenance	5 years *(see Note)*	11.4.6(B)
Balancing valve diaphragm	Maintenance	5 years	11.4.6(C)
Foam concentrate tank	Maintenance	10 years	11.4.6(D)
In-line balanced pressure type			
Foam concentrate pump(s)	Maintenance	5 years *(see Note)*	11.4.7(B)
Balancing valve diaphragm	Maintenance	5 years	11.4.7(C)
Foam concentrate tank	Maintenance	10 years	11.4.7(D)
Pressure vacuum vents	Maintenance	5 years	11.4.8
Water supply tank(s)	Maintenance	See Chapter 9	—
Fire pump(s)	Maintenance	See Chapter 8	—
Water supply	Maintenance	Annually	11.2.6.1
Backflow preventer(s)	Maintenance	See Chapter 12	—
Detector check valve(s)	Maintenance	See Chapter 12	—
Check valve(s)	Maintenance	See Chapter 12	—
Control valve(s)	Maintenance	See Chapter 12	—
Deluge/preaction valves	Maintenance	See Chapter 12	11.2.1
Strainer(s) — mainline	Maintenance	See Chapter 10	—
Detection system	Maintenance	See *NFPA 72*	11.2.2

Note: Also refer to manufacturer's instructions and frequency. Maintenance intervals other than preventive maintenance are not provided, as they depend on the results of the visual inspections and operational tests. For foam-water systems in aircraft hangars, refer to the inspection, test, and maintenance requirements of NFPA 409, *Standard on Aircraft Hangars*, Table 6.1.1.

11.1.1 Fire pumps, water storage tanks, and valves common to other types of water-based fire protection systems shall be inspected, tested, and maintained in accordance with Chapters 8, 9, and 12, respectively, and as specified in Table 11.1.

11.1.2 Foam-Water Systems.

11.1.2.1 This section shall apply to foam-water systems as specified in NFPA 16, *Standard for the Installation of Foam-Water Sprinkler and Foam-Water Spray Systems.*

11.1.2.2 This section shall not include systems detailed in NFPA 11, *Standard for Low-Expansion Foam.*

11.1.3 Foam-Water System.

11.1.3.1 If during routine inspection and testing it is determined that the foam-water system has been altered or changed (e.g., equipment replaced, relocated, or foam concentrate replaced), it shall be determined whether the design intent has been altered and whether the system operates properly.

11.1.3.2 The inspection shall verify that all components, including foam concentrate discharge devices and proportioning equipment, are installed in accordance with their listing.

11.1.4 Proportioning System. The proportioning system shall be permitted to be any of the following types:

(1) Standard pressure proportioner
(2) Bladder tank proportioner
(3) Line proportioner (venturi pickup)
(4) Standard balanced pressure proportioner
(5) In-line balanced pressure proportioner
(6) Orifice plate, either direct or indirect
(7) Other approved proportioning method

11.1.5 Impairments. The procedures outlined in Chapter 14 shall be followed where an impairment to protection occurs.

11.1.6 Notification to Supervisory Service. To avoid false alarms where a supervisory service is provided, the alarm receiving facility shall be notified by the owner or designated representative as follows:

(1) Before conducting any test or procedure that could result in the activation of an alarm
(2) After such tests or procedures are concluded

11.2 Inspection. Systems shall be inspected in accordance with the frequency specified in Table 11.1.

11.2.1 Deluge Valves. Deluge valves shall be inspected in accordance with the provisions of Chapter 12.

11.2.2 Automatic Detection Equipment. Automatic detection equipment shall be inspected, tested, and maintained in accordance with *NFPA 72, National Fire Alarm Code,* to ensure that the detectors are in place, securely fastened, and protected from corrosion, weather, and mechanical damage and that the communication wiring, control panels, or pneumatic tubing system is functional.

11.2.3 System Piping and Fittings. System piping and fittings shall be inspected for the following:

(1) Mechanical damage (e.g., broken piping or cracked fittings)
(2) External conditions (e.g., missing or damaged paint or coatings, rust, and corrosion)
(3) Misalignment or trapped sections
(4) Low point drains (automatic or manual)
(5) Location and condition of rubber-gasketed fittings

11.2.4 Hangers and Supports. Hangers and supports shall be inspected for the following and repaired as necessary:

(1) Condition (e.g., missing or damaged paint or coating, rust, and corrosion)
(2) Secure attachment to structural supports and piping
(3) Damaged or missing hangers

11.2.5* Foam-Water Discharge Devices.

11.2.5.1 Foam-water discharge devices shall be inspected visually and maintained to ensure that they are in place, continue to be aimed or pointed in the direction intended in the system design, and are free from external loading and corrosion.

11.2.5.2 Where caps or plugs are required, the inspection shall confirm they are in place and free to operate as intended.

11.2.5.3 Misaligned discharge devices shall be adjusted (aimed) by visual means, and the discharge patterns shall be checked at the next scheduled flow test.

11.2.5.4 Discharge devices are listed or approved for particular foam concentrates. Inspection shall verify that unlisted combinations of discharge devices and foam concentrate have not been substituted.

11.2.6 Water Supply.

11.2.6.1 The dependability of the water supply shall be ensured by regular inspection and maintenance, whether furnished by a municipal source, on-site storage tanks, a fire pump, or private underground piping systems.

11.2.6.2* Water supply piping shall be maintained free of internal obstructions.

11.2.7 Strainers.

11.2.7.1 Mainline and individual discharge device strainers (basket or screen) shall be inspected in accordance with the provisions of Chapter 10.

11.2.7.2 Foam concentrate strainers shall be inspected visually to ensure the blow-down valve is closed and plugged.

11.2.7.2.1 Baskets or screens shall be removed and inspected after each operation or flow test.

11.2.8 Drainage. The area beneath and surrounding a foam-water spray system shall be inspected to ensure that drainage facilities, such as trap sumps and drainage trenches, are not blocked and retention embankments or dikes are in good repair.

11.2.9* Proportioning Systems.

11.2.9.1 The components of the various proportioning systems described in 11.2.9 shall be inspected in accordance with the frequency specified in Table 11.1.

11.2.9.2 Valves specified to be checked shall be permitted to be open or closed, depending on specific functions within each foam-water system.

11.2.9.3 The position (open or closed) of valves shall be verified in accordance with specified operating conditions.

11.2.9.4* Inspection of the concentrate tank shall include verification that the quantity of foam concentrate satisfies the requirements of the original design.

11.2.9.5 Additional inspection requirements shall be performed as detailed for the proportioning systems specified in 11.2.9.

11.2.9.5.1* Standard Pressure Proportioner. This is a pressure vessel. The pressure shall be removed before the inspection to prevent injury. The inspection shall verify the following:

(1) Ball drip valves (automatic drains) are free and opened.
(2) External corrosion on foam concentrate storage tanks is not present.

11.2.9.5.2* Bladder Tank Proportioner. This is a pressure vessel. The pressure shall be removed before the inspection to prevent injury. The inspection shall include the following:

(1) Water control valves to foam concentrate tank
(2) A check for external corrosion on foam concentrate storage tanks
(3) A check for the presence of foam in the water surrounding the bladder (annual)

11.2.9.5.3 Line Proportioner. The inspection shall include the following:

(1)*Strainers
(2)*Verification that pressure vacuum vent is operating freely
(3) A check for external corrosion on foam concentrate storage tanks

11.2.9.5.4 Standard Balanced Pressure Proportioner. The inspection shall include the following:

(1)*Strainers
(2)*Verification that pressure vacuum vent is operating freely
(3) Verification that gauges are in good operating condition

(4) Verification that sensing line valves are open

(5) Verification that power is available to foam liquid pump

11.2.9.5.5 In-Line Balanced Pressure Proportioner. The inspection shall include the following:

(1)*Strainers

(2)*Verification that pressure vacuum vent is operating freely

(3) Verification that gauges are in good working condition

(4) Verification that sensing line valves at pump unit and individual proportioner stations are open

(5) Verification that power is available to foam liquid pump

11.2.9.5.6 Orifice Plate Proportioner. The inspection shall include the following:

(1)*Strainers

(2)*Verification that pressure vacuum vent is operating freely

(3) Verification that gauges are in good working condition

(4) Verification that power is available to foam liquid pump

11.2.10 Foam Concentrate Samples. Samples shall be submitted in accordance with the manufacturer's recommended sampling procedures.

11.3* Operational Tests. Frequency of system tests shall be in accordance with Table 11.1.

11.3.1 Owner's Representative. The owner's representative, the authority having jurisdiction, and the fire department or fire brigade shall be notified that testing is to be conducted so they have the opportunity to observe the testing of the foam-water systems.

11.3.2* Test Preparation. Precautions shall be taken to prevent damage to property during the test.

11.3.3* Operational Test Performance.

11.3.3.1 Operational tests shall be conducted to ensure that the foam-water system(s) responds as designed, both automatically and manually.

11.3.3.2 The test procedures shall simulate anticipated emergency events so the response of the foam-water system(s) can be evaluated.

11.3.3.3 Where discharge from the system discharge devices would create a hazardous condition or conflict with local requirements, an approved alternate method to achieve full flow conditions shall be permitted.

11.3.3.4 Response Time. Under test conditions, the automatic fire detection systems, when exposed to a test source, shall operate within the requirements of *NFPA 72, National Fire Alarm Code,* for the type of detector provided and the response time shall be recorded.

11.3.3.5 Discharge Time. The time lapse between operation of detection systems and water delivery time to the protected area shall be recorded for open discharge devices.

11.3.3.6 Discharge Patterns.

11.3.3.6.1 The discharge patterns from all of the open spray devices shall be observed to ensure that patterns are not impeded by plugged discharge devices and to ensure that discharge devices are correctly positioned and that obstructions do not prevent discharge patterns from covering surfaces to be protected.

11.3.3.6.2 Where obstructions occur, the piping and discharge devices shall be cleaned and the system retested.

11.3.3.6.3 Discharge devices shall be permitted to be of different orifice sizes and types.

11.3.3.7* Pressure Readings.

11.3.3.7.1 Pressure readings shall be recorded at the highest, most remote discharge device.

11.3.3.7.2 A second pressure reading shall be recorded at the main control valve.

11.3.3.7.3 Readings shall be compared to the hydraulic design pressures to ensure the original system design requirements are met.

11.3.4 Multiple Systems. The maximum number of systems expected to operate in case of fire shall be tested simultaneously to check the adequacy of the water supply and concentrate pump.

11.3.5 Manual Actuation Devices. Manual actuation devices shall be tested annually.

11.3.6 Concentration Testing.

11.3.6.1 During the full flow foam test, a foam sample shall be taken.

11.3.6.2 This sample shall be checked by refractometric or other methods to verify concentration of the solution.

11.3.6.3 Concentration shall be within 10 percent of the acceptance test results but in no case more than 10 percent below minimum design standards.

11.3.7 Return to Service. After the full flow test, the foam-water system shall be returned to service and the foam concentrate tank shall be replenished to design level.

11.4* Maintenance.

11.4.1 Maintenance of foam-water systems shall be in accordance with the requirements of those chapters covering the specific component parts.

11.4.2 Maintenance of specific foam components shall be in accordance with 11.4.3 through 11.4.7.

11.4.3 Standard Pressure Proportioner.

(A) The ball drip (automatic type) drain valves shall be disassembled, cleaned, and reassembled.

(B)* The foam liquid storage tank shall be drained of foam liquid and flushed. (Foam liquid shall be permitted to be salvaged and reused.)

(C) The foam liquid tank shall be inspected for internal and external corrosion and hydrostatically tested to the specified working pressure.

11.4.4 Bladder Tank Proportioner.

(A) Sight glass, where provided, shall be removed and cleaned.

(B)* The foam concentrate tank shall be hydrostatically tested to the specified working pressure.

11.4.5 Line Proportioner.

(A) The foam concentrate tank shall be inspected for internal corrosion. Pickup pipes inside the tank shall be inspected for corrosion, separation, or plugging.

(B) The foam concentrate tank shall be drained and flushed. (Foam concentrate shall be permitted to be salvaged and re-used.)

11.4.6 Standard Balanced Pressure Proportioner.

(A) The foam concentrate pump shall be operated. Foam concentrate shall be circulated back to the tank.

(B) Foam pumps, drive train, and drivers shall be serviced in accordance with the manufacturer's instructions and frequency, but not at intervals of more than 5 years.

(C) The diaphragm balancing valve shall be flushed through the diaphragm section with water or foam concentrate until fluid appears clear or new.

(D) The foam concentrate tank shall be inspected internally for corrosion and sediment. Excessive sediment shall require draining and flushing of the tank.

11.4.7 In-Line Balanced Pressure Proportioner.

(A) The foam concentrate pump shall be operated. Foam concentrate shall be circulated back to the tank.

(B) Foam pumps, drive train, and drivers shall be serviced in accordance with the manufacturer's instructions and frequency, but not at intervals of more than 5 years.

(C) The diaphragm balancing valve shall be flushed through the diaphragm section with water or foam concentrate until fluid appears clear or new.

(D) The foam concentrate tank shall be inspected internally for corrosion and sediment. Excessive sediment shall require draining and flushing of the tank.

11.4.8 Pressure Vacuum Vents. The procedures specified in 11.4.8(A) through 11.4.8(H) shall be performed on pressure vacuum vents every 5 years.

(A) The vent shall be removed from the expansion dome. While the vent is removed, it shall be ensured that the opening is not blocked and that dirt or other foreign objects do not enter the tank.

(B) The vest bonnet shall be removed. The vacuum valve and pressure valve shall be lifted out.

(C) The vent body shall be flushed internally and the vacuum valve and the pressure valve shall be washed thoroughly. It shall be ensured that the screen is not clogged, and the use of any hard, pointed objects to clear the screen shall be avoided.

(D) If the liquid has become excessively gummy or solidified, the vent body and parts shall be soaked in hot soapy water.

(E) The vent body shall be turned upside down and drained thoroughly. Parts shall be dried by placing them in a warm and dry area or by using an air hose.

(F) Parts shall be sprayed with a light Teflon® coating, and the vent shall be reassembled. The use of any type of oil for lubrication purposes shall be avoided, as oil is harmful to the foam liquid.

(G) The vent bonnet shall be replaced, and the vent shall be turned upside down slowly a few times to ensure proper freedom of the movable parts.

(H) The vent shall be attached to the liquid storage tank expansion dome.

Chapter 12 Valves, Valve Components, and Trim

12.1* General. This chapter shall provide the minimum requirements for the routine inspection, testing, and maintenance of valves, valve components, and trim. Table 12.1 shall be used to determine the minimum required frequencies for inspection, testing, and maintenance.

Table 12.1 Summary of Valves, Valve Components, and Trim Inspection, Testing, and Maintenance

Item	Activity	Frequency	Reference
Control Valves			
Sealed	Inspection	Weekly	12.3.2.1
Locked	Inspection	Monthly	12.3.2.1.1
Tamper switches	Inspection	Monthly	12.3.2.1.1
Alarm Valves			
Exterior	Inspection	Monthly	12.4.1.1
Interior	Inspection	5 years	12.4.1.2
Strainers, filters, orifices	Inspection	5 years	12.4.1.2
Check Valves			
Interior	Inspection	5 years	12.4.2.1
Preaction/Deluge Valves			
Enclosure (during cold weather)	Inspection	Daily/weekly	12.4.3.1
Exterior	Inspection	Monthly	12.4.3.1.6
Interior	Inspection	Annually/5 years	12.4.3.1.7
Strainers, filters, orifices	Inspection	5 years	12.4.3.1.8
Dry Pipe Valves/ Quick-Opening Devices			
Enclosure (during cold weather)	Inspection	Daily/weekly	12.4.4.1.1
Exterior	Inspection	Monthly	12.4.4.1.4
Interior	Inspection	Annually	12.4.4.1.5
Strainers, filters, orifices	Inspection	5 years	12.4.4.1.6
Pressure Reducing and Relief Valves			
Sprinkler systems	Inspection	Quarterly	12.5.1.1

Table 12.1 *Continued*

Item	Activity	Frequency	Reference
Hose connections	Inspection	Quarterly	12.5.2.1
Hose racks	Inspection	Quarterly	12.5.3.1
Fire pumps			
Casing relief valves	Inspection	Weekly	12.5.6.1, 12.5.6.1.1
Pressure relief valves	Inspection	Weekly	12.5.6.2, 12.5.6.2.1
Backflow Prevention Assemblies			
Reduced pressure	Inspection	Weekly/monthly	12.6.1
Reduced pressure detectors	Inspection	Weekly/monthly	12.6.1
Fire Department Connections	Inspection	Quarterly	12.7.1
Main Drains	Test	Annually/quarterly	12.2.6, 12.2.6.1, 12.3.3.4
Water-Flow Alarms	Test	Quarterly	12.2.7
Control Valves			
Position	Test	Annually	12.3.3.1
Operation	Test	Annually	12.3.3.1
Supervisory	Test	Semiannually	12.3.3.5
Preaction/Deluge Valves			
Priming water	Test	Quarterly	12.4.3.2.1
Low air pressure alarms	Test	Quarterly	12.4.3.2.10
Full flow	Test	Annually	12.4.3.2.2
Dry Pipe Valves/			
Quick-Opening Devices			
Priming water	Test	Quarterly	12.4.4.2.1
Low air pressure alarm	Test	Quarterly	12.4.4.2.6
Quick-opening devices	Test	Quarterly	12.4.4.2.4
Trip test	Test	Annually	12.4.4.2.2
Full flow trip test	Test	3 years	12.4.4.2.2.2
Pressure Reducing and Relief Valves			
Sprinkler systems	Test	5 years	12.5.1.2
Circulation relief	Test	Annually	12.5.6.1.2
Pressure relief valves	Test	Annually	12.5.6.2.2
Hose connections	Test	5 years	12.5.2.2
Hose racks	Test	5 years	12.5.3.2
Backflow Prevention Assemblies	Test	Annually	12.6.2
Control Valves	Maintenance	Annually	12.3.4
Preaction/Deluge Valves	Maintenance	Annually	12.4.3.3.2
Dry Pipe Valves/	Maintenance	Annually	12.4.4.3.2
Quick-Opening Devices			

12.2 General Provisions.

12.2.1 The owner shall have manufacturer's literature available to provide specific instructions for inspecting, testing, and maintaining the valves and associated equipment.

12.2.2 All pertinent personnel, departments, authorities having jurisdiction, or agencies shall be notified that testing or maintenance of the valve and associated alarms is to be conducted.

12.2.3* All system valves shall be protected from physical damage and shall be accessible.

12.2.4 Before opening a test or drain valve, it shall be verified that adequate provisions have been made for drainage.

12.2.5 The general appearance and condition of all valves shall be observed and noted, and it shall be verified that all valves are in the appropriate open or closed position.

12.2.6* Main Drain Test. A main drain test shall be conducted annually at each water-based fire protection system riser to determine whether there has been a change in the condition of the water supply piping and control valves. *(See also 12.3.4.2.)*

12.2.6.1 Systems where the sole water supply is through a backflow preventer and/or pressure reducing valves, the main drain test of at least one system downstream of the device shall be conducted on a quarterly basis.

12.2.7 Water-Flow Alarm. All water-flow alarms shall be tested quarterly in accordance with the manufacturer's instructions.

12.2.8 Gauges.

12.2.8.1 Gauges shall be inspected monthly to verify that they are in good condition and that normal pressure is being maintained.

12.2.8.1.1 Where other sections of this standard have different frequency requirements for specific gauges, those requirements shall be used.

12.2.8.2 Gauges shall be replaced every 5 years or tested every 5 years by comparison with a calibrated gauge.

12.2.8.3 Gauges not accurate to within 3 percent of the full scale shall be recalibrated or replaced.

12.2.9 Records. Records shall be maintained in accordance with Section 4.3.

12.3 Control Valves in Water-Based Fire Protection Systems.

12.3.1* Each control valve shall be identified and have a sign indicating the system or portion of the system it controls.

12.3.1.1* When a normally open valve is closed, the procedures established in Chapter 14 shall be followed.

12.3.1.1.1 When the valve is returned to service, a drain test (either main or sectional drain, as appropriate) shall be conducted to determine that the valve is open.

12.3.1.2 Each normally open valve shall be secured by means of a seal or a lock or shall be electrically supervised in accordance with the applicable NFPA standards.

12.3.1.3 Normally closed valves shall be secured by means of a seal or shall be electrically supervised in accordance with the applicable NFPA standard.

12.3.1.3.1 Sealing or electrical supervision shall not be required for hose valves.

12.3.2 Inspection.

12.3.2.1 All valves shall be inspected weekly.

12.3.2.1.1 Valves secured with locks or supervised in accordance with applicable NFPA standards shall be permitted to be inspected monthly.

12.3.2.1.2 After any alterations or repairs, an inspection shall be made by the owner to ensure that the system is in service and all valves are in the normal position and properly sealed, locked, or electrically supervised.

12.3.2.2* The valve inspection shall verify that the valves are in the following condition:

(1) In the normal open or closed position
(2)*Properly sealed, locked, or supervised
(3) Accessible
(4) Provided with appropriate wrenches
(5) Free from external leaks
(6) Provided with appropriate identification

12.3.3 Testing.

12.3.3.1 Each control valve shall be operated annually through its full range and returned to its normal position.

12.3.3.2* Post indicator valves shall be opened until spring or torsion is felt in the rod, indicating that the rod has not become detached from the valve.

12.3.3.2.1 This test shall be conducted every time the valve is closed.

12.3.3.3 Post indicator and outside screw and yoke valves shall be backed a one-quarter turn from the fully open position to prevent jamming.

12.3.3.4 A main drain test shall be conducted annually at each system riser and any time the valve is closed at each system riser or feed main after the control valve has been closed to determine whether there has been a change in the condition of the water supply piping and control valves.

12.3.3.5* Supervisory Switches.

12.3.3.5.1 Valve supervisory switches shall be tested semiannually.

12.3.3.5.2 A distinctive signal shall indicate movement from the valve's normal position during either the first two revolutions of a hand wheel or when the stem of the valve has moved one-fifth of the distance from its normal position.

12.3.3.5.3 The signal shall not be restored at any valve position except the normal position.

12.3.4 Maintenance.

12.3.4.1 The operating stems of outside screw and yoke valves shall be lubricated annually.

12.3.4.2 The valve then shall be completely closed and re-opened to test its operation and distribute the lubricant.

12.4 System Valves.

12.4.1 Inspection of Alarm Valves. Alarm valves shall be inspected as described in 12.4.1.1 and 12.4.1.2.

12.4.1.1* Alarm valves shall be externally inspected monthly and shall verify the following:

(1) The gauges indicate normal supply water pressure is being maintained.
(2) The valve is free of physical damage.
(3) All valves are in the appropriate open or closed position.
(4) The retarding chamber or alarm drains are not leaking.

12.4.1.2* Alarm valves and their associated strainers, filters, and restriction orifices shall be inspected internally every 5 years unless tests indicate a greater frequency is necessary.

12.4.1.3 Maintenance.

12.4.1.3.1 Internal components shall be cleaned/repaired as necessary in accordance with the manufacturer's instructions.

12.4.1.3.2 The system shall be returned to service in accordance with the manufacturer's instructions.

12.4.2 Check Valves.

12.4.2.1 Inspection. Valves shall be inspected internally every 5 years to verify that all components operate correctly, move freely, and are in good condition.

12.4.2.2 Maintenance. Internal components shall be cleaned, repaired, or replaced as necessary in accordance with the manufacturer's instructions.

12.4.3 Preaction Valves and Deluge Valves.

12.4.3.1 Inspection. Valve enclosure heating equipment for preaction and deluge valves subject to freezing shall be inspected daily during cold weather for its ability to maintain a minimum temperature of at least 4°C (40°F).

12.4.3.1.1 Valve enclosures equipped with low temperature alarms shall be inspected weekly.

12.4.3.1.2 Low temperature alarms, if installed in valve enclosures, shall be inspected annually at the beginning of the heating season.

12.4.3.1.3 Gauges shall be inspected weekly.

12.4.3.1.3.1 The gauge on the supply side of the preaction or deluge valve shall indicate that the normal supply water pressure is being maintained.

12.4.3.1.4 The gauge monitoring the preaction system supervisory air pressure, if provided, shall be inspected monthly to verify that it indicates that normal pressure is being maintained.

12.4.3.1.5 The gauge monitoring the detection system pressure, if provided, shall be tested monthly to verify that it indicates that normal pressure is being maintained.

12.4.3.1.6 The preaction or deluge valve shall be externally inspected monthly to verify the following:

(1) The valve is free from physical damage.
(2) All trim valves are in the appropriate open or closed position.
(3) The valve seat is not leaking.
(4) Electrical components are in service.

12.4.3.1.7 The interior of the preaction or deluge valve and the condition of detection devices shall be inspected annually when the trip test is conducted.

12.4.3.1.7.1 Internal inspection of valves that can be reset without removal of a faceplate shall be permitted to be conducted every 5 years.

12.4.3.1.8 Strainers, filters, restricted orifices, and diaphragm chambers shall be inspected internally every 5 years unless tests indicate a greater frequency is necessary.

12.4.3.2 Testing.

12.4.3.2.1* The priming water level in supervised preaction systems shall be tested quarterly for compliance with the manufacturer's instructions.

12.4.3.2.2* Each deluge or preaction valve shall be trip tested annually at full flow in warm weather and in accordance with the manufacturer's instructions. Protection shall be provided for any devices or equipment subject to damage by system discharge during tests.

12.4.3.2.2.1 Where the nature of the protected property is such that water cannot be discharged for test purposes, the trip test shall be conducted in a manner that does not necessitate discharge in the protected area.

12.4.3.2.2.2 Where the nature of the protected property is such that water cannot be discharged unless protected equipment is shut down (e.g., energized electrical equipment), a full flow system test shall be conducted at the next scheduled shutdown. In all cases, the test frequency shall not exceed 3 years.

12.4.3.2.2.3 Preaction or deluge valves protecting freezers shall be trip tested in a manner that does not introduce moisture into the piping in the freezer.

12.4.3.2.3 The water discharge patterns from all open sprinklers or spray nozzles shall be observed to ensure that patterns are not impeded by plugging and to ensure that they are correctly positioned and that obstructions do not prevent discharge patterns from wetting surfaces to be protected.

12.4.3.2.3.1 Where obstructions occur, the piping and sprinklers or nozzles shall be cleaned and the system retested.

12.4.3.2.4 Pressure Readings.

12.4.3.2.4.1 Pressure readings shall be recorded at the hydraulically most remote nozzle or sprinkler.

12.4.3.2.4.2 A second pressure reading shall be recorded at the deluge valve.

12.4.3.2.4.3 These readings shall be compared to the hydraulic design pressures to ensure the original system design requirements are met by the water supply.

12.4.3.2.4.4 Where the hydraulically most remote nozzle or sprinkler is inaccessible, nozzles or sprinklers in other than foam-water systems shall be permitted to be checked visually without taking a pressure reading on the most remote nozzle or sprinkler.

12.4.3.2.4.5 Where the reading taken at the riser indicates that the water supply has deteriorated, a gauge shall be placed on the hydraulically most remote nozzle or sprinkler and the results compared with the required design pressure.

12.4.3.2.5 Multiple Systems. The maximum number of systems expected to operate in case of fire shall be tested simultaneously to check the adequacy of the water supply.

12.4.3.2.6 Manual Operation. Manual actuation devices shall be operated annually.

12.4.3.2.7 Return to Service. After the full flow test, the system shall be returned to service in accordance with the manufacturer's instructions.

12.4.3.2.8 Grease or other sealing materials shall not be applied to the seating surfaces of preaction or deluge valves.

12.4.3.2.9* Records indicating the date the preaction or deluge valve was last tripped and the tripping time as well as the individual and organization conducting the test shall be maintained at a location or in a manner readily available for review by the authority having jurisdiction.

12.4.3.2.10 Low air pressure alarms, if provided, shall be tested quarterly in accordance with the manufacturer's instructions.

12.4.3.2.11 Low temperature alarms, if installed in valve enclosures, shall be tested annually at the beginning of the heating season.

12.4.3.2.12 Automatic air pressure maintenance devices, if provided, shall be tested yearly at the time of the annual preaction or deluge valve trip test, in accordance with the manufacturer's instructions.

12.4.3.3 Maintenance.

12.4.3.3.1 Leaks causing drops in supervisory pressure sufficient to sound warning alarms and electrical malfunctions causing alarms to sound shall be located and repaired.

12.4.3.3.2 During the annual trip test, the interior of the preaction or deluge valve shall be cleaned thoroughly and the parts replaced or repaired as necessary.

12.4.3.3.2.1 Interior cleaning and parts replacement or repair shall be permitted every 5 years for valves that can be reset without removal of a faceplate.

12.4.3.3.3* Low points in preaction or deluge systems shall be drained after each operation and before the onset of freezing weather conditions.

12.4.3.3.4 Additional maintenance as required by the manufacturer's instructions shall be provided.

12.4.4 Dry Pipe Valves/Quick-Opening Devices.

12.4.4.1 Inspection.

12.4.4.1.1 Valve enclosure heating equipment shall be inspected daily during cold weather for its ability to maintain a minimum temperature of at least 4°C (40°F).

12.4.4.1.1.1 Valve enclosures equipped with low temperature alarms shall be inspected weekly.

12.4.4.1.1.2 Low temperature alarms, if installed in valve enclosures, shall be inspected annually at the beginning of the heating season.

12.4.4.1.2 Gauges shall be inspected weekly.

(A) The gauge on the supply side of the dry pipe valve shall indicate that the normal supply water pressure is being maintained.

(B) The gauge on the system side of the dry pipe valve shall indicate that the proper ratio of air or nitrogen pressure to water supply pressure is being maintained in accordance with the manufacturer's instructions.

(C)* The gauge on the quick-opening device, if provided, shall indicate the same pressure as the gauge on the system side of the dry pipe valve.

12.4.4.1.3 Systems equipped with low air or nitrogen pressure alarms shall be inspected monthly.

12.4.4.1.4 The dry pipe valve shall be externally inspected monthly to verify the following:

(1) The valve is free of physical damage.
(2) All trim valves are in the appropriate open or closed position.
(3) The intermediate chamber is not leaking.

12.4.4.1.5 The interior of the dry pipe valve shall be inspected annually when the trip test is conducted.

12.4.4.1.6 Strainers, filters, and restricted orifices shall be inspected internally every 5 years unless tests indicate a greater frequency is necessary.

12.4.4.2 Testing.

12.4.4.2.1* The priming water level shall be tested quarterly.

12.4.4.2.2* Each dry pipe valve shall be trip tested annually during warm weather.

12.4.4.2.2.1 Dry pipe valves protecting freezers shall be trip tested in a manner that does not introduce moisture into the piping in the freezers.

12.4.4.2.2.2* Every 3 years and whenever the system is altered, the dry pipe valve shall be trip tested with the control valve fully open and the quick-opening device, if provided, in service.

12.4.4.2.2.3* During those years when full flow testing in accordance with 12.4.4.2.2.2 is not required, each dry pipe valve shall be trip tested with the control valve partially open.

12.4.4.2.3 Grease or other sealing materials shall not be applied to the seating surfaces of dry pipe valves.

12.4.4.2.4* Quick-opening devices, if provided, shall be tested quarterly.

12.4.4.2.5 A tag or card that shows the date on which the dry pipe valve was last tripped and the name of the person and organization conducting the test shall be attached to the valve.

12.4.4.2.5.1 Separate records of initial air and water pressure, tripping air pressure, and dry pipe valve operating conditions shall be maintained on the premises for comparison with previous test results.

12.4.4.2.5.2 Records of tripping time shall be maintained for full flow trip tests.

12.4.4.2.6 Low air pressure alarms, if provided, shall be tested quarterly in accordance with the manufacturer's instructions.

12.4.4.2.7 Low temperature alarms, if installed in valve enclosures, shall be tested annually at the beginning of the heating season.

12.4.4.2.8 Automatic air pressure maintenance devices, if provided, shall be tested annually during the dry pipe valve trip test in accordance with the manufacturer's instructions.

12.4.4.3 Maintenance.

12.4.4.3.1* Leaks resulting in air pressure losses greater than 0.7 bar (10 psi) per week shall be located and repaired.

12.4.4.3.2 During the annual trip test, the interior of the dry pipe valve shall be cleaned thoroughly and parts replaced or repaired as necessary.

12.4.4.3.3* Low points in dry pipe sprinkler systems shall be drained after each operation and before the onset of freezing weather conditions.

12.5 Pressure Reducing Valves and Relief Valves.

12.5.1 Inspection and Testing of Sprinkler Pressure Reducing Control Valves. Sprinkler pressure reducing control valves shall be inspected and tested as described in 12.5.1.1 and 12.5.1.2.

12.5.1.1 All valves shall be inspected quarterly to verify that the valves are in the following condition:

(1) In the open position
(2) Not leaking
(3) Maintaining downstream pressures in accordance with the design criteria
(4) In good condition, with handwheels installed and unbroken

12.5.1.2* A full flow test shall be conducted on each valve at 5-year intervals and shall be compared to previous test results.

12.5.1.2.1 Adjustments shall be made in accordance with the manufacturer's instructions.

12.5.1.3 A partial flow test adequate to move the valve from its seat shall be conducted annually.

12.5.2 Hose Connection Pressure Reducing Valves.

12.5.2.1 All valves shall be inspected quarterly to verify the following:

(1) The handwheel is not broken or missing.
(2) The outlet hose threads are not damaged.
(3) No leaks are present.
(4) The reducer and the cap are not missing.

12.5.2.2* A full flow test shall be conducted on each valve at 5-year intervals and shall be compared to previous test results.

12.5.2.2.1 Adjustments shall be made in accordance with the manufacturer's instructions.

12.5.2.3 A partial flow test adequate to move the valve from its seat shall be conducted annually.

12.5.3 Hose Rack Assembly Pressure Reducing Valves.

12.5.3.1 All valves shall be inspected quarterly to verify the following:

(1) The handwheel is not missing or broken.

(2) No leaks are present.

12.5.3.2 A full flow test shall be conducted on each valve at 5-year intervals and compared to previous test results.

12.5.3.2.1 Adjustments shall be made in accordance with the manufacturer's instructions.

12.5.3.3 A partial flow test adequate to move the valve from its seat shall be conducted annually.

12.5.4 Pressure Reducing Valves.

12.5.4.1 All pressure reducing valves installed on fire protection systems not covered by 12.5.1, 12.5.2, or 12.5.3 shall be inspected in accordance with 12.5.1.1.

12.5.4.2 All pressure reducing valves installed on fire protection systems not covered by 12.5.1, 12.5.2, or 12.5.3 shall be tested in accordance with 12.5.1.2.

12.5.5 Hose Valves.

12.5.5.1 Inspection.

12.5.5.1.1 Hose valves shall be inspected quarterly.

12.5.5.1.2 All deficiencies shall be corrected.

12.5.5.1.3 Hose valves shall be inspected to ensure that hose caps are in place and not damaged.

12.5.5.1.4 Hose threads shall be inspected for damage.

12.5.5.1.5 Valve handles shall be present and not damaged.

12.5.5.1.6 Gaskets shall be inspected for damage or deterioration.

12.5.5.1.7 Hose valves shall be inspected for leaks.

12.5.5.1.8 Hose valves shall be inspected to ensure no obstructions are present.

12.5.5.1.9 Hose valves shall be inspected to ensure that restricting devices are present.

12.5.5.2 Testing.

12.5.5.2.1* Class I and Class III standpipe system hose valves shall be tested annually by opening and closing the valves.

12.5.5.2.1.1 Hose valves that are difficult to operate or leak shall be repaired or replaced.

12.5.5.2.2* Hose valves on hose stations attached to sprinkler systems and Class II standpipe systems shall be tested every 3 years by opening and closing the valves.

12.5.5.2.2.1 Hose valves that are difficult to operate or leak shall be repaired or replaced.

12.5.5.3 Maintenance. Hose valves that do not operate smoothly or open fully shall be lubricated, repaired, or replaced.

12.5.6 Fire Pump Pressure Relief Valves.

12.5.6.1 All circulation relief valves shall be inspected weekly.

12.5.6.1.1 The inspection shall verify that water flows through the valve when the fire pump is operating at shut-off pressure (i.e., churn) to prevent the pump from overheating.

12.5.6.1.2 During the annual fire pump test, the closure of the circulation relief valve shall be verified to be in accordance with the manufacturer's specifications.

12.5.6.2 All pressure relief valves shall be inspected weekly.

12.5.6.2.1 The inspection shall verify that the pressure downstream of the relief valve fittings in the fire pump discharge piping does not exceed the pressure for which the system components are rated.

12.5.6.2.2 During the annual fire pump flow test, the pressure relief valve shall be verified to be correctly adjusted and set to relieve at the correct pressure and to close below that pressure setting.

12.5.7 Maintenance. All damaged or missing components noted during the inspections specified in 12.5.5.1 through 12.5.5.2.2 shall be repaired or replaced in accordance with the manufacturer's instructions.

12.6 Backflow Prevention Assemblies.

12.6.1 Inspection. Inspection of backflow prevention assemblies shall be as described in 12.6.1.1 through 12.6.1.2.2.

12.6.1.1 The double check assembly (DCA) valves and double check detector assembly (DCDA) valve shall be inspected weekly to ensure that the OS&Y isolation valves are in the normal open position.

12.6.1.1.1 Valves secured with locks or electrically supervised in accordance with applicable NFPA standards shall be inspected monthly.

12.6.1.2* Reduced pressure assemblies (RPA) and reduced pressure detector assemblies (RPDA) shall be inspected weekly to ensure that the differential-sensing valve relief port is not continuously discharging and the OS&Y isolation valves are in the normal open position.

12.6.1.2.1 Valves secured with locks or electrically supervised in accordance with applicable NFPA standards shall be inspected monthly.

12.6.1.2.2 After any testing or repair, an inspection by the owner shall be made to ensure that the system is in service and all isolation valves are in the normal open position and properly locked or electrically supervised.

12.6.2 Testing.

12.6.2.1* All backflow preventers installed in fire protection system piping shall be tested annually in accordance with the following:

(1) A forward flow test shall be conducted at the system demand, including hose stream demand, where hydrants or inside hose stations are located downstream of the backflow preventer.

(2) A backflow performance test, as required by the authority having jurisdiction, shall be conducted at the completion of the forward flow test.

12.6.2.1.1 For backflow preventers sized 50.8 mm (2 in.) and under, the forward flow test shall be acceptable to conduct without measuring flow, where the test outlet is of a size to flow the system demand.

12.6.2.1.2 Where water rationing shall be enforced during shortages lasting more than 1 year, an internal inspection of the backflow preventer to ensure the check valves will fully open shall be acceptable in lieu of conducting the annual forward flow test.

12.6.2.1.3 Where connections do not permit a full flow test, tests shall be completed at the maximum flow rate possible.

12.6.2.1.4 The forward flow test shall not be required where annual fire pump testing causes the system demand to flow through the backflow preventer device.

12.6.2.2* All backflow devices installed in fire protection water supply shall be tested annually at the designed flow rate of the fire protection system, including required hose stream demands.

12.6.2.2.1 Where connections do not permit a full flow test, tests shall be conducted at the maximum flow rate possible.

12.6.3 Maintenance.

12.6.3.1 Maintenance of all backflow prevention assemblies shall be conducted by a trained individual following the manufacturer's instructions in accordance with the procedure and policies of the authority having jurisdiction.

12.6.3.2 Rubber parts shall be replaced in accordance with the frequency required by the authority having jurisdiction and the manufacturer's instructions.

12.7 Fire Department Connections.

12.7.1 Fire department connections shall be inspected quarterly. The inspection shall verify the following:

(1) The fire department connections are visible and accessible.
(2) Couplings or swivels are not damaged and rotate smoothly.
(3) Plugs or caps are in place and undamaged.
(4) Gaskets are in place and in good condition.
(5) Identification signs are in place.
(6) The check valve is not leaking.
(7) The automatic drain valve is in place and operating properly.
(8) The fire department connection clapper(s) is in place and operating properly.

12.7.2 If fire department connection plugs or caps are not in place, the interior of the connection shall be inspected for obstructions, and it shall be verified that the fire department connection clapper is operational over its full range.

12.7.3 Components shall be repaired or replaced as necessary in accordance with the manufacturer's instructions. Any obstructions that are present shall be removed.

Chapter 13   Obstruction Investigation

13.1 General. This chapter shall provide the minimum requirements for conducting investigations of fire protection system piping for possible sources of materials that can cause pipe blockage.

13.2* Obstruction Investigation and Prevention.

13.2.1 An investigation of piping and branch line conditions shall be conducted every 5 years by opening a flushing connection at the end of one main and by removing a sprinkler toward the end of one branch line for the purpose of investigating for the presence of foreign organic and inorganic material.

13.2.1.1 Alternative nondestructive examination methods shall be permitted.

13.2.1.2 Tubercules or slime, if found, shall be tested for indications of microbiologically influenced corrosion (MIC).

13.2.2* An obstruction investigation shall be conducted for system or yard main piping wherever any of the following conditions exist:

(1) Defective intake for fire pumps taking suction from open bodies of water
(2) The discharge of obstructive material during routine water tests
(3) Foreign materials in fire pumps, in dry pipe valves, or in check valves
(4) Foreign material in water during drain tests or plugging of inspector's test connection(s)
(5) Plugged sprinklers
(6) Plugged piping in sprinkler systems dismantled during building alterations
(7) Failure to flush yard piping or surrounding public mains following new installations or repairs
(8) A record of broken public mains in the vicinity
(9) Abnormally frequent false tripping of a dry pipe valve(s)
(10) A system that is returned to service after an extended shutdown (greater than 1 year)
(11) There is reason to believe that the sprinkler system contains sodium silicate or highly corrosive fluxes in copper systems
(12) A system has been supplied with raw water via the fire department connection
(13) Pinhole leaks
(14) A 50-percent increase in the time it takes water to travel to the inspector's test connection from the time the valve trips during a full flow trip test of a dry pipe sprinkler system when compared to the original system acceptance test

13.2.3* Systems shall be examined for internal obstructions where conditions exist that could cause obstructed piping.

13.2.3.1 If the condition has not been corrected or the condition is one that could result in obstruction of the piping despite any previous flushing procedures that have been performed, the system shall be examined for internal obstructions every 5 years.

13.2.3.2 Internal inspections shall be accomplished by examining the interior of the following four points:

(1) System valve
(2) Riser
(3) Cross main
(4) Branch line

13.2.3.3 Alternative nondestructive examination methods shall be permitted.

13.2.4* If an obstruction investigation carried out in accordance with 13.2.1 indicates the presence of sufficient material to obstruct sprinklers, a complete flushing program shall be conducted by qualified personnel.

13.3 Prevention of Ice Obstruction. Dry pipe or preaction sprinkler system piping that protects or passes through freezers or cold storage rooms shall be inspected internally on an annual basis for ice obstructions at the point where the piping enters the refrigerated area.

13.3.1 Alternative nondestructive examinations shall be permitted.

13.3.2 All penetrations into the cold storage areas shall be inspected and, if an ice obstruction is found, additional pipe shall be examined to ensure no ice blockage exists.

Chapter 14   Impairments

14.1 General. This chapter shall provide the minimum requirements for a water-based fire protection system impairment program. Measures shall be taken during the impairment to ensure that increased risks are minimized and the duration of the impairment is limited.

14.2 Impairment Coordinator.

14.2.1 The building owner shall assign an impairment coordinator to comply with the requirements of this chapter.

14.2.2 In the absence of a specific designee, the owner shall be considered the impairment coordinator.

14.2.3 Where the lease, written use agreement, or management contract specifically grants the authority for inspection, testing, and maintenance of the fire protection system(s) to the tenant, management firm, or managing individual, the tenant, management firm, or managing individual shall assign a person as impairment coordinator.

14.3 Tag Impairment System.

14.3.1* A tag shall be used to indicate that a system, or part thereof, has been removed from service.

14.3.2* The tag shall be posted at each fire department connection and system control valve indicating which system, or part thereof, has been removed from service.

14.3.3 The authority having jurisdiction shall specify where the tag is to be placed.

14.4 Impaired Equipment.

14.4.1 The impaired equipment shall be considered to be the water-based fire protection system, or part thereof, that is removed from service.

14.4.2 The impaired equipment shall include, but shall not be limited to, the following:

(1) Sprinkler systems
(2) Standpipe systems
(3) Fire hose systems
(4) Underground fire service mains
(5) Fire pumps
(6) Water storage tanks
(7) Water spray fixed systems
(8) Foam-water systems
(9) Fire service control valves

14.5* Preplanned Impairment Programs.

14.5.1 All preplanned impairments shall be authorized by the impairment coordinator.

14.5.2 Before authorization is given, the impairment coordinator shall be responsible for verifying that the following procedures have been implemented:

(1) The extent and expected duration of the impairment have been determined.
(2) The areas or buildings involved have been inspected and the increased risks determined.

(3) Recommendations have been submitted to management or building owner/manager. Where a required fire protection system is out of service for more than 4 hours in a 24-hour period, the impairment coordinator shall arrange for one of the following:
  (a) Evacuation of the building or portion of the building affected by the system out of service
  (b)*An approved fire watch
  (c)*Establishment of a temporary water supply
  (d)*Establishment and implementation of an approved program to eliminate potential ignition sources and limit the amount of fuel available to the fire
(4) The fire department has been notified.
(5) The insurance carrier, the alarm company, building owner/manager, and other authorities having jurisdiction have been notified.
(6) The supervisors in the areas to be affected have been notified.
(7) A tag impairment system has been implemented. (*See Section 14.3.*)
(8) All necessary tools and materials have been assembled on the impairment site.

14.6 Emergency Impairments.

14.6.1 Emergency impairments include but are not limited to system leakage, interruption of water supply, frozen or ruptured piping, and equipment failure.

14.6.2 When emergency impairments occur, emergency action shall be taken to minimize potential injury and damage.

14.6.3 The coordinator shall implement the steps outlined in Section 14.5.

14.7 Restoring Systems to Service. When all impaired equipment is restored to normal working order, the impairment coordinator shall verify that the following procedures have been implemented:

(1) Any necessary inspections and tests have been conducted to verify that affected systems are operational. The appropriate chapter of this standard shall be consulted for guidance on the type of inspection and test required.
(2) Supervisors have been advised that protection is restored.
(3) The fire department has been advised that protection is restored.
(4) The building owner/manager, insurance carrier, alarm company, and other authorities having jurisdiction have been advised that protection is restored.
(5) The impairment tag has been removed.

Annex A   Explanatory Material

Annex A is not a part of the requirements of this NFPA document but is included for informational purposes only. This annex contains explanatory material, numbered to correspond with the applicable text paragraphs.

A.1.2 History has shown that the performance reliability of a water-based fire protection system under fire-related conditions increases where comprehensive inspection, testing, and maintenance procedures are enforced. Diligence during an inspection is important. The inspection, testing, and maintenance of some items in the standard might not be practical or possible, depending on existing conditions. The inspector should use good judgment when making inspections.

A.1.3 An entire program of quality control includes, but is not limited to, maintenance of equipment, inspection frequency, testing of equipment, on-site fire brigades, loss control provisions, and personnel training. Personnel training can be used as an alternative even if a specific frequency differs from that specified in this standard.

A.1.4 The liter and bar units, which are not part of but are recognized by SI, commonly are used in international fire protection. These units are provided in Table A.1.4 with their conversion factors.

Table A.1.4 Metric Conversions

Name of Unit	Unit Symbol	Conversion Factor
liter	L	1 gal = 3.785 L
liter per minute per square meter	L/min·m²	1 gpm/ft² = 40.746 L/min·m²
cubic decimeter	dm³	1 gal = 3.785 dm³
pascal	Pa	1 psi = 6894.757 Pa
bar	bar	1 psi = 0.0689 bar
bar	bar	1 bar = 10^5 Pa

Note: For additional conversions and information, see ASTM E 380, *Standard for Metric Practice.*

A.3.2.1 Approved. The National Fire Protection Association does not approve, inspect, or certify any installations, procedures, equipment, or materials; nor does it approve or evaluate testing laboratories. In determining the acceptability of installations, procedures, equipment, or materials, the authority having jurisdiction may base acceptance on compliance with NFPA or other appropriate standards. In the absence of such standards, said authority may require evidence of proper installation, procedure, or use. The authority having jurisdiction may also refer to the listings or labeling practices of an organization that is concerned with product evaluations and is thus in a position to determine compliance with appropriate standards for the current production of listed items.

A.3.2.2 Authority Having Jurisdiction (AHJ). The phrase "authority having jurisdiction," or its acronym AHJ, is used in NFPA documents in a broad manner, since jurisdictions and approval agencies vary, as do their responsibilities. Where public safety is primary, the authority having jurisdiction may be a federal, state, local, or other regional department or individual such as a fire chief; fire marshal; chief of a fire prevention bureau, labor department, or health department; building official; electrical inspector; or others having statutory authority. For insurance purposes, an insurance inspection department, rating bureau, or other insurance company representative may be the authority having jurisdiction. In many circumstances, the property owner or his or her designated agent assumes the role of the authority having jurisdiction; at government installations, the commanding officer or departmental official may be the authority having jurisdiction.

A.3.2.3 Listed. The means for identifying listed equipment may vary for each organization concerned with product evaluation; some organizations do not recognize equipment as listed unless it is also labeled. The authority having jurisdiction should utilize the system employed by the listing organization to identify a listed product.

A.3.3.2 Automatic Detection Equipment. Water spray systems can use fixed temperature, rate-of-rise, rate-compensation fixed temperature, optical devices, flammable gas detectors or products of combustion detectors, and manual means to initiate water flow.

A.3.3.10 Fire Hydrant. See Figure A.3.3.10(a) and Figure A.3.3.10(b).

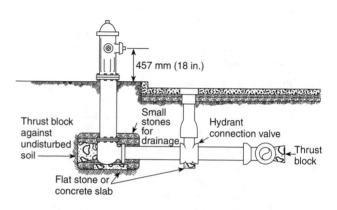

FIGURE A.3.3.10(a)   Typical Fire Hydrant Connection.

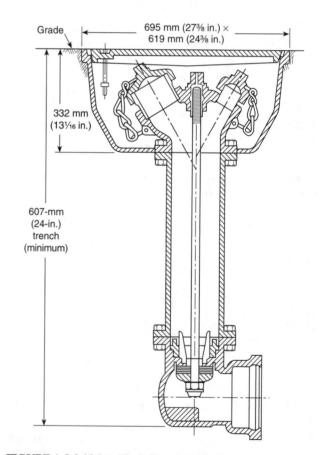

FIGURE A.3.3.10(b)   Flush-Type Hydrant.

A.3.3.10.1 Dry Barrel Hydrant (Frostproof Hydrant). See Figure A.3.3.10.1.

A.3.3.10.2 Monitor Nozzle Hydrant. See Figure A.3.3.10.2.

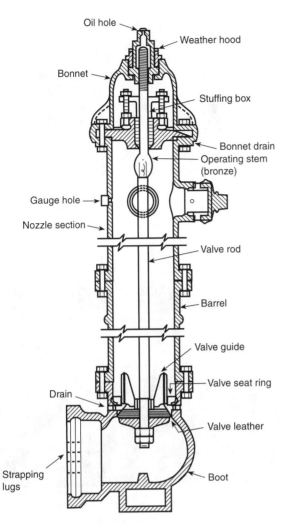

FIGURE A.3.3.10.1   Dry Barrel Hydrant.

A.3.3.10.3 Wall Hydrant. See Figure A.3.3.10.3.

A.3.3.10.4 Wet Barrel Hydrant. See Figure A.3.3.10.4.

A.3.3.14 Hose House. See Figure A.3.3.14(a) through Figure A.3.3.14(c).

A.3.3.17.1 Conventional Pin Rack. See Figure A.3.3.17.1.

A.3.3.17.2 Horizontal Rack. See Figure A.3.3.17.2.

A.3.3.17.3 Hose Reel. See Figure A.3.3.17.3.

A.3.3.17.4 Semiautomatic Hose Rack Assembly. See Figure A.3.3.17.4.

A.3.3.24.1 Monitor Nozzle. See Figure A.3.3.24.1(a) and Figure A.3.3.24.1(b).

A.3.3.24.2 Water Spray Nozzle. The selection of the type and size of spray nozzles should be made with proper consideration given to such factors as physical character of the hazard involved, draft or wind conditions, material likely to be burning, and the general purpose of the system.

High-velocity spray nozzles, generally used in piped installations, discharge in the form of a spray-filled cone. Low-velocity spray nozzles usually deliver a much finer spray in the form of either a spray-filled spheroid or cone. Due to differ-

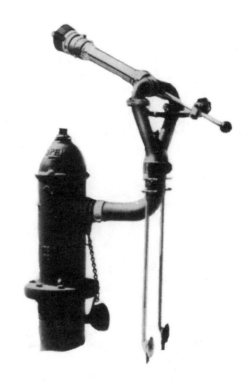

FIGURE A.3.3.10.2   Hydrant with Monitor Nozzle.

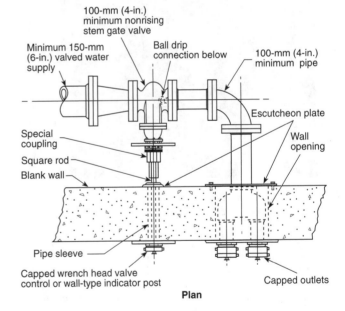

FIGURE A.3.3.10.3   Wall Hydrant.

ences in the size of orifices or waterways in the various nozzles and the range of water particle sizes produced by each type, nozzles of one type cannot ordinarily be substituted for those of another type in an individual installation without seriously affecting fire extinguishment. In general, the higher the velocity and the coarser the size of the water droplets, the greater the effective "reach" or range of the spray.

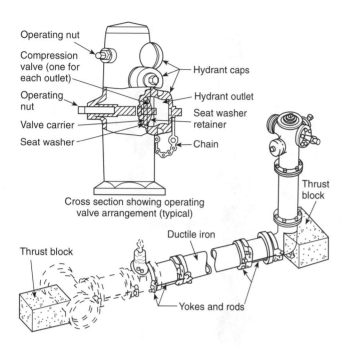

FIGURE A.3.3.10.4 Wet Barrel Hydrant. *(Courtesy of the Los Angeles Department of Water and Power.)*

FIGURE A.3.3.14(b) Steel Hose House of Compact Dimensions for Installation over a Private Hydrant. House Is Shown Closed; Top Lifts Up and Doors on Front Side Open for Complete Accessibility.

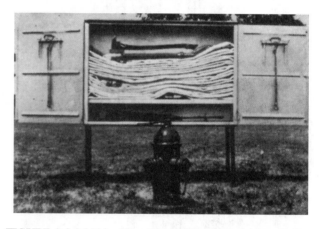

FIGURE A.3.3.14(c) Hose House That Can Be Installed on Legs, As Pictured, or on a Wall Near, but Not Directly over, a Private Hydrant.

FIGURE A.3.3.14(a) Hose House of Five-Sided Design for Installation over a Private Hydrant.

Another type of water spray nozzle uses the deflector principle of the standard sprinkler. The angle of the spray discharge cones is governed by the design of the deflector. Some manufacturers make spray nozzles of this type individually automatic by constructing them with heat-responsive elements as used in standard automatic sprinklers.

A.3.3.28 Pressure Vacuum Vent. See Figure A.3.3.28.

A.3.3.29 Proportioners. See Figure A.3.3.29.

A.3.3.29.1 Bladder Tank Proportioner. See Figure A.3.3.29.1.

A.3.3.29.2 In-Line Balanced Pressure Proportioner. See Figure A.3.3.29.2.

A.3.3.29.3 Line Proportioner. See Figure A.3.3.29.3.

A.3.3.29.4 Standard Balanced Pressure Proportioner. See Figure A.3.3.29.4.

A.3.3.29.5 Standard Pressure Proportioner. See Figure A.3.3.29.5.

A.3.3.34 Strainer. There are two types of strainers. Pipeline strainers are used in water supply connections. These are capable of removing from the water all solids of sufficient size to obstruct the spray nozzles [3.2-mm (⅛-in.) perforations usually are suitable]. Pipeline strainer designs should incorporate a flushout connection or should be capable of flushing through the main drain.

Individual strainers for spray nozzles, where needed, are capable of removing from the water all solids of sufficient size to obstruct the spray nozzle that they serve.

A.3.5.1 Control Valve. Experience has shown that closed valves are the primary cause of failure of water-based fire protection systems in protected occupancies.

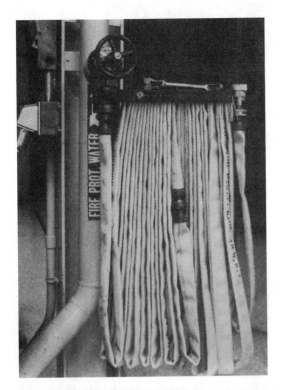

FIGURE A.3.3.17.1 Conventional Pin Rack.

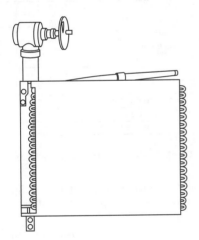

FIGURE A.3.3.17.2 Horizontal Rack.

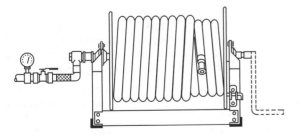

FIGURE A.3.3.17.3 Constant Flow Hose Reel.

FIGURE A.3.3.17.4 Semiautomatic Hose Rack Assembly.

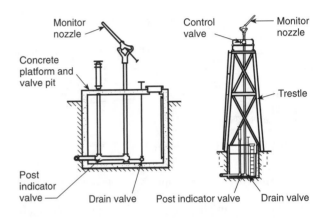

FIGURE A.3.3.24.1(a) Standard Monitor Nozzles; Gear Control Nozzles Also Are Permitted.

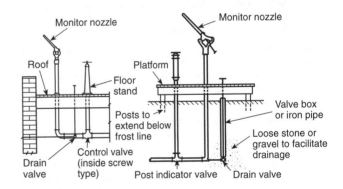

FIGURE A.3.3.24.1(b) Alternative Arrangement of Standard Monitor Nozzles.

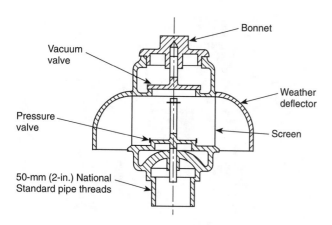

FIGURE A.3.3.28   Pressure Vacuum Vent.

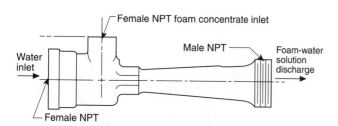

FIGURE A.3.3.29   Proportioner.

A.3.6.4 Sprinkler System. A sprinkler system is considered to have a single system riser control valve. The design and installation of water supply facilities such as gravity tanks, fire pumps, reservoirs, or pressure tanks are covered by NFPA 20, *Standard for the Installation of Stationary Pumps for Fire Protection,* and NFPA 22, *Standard for Water Tanks for Private Fire Protection.*

A.3.6.4.6 Wet Pipe Sprinkler System. Hose connections [40-mm (1½-in.) hose, valves, and nozzles] supplied by sprinkler system piping are considered components of the sprinkler system.

A.4.1.1 The components are not required to be open or exposed. Doors, removable panels, or valve pits can be permitted to satisfy the need for accessibility. Such equipment should not be obstructed by features such as walls, ducts, columns, direct burial, or stock storage.

A.4.1.2 Inspection, testing, and maintenance can be permitted to be contracted with an inspection, testing, and maintenance service.

A.4.1.4 Recalled products should be replaced or remedied. Such replacement or remedial product should be installed in accordance with the manufacturer's instructions and the appropriate NFPA installation standards. A recalled product is a product subject to a statute or administrative regulation specifically requiring the manufacturer, importer, distributor, wholesaler, or retailer of a product, or any combination of such entities, to recall the product, or a product voluntarily recalled by a combination of such entities.

A.4.1.5 Fire protection systems should not be removed from service when the building is not in use; however, where a system that has been out of service for a prolonged period (such as in the case of idle or vacant properties) is returned to service, it is recommended that a responsible and experienced contractor be retained to perform all inspections and tests.

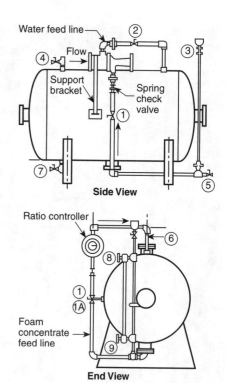

Valve description		Normal position	
Valve no.	Description	Manual system	Auto system
1	Concentrate shutoff	Closed	Closed
1A	Auto. conc. shutoff	N/A	Closed
2	Water pres. shutoff	Open	Open
3	Fill cup shutoff	Closed	Closed
4	Tank water vent	Closed	Closed
5	Diaph. conc. vent	Closed	Closed
6	Water fill	Closed	Closed
7	Concentrate drain/fill	Closed	Closed
8	Upr. sight gauge (opt.)	Closed	Closed
9	Lwr. sight gauge (opt.)	Closed	Closed

FIGURE A.3.3.29.1   Bladder Tank Proportioner.

A.4.3.1 Typical records include, but are not limited to, valve inspections; flow, drain, and pump tests; and trip tests of dry pipe, deluge, and preaction valves.

Computer programs that file inspection and test results should provide a means of comparing current and past results and should indicate the need for corrective maintenance or further testing.

Acceptance test records should be retained for the life of the system or its special components. Subsequent test records should be retained for a period of 1 year after the next test. The comparison determines deterioration of system performance or condition and the need for further testing or maintenance.

A.4.4 Inspection and periodic testing determine what, if any, maintenance actions are required to maintain the operability of a water-based fire protection system. The standard establishes minimum inspection/testing frequencies, responsibilities, test routines, and reporting procedures but does not define precise limits of anomalies where maintenance actions are required.

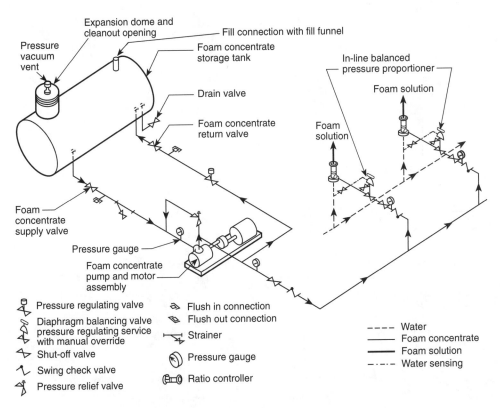

FIGURE A.3.3.29.2 In-Line Balanced Pressure Proportioner.

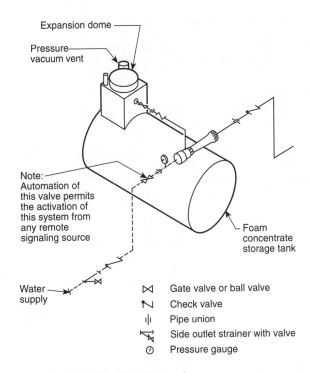

FIGURE A.3.3.29.3 Line Proportioner.

Substandard conditions, such as a closed valve, subnormal water pressure, loss of building heat or power, or obstruction of sprinklers, nozzles, detectors, or hose stations, can delay or prevent system actuation and impede manual fire-fighting operations.

A.4.5.6 Examples of components or subsystems are fire pumps, drivers or controllers, pressure regulating devices, detection systems and controls, alarm check, and dry pipe, deluge, and preaction valves.

A.4.6 Preventive maintenance includes, but is not limited to, lubricating control valve stems; adjusting packing glands on valves and pumps; bleeding moisture and condensation from air compressors, air lines, and dry pipe system auxiliary drains; and cleaning strainers. Frequency of maintenance is indicated in the appropriate chapter.

Corrective maintenance includes, but is not limited to, replacing loaded, corroded, or painted sprinklers; replacing missing or loose pipe hangers; cleaning clogged fire pump impellers; replacing valve seats and gaskets; restoring heat in areas subject to freezing temperatures where water-filled piping is installed; and replacing worn or missing fire hose or nozzles.

Emergency maintenance includes, but is not limited to, repairs due to piping failures caused by freezing or impact damage; repairs to broken underground fire mains; and replacement of frozen or fused sprinklers, defective electric power, or alarm and detection system wiring.

A.4.7.4 Most places using or storing hazardous materials have stations set up for employees where material safety data sheets (MSDSs) are stored. The inspector should be familiar with the types of materials present and the appropriate actions to take in an emergency.

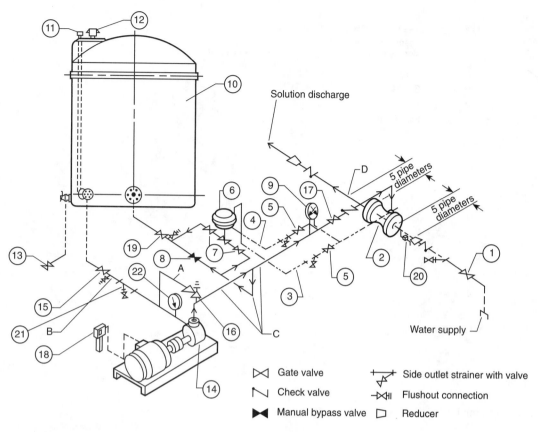

Gate valve

Check valve

Manual bypass valve

Side outlet strainer with valve

Flushout connection

Reducer

Legend:
1   Water supply valve (normally closed)
2   Ratio controller
3   Water balance line — minimum 5-mm (³/₁₆-in.) I.D. pipe
    or tubing recommended
4   Concentrate balance line — minimum 5-mm (³/₁₆-in.) I.D.
    pipe or tubing recommended
5   Sensing line valves (normally open)
6   Diaphragm control valve — automatic pressure
    balance — must be in vertical position
7   Block valves (normally open)
8   Manual bypass valve (normally open)
9   Water and concentrate pressure gauge (duplex)
10 Foam concentrate storage tank
11 Concentrate storage tank fill connection
12 Pressure vacuum vent
13 Concentrate storage tank drain valve (normally closed)
14 Foam concentrate pump and motor
15 Concentrate pump supply valve (normally open)
16 Pressure relief valve (setting as required by system)
17 Concentrate pump discharge valve (normally open)
18 Electric motor starter and switch
19 Concentrate return line valve (normally open)
20 Ball drip valve — 20 mm (³/₄ in.) (install in horizontal position)
21 Strainer with valved side outlet
22 Compound gauge

Operation:
Start concentrate pump (18). Open water supply valve (1).
Open concentrate pump discharge valve (17). Equal gauge
readings then maintained at (9) by the automatic valve (6).
For manual operation, valves (7) can be closed and equal
gauge readings maintained by regulating valve (8) manually.

System Automation:
By automating certain valves, the balanced pressure
proportioning system can be activated from any remote
signaling source.

• Water supply valve (1), normally closed, to be automatically
  operated;
• Concentrate pump discharge valve (17), normally closed, to
  be automatically operated;
• Electric motor starter switch (18) to be automatically operated.

FIGURE A.3.3.29.4   Standard Balanced Pressure Proportioner.

A.4.8 WARNING: NFPA 20, *Standard for the Installation of Stationary Pumps for Fire Protection,* includes electrical requirements that discourage the installation of a disconnect means in the power supply to electric motor-driven fire pumps. This is intended to ensure the availability of power to the fire pumps. Where equipment connected to those circuits is serviced or maintained, the service person could be subject to unusual exposure to electrical and other hazards. It could be necessary to establish special safe work practices and to use safeguards or personal protective clothing, or both.

A.5.2 The provisions of the standard are intended to apply to routine inspections. In the event of a fire, a post-fire inspection should be made of all sprinklers within the fire area. In

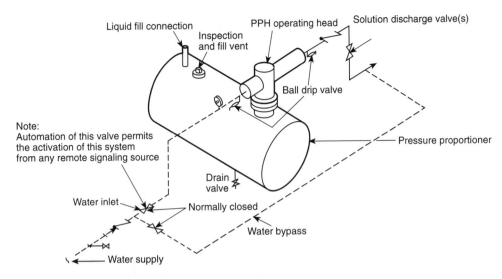

FIGURE A.3.3.29.5 Standard Pressure Proportioner.

situations where the fire was quickly controlled or extinguished by one or two sprinklers, it may only be necessary to replace the activated sprinklers. Care should be taken that the replacement sprinklers are of the same make and model or that they have compatible performance characteristics (*see 5.4.1.1*). Soot-covered sprinklers should be replaced because deposits can result in corrosion of operating parts. In the event of a substantial fire, special consideration should be given to replacing the first ring of sprinklers surrounding the operated sprinklers due to the potential for excessive thermal exposure, which could weaken the response mechanisms.

A.5.2.1.1 The conditions described in this section can have a detrimental effect on the performance of sprinklers by affecting water distribution patterns, insulating thermal elements, delaying operation, or otherwise rendering the sprinkler inoperable or ineffectual.

Severely loaded or corroded sprinklers should be rejected as part of the visual inspection. Such sprinklers could be affected in their distribution or other performance characteristics not addressed by routine sample testing. Lightly loaded or corroded sprinklers could be permitted for continued use if samples are selected for testing based on worst-case conditions and the samples successfully pass the tests.

A.5.2.1.1.4 Examples include some floor/ceiling or roof/ceiling assemblies, areas under theater stages, pipe chases, and other inaccessible areas.

A.5.2.1.2 Obstructions to spray patterns include continuous or noncontinuous obstructions less than or equal to 457 mm (18 in.) below the sprinkler deflector that prevent the pattern from fully developing. Obstructions that prevent sprinkler discharge from reaching the hazard include continuous or noncontinuous obstructions that interrupt the water discharge in a horizontal plane more than 457 mm (18 in.) below the sprinkler deflector in a manner to limit the distribution from reaching the protected hazard. Specific guidance for clearance and obstructions is found in NFPA 13, *Standard for the Installation of Sprinkler Systems*, and specific sprinkler listings.

A.5.2.2 The conditions described in this section can have a detrimental effect on the performance and life of pipe by affecting corrosion rates or pipe integrity or otherwise rendering the pipe ineffectual.

A.5.2.2.3 Examples include some floor/ceiling or roof/ceiling assemblies, areas under theater stages, pipe chases, and other inaccessible areas.

A.5.2.3 The conditions described in this section can have a detrimental effect on the performance of hangers and braces by allowing failures if the components become loose.

A.5.2.3.3 Examples of hangers and seismic braces installed in concealed areas include some floor/ceiling or roof/ceiling assemblies, areas under theater stages, pipe chases, and other inaccessible areas.

A.5.2.4.1 Due to the high probability of a buildup of excess pressure, gridded wet pipe systems should be provided with a relief valve not less than 6.3 mm (¼ in.) in accordance with NFPA 13, *Standard for the Installation of Sprinkler Systems*.

A.5.2.4.4 See Figure A.5.2.4.4.

A.5.2.7 The hydraulic nameplate should be secured to the riser with durable wire, chain, or equivalent. *(See Figure A.5.2.7.)*

A.5.3.1 The sprinkler field service testing described in this section is considered routine testing. Non-routine testing should be conducted to address unusual conditions not associated with the routine test cycles mandated within this standard. Due to the nature of non-routine testing, specific tests cannot be identified in this standard. The type of tests to be conducted and number and location of samples to be submitted should be appropriate to the problem discovered or being investigated and based on consultation with the manufacturer, listing agency, and the authority having jurisdiction.

A.5.3.1.1 Sprinklers should be first given a visual inspection for signs of mechanical damage, cleaning, painting, leakage in service, or severe loading or corrosion, all of which are considered causes for immediate replacement. Devices that have passed the visual inspection should then be laboratory tested for sensitivity and functionality. The waterway should clear when sensitivity/functionality tested at .4 bar (5 psi) or the minimum listed operating pressure for dry sprinklers.

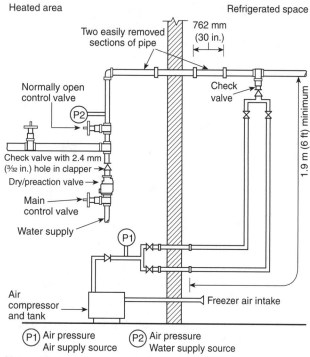

Notes:
1. Check valve with 2.4-mm (³⁄₃₂-in.) hole in clapper not required if prime water not used.
2. Supply air to be connection to top or side of system pipe.
3. Each removable air line shall be a minimum of 25 mm (1 in.) diameter and minimum of 1.9 m (6 ft) long.

FIGURE A.5.2.4.4 Refrigerator Area Sprinkler System Used to Minimize the Chances of Developing Ice Plugs.

This system as shown on _____ company

print no _____ dated _____

for _____

at _____ contract no _____

is designed to discharge at a rate of _____

L/min per m² (gpm per ft²) of floor area over a maximum

area of _____ m² (ft²) when supplied

with water at a rate of _____ L/min (gpm)

at _____ bar (psi) at the base of the riser.

Hose stream allowance of _____

L/min (gpm) is included in the above.

FIGURE A.5.2.7 Sample Hydraulic Nameplate.

Thermal sensitivity should be not less than that permitted in post-corrosion testing of new sprinklers of the same type.

Sprinklers that have been in service for a number of years should not be expected to have all of the performance qualities of a new sprinkler. However, if there is any question about their continued satisfactory performance, the sprinklers should be replaced.

See Figure A.5.3.1.1.

Fast response
3-mm bulb

Standard response
5-mm bulb

Fast response
element

Fast response
link

Standard response
solder link sprinkler

FIGURE A.5.3.1.1 Sprinkler Operating Element Identification.

A.5.3.1.1.1.3 Due to solder migration caused by the high temperatures to which these devices are exposed, it is important to test them every 5 years. Because of this phenomenon, the operating temperature can vary over a wide range.

A.5.3.1.1.2 Examples of these environments are paper mills, packing houses, tanneries, alkali plants, organic fertilizer plants, foundries, forge shops, fumigation, pickle and vinegar works, stables, storage battery rooms, electroplating rooms, galvanizing rooms, steam rooms of all descriptions including moist vapor dry kilns, salt storage rooms, locomotive sheds or houses, driveways, areas exposed to outside weather, around bleaching equipment in flour mills, all portions of cold storage areas, and portions of any area where corrosive vapors prevail. Harsh water environments include water supplies that are chemically reactive.

A.5.3.1.2 A sample should represent a given environment, and the sample size should consist of 1 percent or minimum of 4 of each type used in that environment. For example, a loading dock would be considered a different environment from the adjoining warehouse.

Within an environment, similar sidewall, upright, and pendent sprinklers produced by the same manufacturer could be considered part of the same sample but would be considered different samples if produced by different manufacturers.

A.5.3.2 The normal life expectancy of a gauge is between 10 and 15 years. A gauge can be permitted to have a reading with an error of ±3 percent of the maximum (full scale) gauge reading. For example, a gauge having 13.8 bar (200 psi) maximum radius installed on a system with 4.1 bar (60 psi) normal pressure can be permitted if the gauge reads from 3.7 bar to 4.5 bar (54 psi to 66 psi).

A.5.3.3 Testing of the water-flow alarm on wet pipe systems should be completed by opening the inspector's test connection. This simulates activation of a sprinkler. Where freezing weather conditions or other circumstances prohibit using the inspector's test connection, the bypass test connection can be permitted to be used.

A.5.3.3.2 Data concerning reliability of vane-type waterflow devices indicate no appreciable change in failure rates for those tested quarterly and those tested semiannually. Mechanical motor gongs and pressure switches, however, have additional mechanical and environmental failure modes and need to be tested more often.

A.5.3.3.3 Opening the inspector's test connection simulates activation of a sprinkler.

A.5.3.3.5 Opening the inspector's test connection can cause the system to trip accidentally.

A.5.3.4 Listed CPVC sprinkler pipe and fittings should be protected from freezing with glycerin only. The use of diethylene, ethylene, or propylene glycols is specifically prohibited. Where inspecting antifreeze systems employing listed CPVC piping, the solution should be verified to be glycerin based.

A.5.4.1.1.1 Old-style sprinklers are permitted to replace existing old-style sprinklers. Old-style sprinklers should not be used to replace standard sprinklers without a complete engineering review of the system. The old-style sprinkler is the type manufactured before 1953. It discharges approximately 40 percent of the water upward to the ceiling, and it can be installed in either the upright or pendent position.

A.5.4.1.3 It is imperative that any replacement sprinkler have the same characteristics as the sprinkler being replaced. If the same temperature range, response characteristics, spacing requirements, flow rates, and K-factors cannot be obtained, a sprinkler with similar characteristics should be used, and the system should be evaluated to verify the sprinkler is appropriate for the intended use. With regard to response characteristics, matching identical Response Time Index (RTI) and conductivity factors is not necessary unless special design considerations are given for those specific values.

A.5.4.1.4 A minimum of two sprinklers of each type and temperature rating installed should be provided.

A.5.4.1.6 Other types of wrenches could damage the sprinklers.

A.5.4.1.8 Corrosion-resistant or specially coated sprinklers should be installed in locations where chemicals, moisture, or other corrosive vapors exist.

A.5.4.2 Conversion of dry pipe systems to wet pipe systems causes corrosion and accumulation of foreign matter in the pipe system and loss of alarm service.

A.5.4.3 Where pressure testing listed CPVC piping, the sprinkler systems should be filled with water and air should be bled from the highest and farthest sprinkler before test pressure is applied. Air or compressed gas should never be used for pressure testing.

A.5.4.4 Certain sprinkler systems, such as those installed aboard ships, are maintained under pressure by a small freshwater supply but are supplied by a raw water source following system activation. In these systems, the effects of raw water are minimized by draining and refilling with fresh water. For systems on ships, flushing within 45 days or the vessel's next port of call, whichever is longer, is considered acceptable.

A.6.3.1.1 The hydraulically most remote hose connections in a building are generally at a roof manifold, if provided, or at the top of a stair leading to the roof. In a multizone system, the testing means is generally at a test header at grade or at a suction tank on higher floors.

Where a flow test at the hydraulically most remote hose connection is not practicable, the authority having jurisdiction should be consulted for the appropriate location of the test.

A.6.3.2.2 The intent of this paragraph is to ascertain whether the system retains its integrity under fire conditions. Minimum leakage existing only under test pressure is not cause for repair.

A.7.2.2 The requirements in 7.2.2 outline inspection intervals, conditions to be inspected, and corrective actions necessary for private fire service mains and associated equipment.

A.7.2.2.3 Any flow in excess of the flow through the main drain connection should be considered significant.

A.7.3.1 Full flow tests of underground piping can be accomplished by methods including, but not limited to, flow through yard hydrants, fire department connections once the check valve has been removed, main drain connections, and hose connections.

A.7.4.3.2 The intent of this section is to maintain adequate space for use of hydrants during a fire emergency. The amount of space needed depends on the configuration as well as the type and size of accessory equipment, such as hose, wrenches, and other devices that could be used.

A.8.1 A fire pump assembly provides water flow and pressure for private fire protection. The assembly includes the water supply suction and discharge piping and valving; pump; electric, diesel, or steam turbine driver and control; and the auxiliary equipment appurtenant thereto.

A.8.1.2 Types of centrifugal fire pumps include single and multistage units of horizontal or vertical shaft design. Listed fire pumps have rated capacities of 95 L/min to 18,925 L/min (25 gpm to 5000 gpm) with a net pressure range from approximately 2.75 bar to 27.6 bar (40 psi to 400 psi).

(1) *Horizontal Split Case.* This pump has a double suction impeller with an inboard and outboard bearing and is used with a positive suction supply. A variation of this design can be mounted with the shaft in a vertical plane. *[See Figure A.8.1.2(1).]*

(2) *End Suction and Vertical In-Line.* This pump can have either a horizontal or vertical shaft with a single suction impeller and a single bearing at the drive end. *[See Figure A.8.1.2(2).]*

(3) *Vertical Shaft, Turbine Type.* This pump has multiple impellers and is suspended from the pump head by a column pipe that also serves as a support for the shaft and bearings. This pump is necessary where a suction lift is needed, such as from an underground reservoir, well, river, or lake. *[See Figure A.8.1.2(3).]*

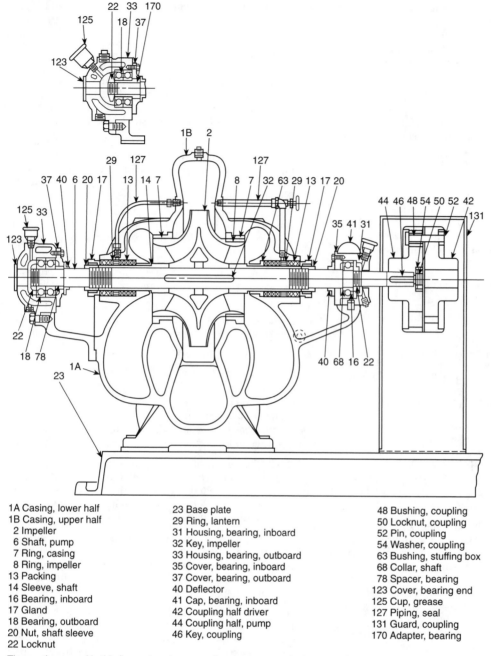

The numbers used in this figure do not necessarily represent standard part numbers used by any manufacturer.

1A Casing, lower half	23 Base plate	48 Bushing, coupling
1B Casing, upper half	29 Ring, lantern	50 Locknut, coupling
2 Impeller	31 Housing, bearing, inboard	52 Pin, coupling
6 Shaft, pump	32 Key, impeller	54 Washer, coupling
7 Ring, casing	33 Housing, bearing, outboard	63 Bushing, stuffing box
8 Ring, impeller	35 Cover, bearing, inboard	68 Collar, shaft
13 Packing	37 Cover, bearing, outboard	78 Spacer, bearing
14 Sleeve, shaft	40 Deflector	123 Cover, bearing end
16 Bearing, inboard	41 Cap, bearing, inboard	125 Cup, grease
17 Gland	42 Coupling half driver	127 Piping, seal
18 Bearing, outboard	44 Coupling half, pump	131 Guard, coupling
20 Nut, shaft sleeve	46 Key, coupling	170 Adapter, bearing
22 Locknut		

FIGURE A.8.1.2(1)   Impeller between Bearings, Separately Coupled, Single-Stage Axial (Horizontal) Split Case. *(Courtesy of Hydraulic Institute Standard for Centrifugal, Rotary and Reciprocating Pumps.)*

A.8.1.6 Controllers include air-, hydraulic-, or electric-operated units. These units can take power from the energy source for their operation, or the power can be obtained elsewhere. Controllers used with electric power sources can apply the source to the driver in one (across-the-line) or two (reduced voltage or current) steps. Controllers can be used with automatic and manual transfer switches to select the available electric power source where more than one is provided.

A.8.2.2 See Table A.8.2.2 and Figure A.8.2.2.

A.8.2.2(5) Visual indicators other than pilot lights can be used for the same purpose.

A.8.3 The purpose of testing the pump assembly is to ensure automatic or manual operation upon demand and continuous delivery of the required system output. An additional purpose is to detect deficiencies of the pump assembly not evident by inspection.

A.8.3.2.1 See Table A.8.3.2.1.

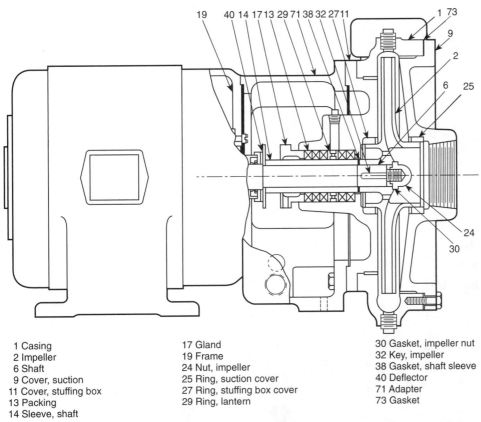

1 Casing	17 Gland	30 Gasket, impeller nut
2 Impeller	19 Frame	32 Key, impeller
6 Shaft	24 Nut, impeller	38 Gasket, shaft sleeve
9 Cover, suction	25 Ring, suction cover	40 Deflector
11 Cover, stuffing box	27 Ring, stuffing box cover	71 Adapter
13 Packing	29 Ring, lantern	73 Gasket
14 Sleeve, shaft		

The numbers used in this figure do not necessarily represent standard part numbers used by any manufacturer.

FIGURE A.8.1.2(2)   Overhung Impeller, Close-Coupled, Single-Stage, End Suction. (*Courtesy of Hydraulic Institute Standard for Centrifugal, Rotary and Reciprocating Pumps.*)

A.8.3.3.1.1 Peak flow for a fire pump is 150 percent of the rated flow. Minimum flow for a pump is the churn pressure.

A.8.3.3.1.2 The method described in 8.3.3.1.2.1 is not considered as complete as those in 8.3.3.1.2.2 and 8.3.3.1.2.3, because it does not test the adequacy of the water supply for compliance with the requirements of 8.1.3 at the suction flange.

A.8.3.3.3 A pressure relief valve that opens during a flow condition is discharging water that is not measured by the recording device(s). It can be necessary to temporarily close the pressure relief valve to achieve favorable pump test results. At the conclusion of the pump test, the pressure relief valve must be readjusted to relieve pressures in excess of the normal operating pressure of the system components.

If the pressure relief valve is open during the flowing conditions due to the fact that the pressure is too high for the components in the fire protection system, the discharge control valve should be closed prior to closing the pressure relief valve to make sure that the fire protection system is not overpressurized. After the test, make sure that the valve is opened again.

A.8.3.3.7 During periods of unusual water supply conditions such as floods, inspection should be on a daily basis.

A.8.3.4.4 If pumps and drivers were shipped from the factory with both machines mounted on a common base plate, they were accurately aligned before shipment. All base plates are flexible to some extent and, therefore, must not be relied upon to maintain the factory alignment. Realignment is necessary after the complete unit has been leveled on the foundation and again after the grout has set and foundation bolts have been tightened. The alignment should be checked after the unit is piped and rechecked periodically. To facilitate accurate field alignment, most manufacturers either do not dowel the pumps or drivers on the base plates before shipment, or at most dowel the pump only.

After the pump and driver unit has been placed on the foundation, the coupling halves should be disconnected. The coupling should not be reconnected until the alignment operations have been completed.

The purpose of the flexible coupling is to compensate for temperature changes and to permit end movement of the shafts without interference with each other while transmitting power from the driver to the pump.

There are two forms of misalignment between the pump shaft and the driver shaft, as follows:

(1) Angular Misalignment. Shafts with axes concentric but not parallel.
(2) Parallel Misalignment. Shafts with axes parallel but not concentric.

The faces of the coupling halves should be spaced within the manufacturer's recommendations and far enough apart so that they cannot strike each other when the driver rotor is moved hard over toward the pump. Due allowance should be

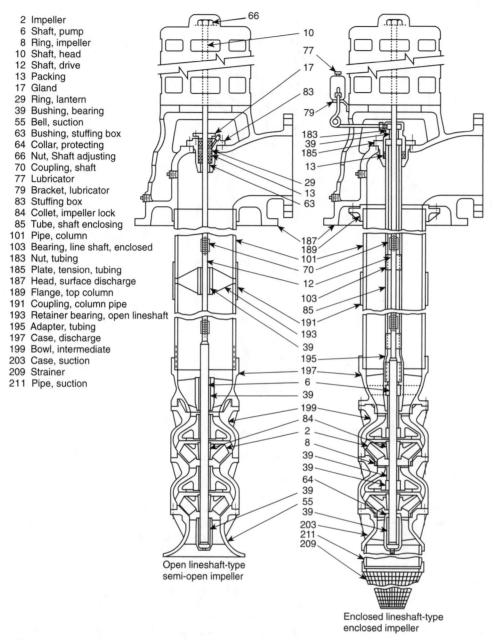

2 Impeller
6 Shaft, pump
8 Ring, impeller
10 Shaft, head
12 Shaft, drive
13 Packing
17 Gland
29 Ring, lantern
39 Bushing, bearing
55 Bell, suction
63 Bushing, stuffing box
64 Collar, protecting
66 Nut, Shaft adjusting
70 Coupling, shaft
77 Lubricator
79 Bracket, lubricator
83 Stuffing box
84 Collet, impeller lock
85 Tube, shaft enclosing
101 Pipe, column
103 Bearing, line shaft, enclosed
183 Nut, tubing
185 Plate, tension, tubing
187 Head, surface discharge
189 Flange, top column
191 Coupling, column pipe
193 Retainer bearing, open lineshaft
195 Adapter, tubing
197 Case, discharge
199 Bowl, intermediate
203 Case, suction
209 Strainer
211 Pipe, suction

Open lineshaft-type
semi-open impeller

Enclosed lineshaft-type
enclosed impeller

The cross-sectional views illustrate the largest possible number of parts in their proper relationship and some construction modifications but do not necessarily represent recommended design.

FIGURE A.8.1.2(3)   Turbine-Type, Vertical, Multistage, Deep Well. *(Courtesy of Hydraulic Institute Standard for Centrifugal, Rotary and Reciprocating Pumps.)*

made for wear of the thrust bearings. The necessary tools for an approximate check of the alignment of a flexible coupling are a straight edge and a taper gauge or a set of feeler gauges.

A check for angular alignment is made by inserting the taper gauge or feelers at four points between the coupling faces and comparing the distance between the faces at four points spaced at 90-degree intervals around the coupling [*see Figure A.8.3.4.4(a)*]. The unit will be in angular alignment when the measurements show that the coupling faces are the same distance apart at all points.

A check for parallel alignment is made by placing a straight edge across both coupling rims at the top, bottom, and at both sides [*see Figure A.8.3.4.4(b)*]. The unit will be in parallel alignment when the straight edge rests evenly on the coupling rim at all positions. Allowance may be necessary for temperature changes and for coupling halves that are not of the same outside diameter. Care must be taken to have the straight edge parallel to the axes of the shafts.

Angular and parallel misalignment are corrected by means of shims under the motor mounting feet. After each change, it

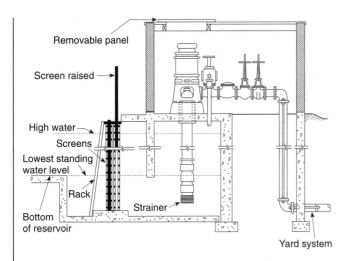

FIGURE A.8.2.2 Wet Pit Suction Screen Installation.

is necessary to recheck the alignment of the coupling halves. Adjustment in one direction may disturb adjustments already made in another direction. It should not be necessary to adjust the shims under the pump.

The permissible amount of misalignment will vary with the type of pump and driver; and coupling manufacturer, model, and size. [**20**: A.3.5]

A.8.3.5.1 Where the information is available, the test plot should be compared with the original acceptance test plot. It should be recognized that the acceptance test plot could exceed the minimum acceptable pump requirements as indicated by the rated characteristics for the pump. While a reduction in output is a matter of concern, this condition should be evaluated in light of meeting the rated characteristics for the pump. [*See Figure A.8.3.5.3(1).*]

The test equipment should be of high quality and accuracy. All equipment should have been calibrated within the last 12 months by an approved calibration facility. Where possible, the calibration facility should provide documentation indicating the instrument reading against the calibrated reading. Instruments that pass the calibration test should be labeled by the calibration facility with the name of the facility and the date of the test.

Pressure gauges should have an accuracy of not greater than 1 percent of full scale. In order to prevent damage to a pressure gauge utilizing a Bourdon tube mechanism, it should not be used where the expected test pressure is greater than 75 percent of the test gauge scale. Some digital gauges can be subjected to twice the full scale pressure without damage. The

Table A.8.2.2 Weekly Observations

Item	Before Pump Is Operated
Horizontal pumps	1. Check drip pockets under packing glands for proper drainage. Standing water in drip pockets is the most common cause of bearing failure. 2. Check packing adjustment — approximately one drop per second is necessary to keep packing lubricated. 3. Observe suction and discharge gauges. Readings higher than suction pressure indicate leakage back from system pressure through either the fire pump or jockey pump.

Table A.8.3.2.1 Weekly Observations

Item	While Pump Is Operating
Horizontal pumps	1. Read suction and discharge gauges — difference between these readings indicates churn pressure, which should match churn pressure as shown on fire pump nameplate. 2. Observe packing glands for proper leakage for cooling of packing. 3. Observe discharge from casing relief valve — adequate flow keeps pump case from overheating.
Vertical pumps	1. Read discharge gauge — add distance to water level in feet and divide by 2.31 to compute psi. This total must match churn pressure as shown on fire pump nameplate. 2. Observe packing glands for proper leakage for cooling of packing. 3. Observe discharge from casing relief valve — adequate flow keeps pump case from overheating.
Diesel engines	1. Observe discharge of cooling water from heat exchanger — if not adequate, check strainer in cooling system for obstructions. If still not adequate, adjust pressure reducing valve for correct flow. 2. Check engine instrument panel for correct speed, oil pressure, water temperature, and ammeter charging rate. 3. Check battery terminal connections for corrosion and clean if necessary. 4. After pump has stopped running, check intake screens, if provided; change diesel system pressure recorder chart and rewind if necessary.

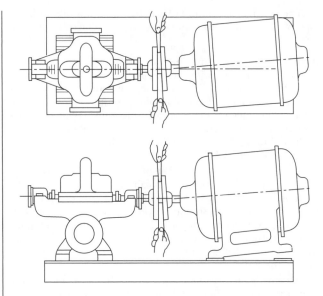

FIGURE A.8.3.4.4(a)   Checking Angular Alignment. *(Courtesy of Hydraulic Institute Standard for Centrifugal, Rotary and Reciprocating Pumps.)*

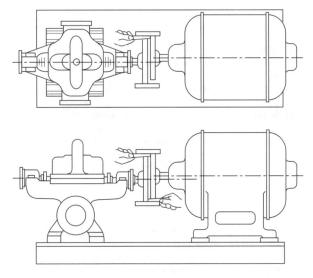

FIGURE A.8.3.4.4(b)   Checking Parallel Alignment. *(Courtesy of Hydraulic Institute Standard for Centrifugal, Rotary and Reciprocating Pumps.)*

manufacturer's recommendations should be consulted for the proper use of the gauge. In order to be able to easily read an analog gauge, the diameter of the face of an analog gauge should be greater than 76 mm (3 in.). Pressure snubbers should be used for all gauges to minimize needle fluctuation. All gauges used in the test should be such that a gauge with the lowest full scale pressure is used. For example, a 20.7-bar (300-psi) gauge should not be used to measure a 1.4-bar (20-psi) pitot pressure.

Equipment other than pressure gauges, such as volt/ammeters, tachometers, and flow meters, should be calibrated to the manufacturer's specifications. The readings from equipment with this level of accuracy and calibration can be used without adjustment for accuracy.

A.8.3.5.3(1) See Figure A.8.3.5.3(1).

A.8.3.5.4 See Annex C.

A.8.4.2 See 8.3.3.4.

A.8.5.1 It is important to provide proper bearing lubrication and to keep bearings clean. Some bearings are the sealed type and need no relubrication. Couplings with rubber drive parts do not need lubrication; other types generally do. The following practices are recommended:

(1) Lubricant fittings should be cleaned before relubricating with grease.
(2) The proper amount of lubricant should be used. Too much lubricant results in churning, causing excessive power loss and overheating.
(3) The correct lubricant should be used.

Engine Maintenance. Engines should be kept clean, dry, and well lubricated. The proper oil level in the crankcase should be maintained.

Battery Maintenance. Only distilled water should be used in battery cells. Plates should be kept submerged at all times. An automatic battery charger is not a substitute for proper maintenance of the battery and charger. Periodic inspection ensures that the charger is operating correctly, the water level in the battery is adequate, and the battery is holding its proper charge.

Fuel Supply Maintenance. The fuel storage tank should be kept at least two-thirds full. Fuel should be maintained free of water and foreign material by draining water and foreign material from the tank sump annually. This necessitates draining approximately 19 L (5 gal).

Temperature Maintenance. The temperature of the pump room, pump house, or area where engines are installed should never be less than the minimum recommended by the engine manufacturer. The manufacturer's temperature recommendations for water and oil heaters should be followed.

A.9.1 One source of information on the inspection and maintenance of steel gravity and suction tanks is the AWWA *Manual of Water Supply Practices — M42 Steel Water-Storage Tanks,* Part III and Annex C.

A.9.1.3 The inspection, testing, and maintenance of water storage tanks can involve or result in a system that is out of service. In cases where a tank is the sole source of supply to a fire protection system, it is recommended that an alternate water supply be arranged while maintenance is performed on the tank.

A.9.2.1.1 More frequent inspections should be made where extreme conditions, such as freezing temperatures or arid climate, can increase the probability of adversely affecting the stored water.

Supervisory water level alarms installed on tanks provide notification that the tank water level is above or below an acceptable level. The water level of the tank is the main concern as opposed to the condition of the water. For convenience, inspection of the condition of the water can take place concurrently with the water level inspection.

A.9.2.5.1 Lightning protection systems, where provided, should be inspected, tested, and maintained in accordance with NFPA 780, *Standard for the Installation of Lightning Protection Systems.*

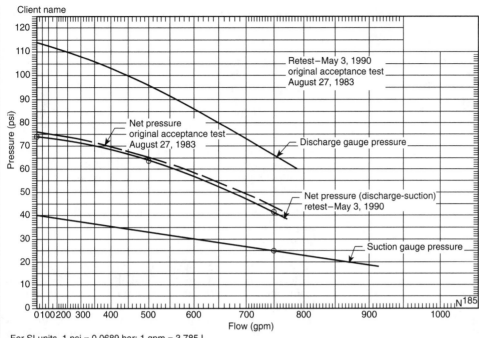

For SI units, 1 psi = 0.0689 bar; 1 gpm = 3.785 L.

FIGURE A.8.3.5.3(1)   Fire Pump Retest.

A.9.2.6.1.1 To aid in the inspection and evaluation of test results, it is a good idea for owners to stencil the last known date of an interior paint job on the exterior of the tank in a conspicuous place. A typical place is near one of the manways at eye level.

A.9.2.6.5 This inspection can be performed by looking for dents on the tank floor. Additionally, walking on the tank floor and looking for buckling of the floor will identify problem areas.

A.9.3.1 The testing procedure for listed mercury gauges is as follows.

To determine that the mercury gauge is accurate, the gauge should be tested every 5 years as follows [steps (1) through (7) coincide with Figure A.9.3.1]:

(1) Overflow the tank.
(2) Close valve F. Open test cock D. The mercury will drop quickly into the mercury pot. If it does not drop, there is an obstruction that needs to be removed from the pipe or pot between the test cock and the gauge glass.
(3) If the mercury does lower at once, close cock D and open valve F. If the mercury responds immediately and comes to rest promptly opposite the "FULL" mark on the gauge board, the instrument is functioning properly.
(4) If the mercury column does not respond promptly and indicate the correct reading during the test, there probably are air pockets or obstructions in the water connecting pipe. Open cock D. Water should flow out forcibly. Allow water to flow through cock D until all air is expelled and rusty water from the tank riser appears. Close cock D. The gauge now likely will read correctly. If air separates from the water in the 25-mm (1-in.) pipe due to being enclosed in a buried tile conduit with steam pipes, the air can be removed automatically by installing a 20-mm (¾-in.) air trap at the high point of the piping. The air trap

usually can be installed most easily in a tee connected by a short piece of pipe at E, with a plug in the top of the tee so that mercury can be added in the future, if necessary, without removing the trap. If there are inaccessible pockets in the piping, as where located below grade or under concrete floors, the air can be removed only through petcock D.

(5) If, in step (4), the water does not flow forcibly through cock D, there is an obstruction that needs to be removed from the outlet of the test cock or from the water pipe between the test cock and the tank riser.
(6) If there is water on top of the mercury column in the gauge glass, it will provide inaccurate readings and should be removed. First, lower the mercury into the pot as in step (2). Close cock D and remove plug G. Open valve F very slowly, causing the mercury to rise slowly and the water above it to drain through plug G. Close valve F quickly when mercury appears at plug G, but have a receptacle ready to catch any mercury that drains out. Replace plug G. Replace any escaped mercury in the pot.
(7) After testing, leave valve F open, except under the following conditions: If it is necessary to prevent forcing mercury and water into the mercury catcher, the controlling valve F can be permitted to be closed when filling the tank but should be left open after the tank is filled. In cases where the gauge is subjected to continual fluctuation of pressure, it could be necessary to keep the gauge shut off except when it needs to be read. Otherwise, it could be necessary to remove water frequently from the top of the mercury column as in step (5).

A.9.3.4 The manufacturer's instructions should be consulted for guidance on testing. In some situations, it might not be possible to test the actual initiating device. In such cases, only the circuitry should be tested.

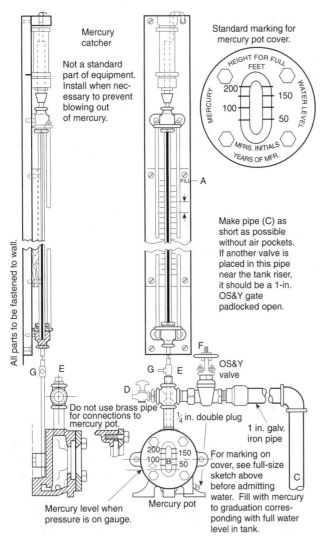

Mercury catcher

Not a standard part of equipment. Install when necessary to prevent blowing out of mercury.

All parts to be fastened to wall.

Standard marking for mercury pot cover.

HEIGHT FOR FULL FEET
MERCURY
200
100
150
50
WATER LEVEL
MFRS. INITIALS
YEARS OF MFR.

FILL — A

Make pipe (C) as short as possible without air pockets. If another valve is placed in this pipe near the tank riser, it should be a 1-in. OS&Y gate padlocked open.

G   E
D

Do not use brass pipe for connections to mercury pot.

Mercury level when pressure is on gauge.

F
OS&Y valve

G   E

¼ in. double plug

1 in. galv. iron pipe

200   150
100   B   50

Mercury pot

C

For marking on cover, see full-size sketch above before admitting water. Fill with mercury to graduation corresponding with full water level in tank.

Note: For SI units, 1 in. = 25.4 mm.

FIGURE A.9.3.1 Mercury Gauge.

A.9.3.5 See A.9.3.4.

A.9.3.6 See A.9.3.4.

A.10.1 The effectiveness and reliability of water spray fixed systems depends on maintenance of the integrity of hydraulic characteristics, water control valves, deluge valves and their fire detection/actuation systems, pipe hangers, and prevention of obstructions to nozzle discharge patterns.

Water spray fixed systems are most commonly used to protect processing equipment and structures, flammable liquid and gas vessels, piping, and equipment such as transformers, oil switches, and motors. They also have been shown to be effective on many combustible solids.

A.10.1.2 Insulation acting in lieu of water spray protection is expected to protect a vessel or structure for the duration of the exposure. The insulation is to prevent the temperature from exceeding 454°C (850°F) for structural members and 393°C (650°F) for vessels. If the insulation is missing, the structure or vessel is not considered to be protected, regardless of water spray protection or insulation on other surfaces. To re-

establish the proper protection, the insulation should be replaced or the water spray protection should be extended, using the appropriate density.

A.10.1.4 The inspection, testing, and maintenance of water spray fixed systems can involve or result in a system that is out of service. Also see Chapter 14.

A.10.1.4.1 Many of the components and subsystems found in a water spray system require the same inspection, test, and maintenance procedures mandated where they are used in automatic sprinkler systems and other fixed water-based fire protection systems. Other chapters of this standard should be consulted for particulars on required inspection and maintenance.

A.10.2.4 The operation of the water spray system is dependent on the integrity of the piping, which should be kept in good condition and free of mechanical damage. The pipe should not be used for support of ladders, stock, or other material. Where piping is subject to a corrosive atmosphere, a protective corrosion-resistant coating should be provided and maintained. Where the age or service conditions warrant, an internal examination of the piping should be made. Where it is necessary to flush all or part of the piping system, this work should be done by sprinkler contractors or other qualified workers.

A.10.2.4.1 Rubber-gasketed fittings in the fire areas are inspected to determine that they are protected by the water spray or other approved means. Unless properly protected, fire could cause loss of the rubber gasket following excessive leakage in a fire situation.

A.10.2.4.2 Hangers and supports are designed to support and restrain the piping from severe movement when the water supply operates and to provide adequate pipe slope for drainage of water from the piping after the water spray system is shut down. Hangers should be kept in good repair. Broken or loose hangers can put undue strain on piping and fittings, cause pipe breaks, and interfere with proper drainage of the pipe. Broken or loose hangers should be replaced or refastened.

A.10.2.5 Systems need inspection to ensure water spray nozzles effectively discharge water unobstructed onto surfaces to be protected from radiant heat (exposure protection) or onto flaming surfaces to extinguish or control combustion. Factors affecting the proper placement of water spray nozzles include the following:

(1) Changes or additions to the protected area that obstruct existing nozzles or require additional coverage for compliance
(2) Removal of equipment from the protected area that results in nozzle placement at excessive distances from the hazard
(3) Mechanical damage or previous flow tests that have caused nozzles to be misdirected
(4) A change in the hazard being protected that requires more or different nozzles to provide adequate coverage for compliance

Spray nozzles can be permitted to be placed in any position necessary to obtain proper coverage of the protected area. Positioning of nozzles with respect to surfaces to be protected, or to fires to be controlled or extinguished, should be guided by the particular nozzle design and the character of water spray produced. In positioning nozzles, care should be taken that the water spray does not miss the targeted surface and reduce the efficiency or calculated discharge rate.

A.10.2.6.2 Water supply piping should be free of internal obstructions that can be caused by debris (e.g., rocks, mud, tubercles) or by closed or partially closed control valves. See Chapter 5 for inspection and maintenance requirements.

A.10.2.7 Mainline strainers should be removed and inspected for damaged and corroded parts every 5 years.

A.10.3.3 The owner's representative should take care to prevent damage to equipment or the structure during the test. Damage could be caused by the system discharge or by runoff from the test site. It should be verified that there is adequate and unobstructed drainage. Equipment should be removed or covered as necessary to prevent damage. Means such as curbing or sandbagging should be used to prevent entry of the water.

A.10.3.4.1 Test methods are as follows:

(1) Some detection circuits can be permitted to be deliberately desensitized in order to override unusual ambient conditions. In such cases, the response in 10.3.4.1 can be permitted to be exceeded.
(2) Testing of integrating tubing systems can be permitted to be related to this test by means of a standard pressure impulse test specified by the listing laboratory.
(3) One method of testing heat detection uses a radiant heat surface at a temperature of 149°C (300°F) and a capacity of 350 watts at a distance of 25 mm (1 in.) but not more than 50 mm (2 in.) from the nearest part of the detector. This method of testing with an electric test set should not be used in hazardous locations. Other test methods can be permitted to be employed, but the results should be obtained under these conditions.

A.10.3.4.3 Spray nozzles can be of different sizes and types. Some are more subject to internal obstructions than others.

A.11.2.5 Directional-type foam-water discharge devices are quite often located in heavy traffic areas and are more apt to be dislocated compared to ordinary sprinkler locations. Of particular concern are low-level discharge devices in loading racks in and around low-level tankage and monitor-mounted devices that have been pushed out of the way for convenience. Inspection frequency might have to be increased accordingly.

A.11.2.6.2 Water supply piping should be free of internal obstructions that can be caused by debris (e.g., rocks, mud, tubercles) or by closed or partially closed control valves. See Chapter 5 for inspection and maintenance requirements.

A.11.2.9 Proportioning systems might or might not include foam concentrate pumps. If pumps are part of the proportioning system, the driver, pump, and gear reducer should be checked in accordance with the manufacturer's recommendations, and the check can include items such as lubrication, fuel, filters, oil levels, and clutches.

A.11.2.9.4 In some cases, an adequate supply of foam liquid is available without a full tank. This is particularly true of foam liquid stored in nonmetallic tanks. If liquid is stored in metallic tanks, the proper liquid level should be one-half the distance into the expansion dome.

A.11.2.9.5.1 Although under normal standby conditions this type of proportioning system should not be pressurized, some installations allow for inadvertent pressurization. Pressure should be removed before inspection.

A.11.2.9.5.2 Where inspecting for a full liquid tank, the manufacturer's instructions should be followed. If checked incorrectly, the tank sight gauges could indicate a full tank when the tank actually is empty of foam liquid. Some foam liquids, due to their viscosity, might not indicate true levels of foam liquid in the tank where checked via the sight glass.

> **CAUTION:** Depending on system configuration, this type of proportioner system might be pressurized or nonpressurized under normal conditions. Pressure should be removed before inspection.

A.11.2.9.5.3(1) See 11.2.7.1.

A.11.2.9.5.3(2) See Figure A.3.3.28.

A.11.2.9.5.4(1) See 11.2.7.1.

A.11.2.9.5.4(2) See Figure A.3.3.28.

A.11.2.9.5.5(1) See 11.2.7.1.

A.11.2.9.5.5(2) See Figure A.3.3.28.

A.11.2.9.5.6(1) See 11.2.7.1.

A.11.2.9.5.6(2) See Figure A.3.3.28.

A.11.3 Operational tests generally should be comprised of the following:

(1) A detection/actuation test with no flow to verify that all components such as automated valves, foam and water pumps, and alarms operate properly
(2) A water-only flow test to check piping continuity, discharge patterns, pressures, and line flushing
(3) A foam flow test to verify solution concentration
(4) Resetting of system to its normal standby condition, including draining of lines and filling of foam liquid tank

A.11.3.2 The owner's representative should take care to prevent damage to equipment or the structure during the test. Damage could be caused by the system discharge or by runoff from the test site. It should be verified that there is adequate and unobstructed drainage. Equipment should be removed or covered as necessary to prevent damage. Means such as curbing or sandbagging should be used to prevent entry of the foam-water solution.

A.11.3.3 An alternate method for achieving flow can be permitted to be an installation as shown in Figure A.11.3.3. This type of testing does not verify system pipe conditions or discharge device performance but only the water supply, foam concentrate supply, and proportioning accuracy.

A.11.3.3.7 Specific foam concentrates typically are listed or approved with specific sprinklers. Part of the approval and listing is a minimum sprinkler operating pressure. Sprinkler operating pressure affects foam quality, discharge patterns, and fire extinguishment (control) capabilities. Discharge pressures less than this specified minimum pressure should be corrected immediately; therefore, it is necessary to test under full flow conditions.

A.11.4 The maintenance items specified in the body of this standard are in addition to the typical inspection and test procedures indicated. Foam-water systems are, as are all fire protection systems, designed to be basically maintenance free. There are, however, some areas that need special attention. Foam concentrate shelf life varies between liquids and is af-

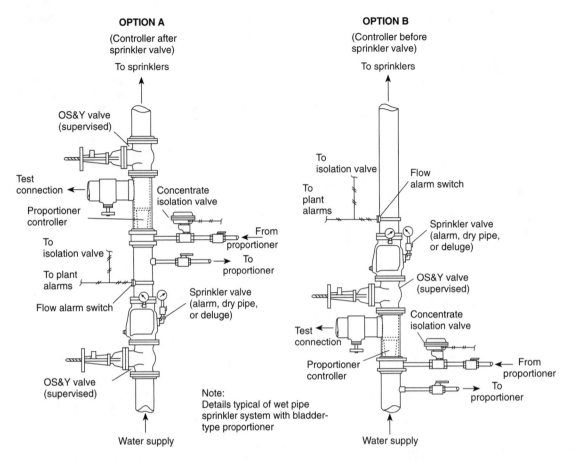

FIGURE A.11.3.3 Foam System/Test Header Combination.

fected by factors such as heat, cold, dilution, contamination, and many others. As with all systems, common sense dictates those maintenance-sensitive areas that should be given attention. Routine testing and inspection generally dictate the need for additional maintenance items. Those maintenance items specified are key procedures that should be performed routinely.

A.11.4.3(B) Foam concentrates tend to settle out over time. Depending on the specific characteristics of the foam concentrate, sedimentation accumulates in the bottom of the storage vessel. This sediment can affect proportioning and foam concentrate integrity. Some concentrates tend to settle out more rapidly than others. If the annual samples indicate excessive sediment, flushing the tank could be required more frequently.

A.11.4.4(B) Where hydrostatically testing bladder tanks, the generation of a pressure differential across the diaphragm should not be allowed. The manufacturer should be consulted for specific procedures.

A.12.1 *Alarm Valves.* Alarm valves are installed in water-based fire protection systems to sound a fire alarm when a flow of water from the system equals or exceeds the flow of a single discharge device. A retarding chamber, which minimizes false alarms due to surges and fluctuating water supply pressure, can be supplied with the alarm valve.

Backflow Prevention Devices. Backflow prevention devices are used to prevent water in a fire protection system from entering the public water supply due to a reverse flow of water, thermal expansion, hydraulic shock, back pressure, or back siphonage. *[See Figure A.12.1(a).]*

Ball Valves. Ball valves are manually operated through their full range of open to closed positions with a one-quarter turn.

Butterfly Valves. Butterfly valves are water supply control valves with gear operators to assist in opening and closing. Butterfly valves can be of the wafer or grooved-end type. *[See Figure A.12.1(b).]*

Check Valves. Check valves allow water flow in one direction only. *[See Figure A.12.1(c).]*

DCA. A double check assembly (DCA) consists of two independently operating spring-loaded check valves. The assembly includes two resilient-seated isolation valves and four test cocks required for testing.

DCDA. A double check detector assembly (DCDA) is hydraulically balanced to include a metered bypass assembly to detect system leakage. The main valve assembly and bypass assembly afford equal levels of backflow prevention and are each equipped with two resilient-seated isolation valves and four test cocks required for testing.

Deluge Valves. Deluge valves hold water at the valve until actuated by the operation of a detection system or manual release. *[See Figure A.12.1(d).]*

Drip Valves. Drip valves automatically drain condensation or small amounts of water that have leaked into system piping or valves. Drip valves close when exposed to system pressure.

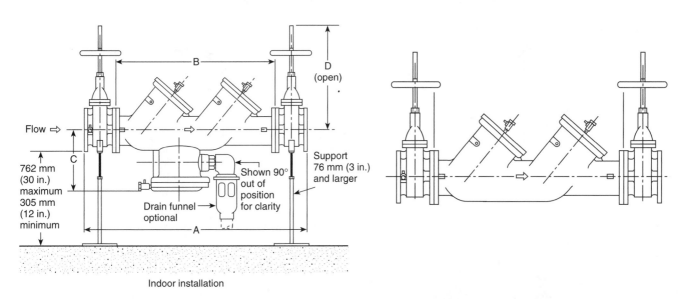

Indoor installation

FIGURE A.12.1(a)   Reduced Pressure Backflow Preventers (left) and Double Check Valve Assemblies (right).

FIGURE A.12.1(b)   Butterfly Post Indicator Valve. *(Courtesy of Henry Pratt Co.)*

FIGURE A.12.1(c)   Detector Check Valve.

Dry Pipe Valves. Dry pipe valves control the flow of water to areas that could be exposed to freezing conditions. Water is held at the valve by air pressure in the system piping. When the air pressure is reduced, the valve operates and floods the system. *[See Figure A.12.1(e) and Figure A.12.1(f).]*

Indicating Valves. Indicating valves provide a dependable, visible indication of the open position, even at a distance.

Indicator Posts. Indicator posts include wall and underground types and are intended for use in operating inside screwed pattern gate valves and for indicating the position of the gates in the valves. *[See Figure A.12.1(g).]*

NRS Gate Valves, OS&Y Gate Valves. Nonrising stem (NRS) gate valves are used underground with indicator posts attached or as roadway box valves (curb-box installation). Outside screw and yoke (OS&Y) gate valves are used indoors and

in pits outdoors. The valve stem moves out when the valve is open and moves in when it is closed. The stem indicates the position of the valve. *[See Figure A.12.1(h) and Figure A.12.1(i).]*

RPA. A reduced-pressure zone principle assembly (RPA) consists of two independently spring-loaded check valves separated by a differential-sensing valve. The differential-sensing valve includes a relief port to atmosphere that discharges excess water resulting from supply system fluctuations. The assembly includes two resilient-seated isolation valves and four test cocks required for testing.

RPDA. A reduced-pressure detector assembly (RPDA) is hydraulically balanced to include a metered bypass assembly to detect system leakage. The main valve assembly and bypass assembly afford equal levels of backflow prevention, and each assembly is equipped with two resilient-seated isolation valves and four test cocks required for testing.

Strainers. Strainers are used for protection against clogging of water discharge openings.

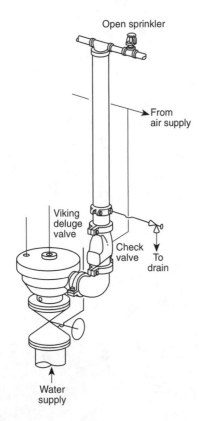

FIGURE A.12.1(d)   Deluge Valve.

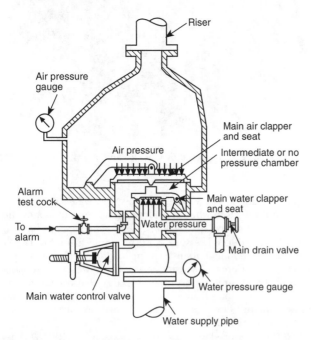

FIGURE A.12.1(e)   Dry Pipe Valve.

Water-Flow Detector Check Valves. Detector-type check valves allow flow in one direction only and have provisions for the connection of a bypass meter around the check valve. *[See Figure A.12.1(c).]*

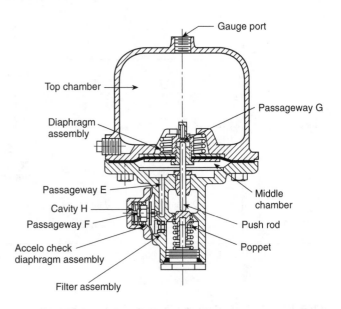

FIGURE A.12.1(f)   Dry Pipe System Accelerator. *(Courtesy of Reliable Automatic Sprinkler Co.)*

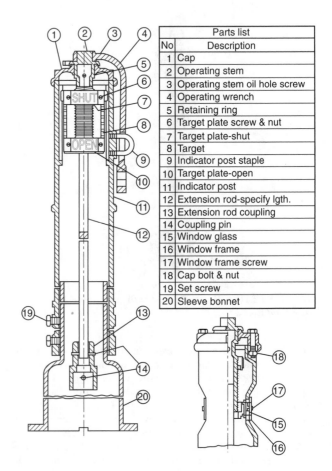

Parts list	
No	Description
1	Cap
2	Operating stem
3	Operating stem oil hole screw
4	Operating wrench
5	Retaining ring
6	Target plate screw & nut
7	Target plate-shut
8	Target
9	Indicator post staple
10	Target plate-open
11	Indicator post
12	Extension rod-specify lgth.
13	Extension rod coupling
14	Coupling pin
15	Window glass
16	Window frame
17	Window frame screw
18	Cap bolt & nut
19	Set screw
20	Sleeve bonnet

FIGURE A.12.1(g)   Vertical Indicator Post.

A.12.2.3 The valves are not required to be exposed. Doors, removable panels, or valve pits can be permitted to satisfy this requirement. Such equipment should not be obstructed by

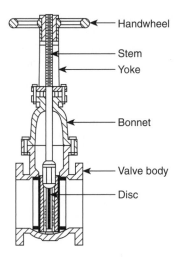

FIGURE A.12.1(h)   OS&Y Gate Valve.

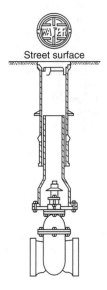

FIGURE A.12.1(i)   Nonindicating-Type Gate Valve.

features such as walls, ducts, columns, direct burial, or stock storage.

A.12.2.6 Main drains are installed on system risers for one principal reason: to drain water from the overhead piping after the system is shut off. This allows the contractor or plant maintenance department to perform work on the system or to replace nozzles after a fire or other incident involving system operation.

The test for standpipe systems should be done at the low point drain for each standpipe or the main drain test connection where the supply main enters the building.

These drains also are used to determine whether there is a major reduction in water flow to the system, such as could be caused by a major obstruction, a dropped gate, a valve that is almost fully closed, or a check valve clapper stuck to the valve seat.

A large drop in the full flow pressure of the main drain (as compared to previous tests) normally is indicative of a dangerously reduced water supply caused by a valve in an almost fully

closed position or other type of severe obstruction. After closing the drain, a slow return to normal static pressure is confirmation of the suspicion of a major obstruction in the waterway and should be considered sufficient reason to determine the cause of the variation.

A satisfactory drain test (i.e., one that reflects the results of previous tests) does not necessarily indicate an unobstructed passage, nor does it prove that all valves in the upstream flow of water are fully opened. The performance of drain tests is not a substitute for a valve check on 100 percent of the fire protection valving.

The main drain test is conducted in the following manner:

(1) Record the pressure indicated by the supply water gauge
(2) Close the alarm control valve on alarm valves
(3) Fully open the main drain valve
(4) After the flow has stabilized, record the residual (flowing) pressure indicated by the water supply gauge
(5) Close the main drain valve slowly
(6) Record the time taken for the supply water pressure to return to the original static (nonflowing) pressure
(7) Open the alarm control valve

A.12.3.1 Signs identifying underground fire service main control valves in roadway boxes should indicate the direction of valve opening, the distance and direction of the valve from the sign location (if the valve is subject to being covered by snow or ice), and the location of the wrench if not located with the sign.

A.12.3.1.1 Valves that normally are closed during cold weather should be removed and replaced with devices that provide continuous fire protection service.

A.12.3.2.2 Valves should be kept free of snow, ice, storage, or other obstructions so that access is ensured.

A.12.3.2.2(2) The purpose of the valve sealing program is as follows:

(1) The presence of a seal on a control valve is a deterrent to closing a valve indiscriminately without obtaining the proper authority.
(2) A broken or missing seal on a valve is cause for the plant inspector to verify that protection is not impaired and to notify superiors of the fact that a valve could have been closed without following procedures.

A.12.3.3.2 These "spring tests" are made to verify that a post indicator valve is fully open. If an operator feels the valve is fully open, he or she should push in the "open" direction. The handle usually moves a short distance (approximately a one-quarter turn) and "springs" back toward the operator in a subtle move when released. This spring occurs when the valve gate pulls up tight against the top of its casting and the valve shaft (being fairly long) twists slightly. The spring indicates that the valve is fully opened and that the gate is attached to the handle. If the gate is jammed due to a foreign particle, the handle is not likely to spring back. If the gate is loose from the handle, the handle continues to turn in the "open" direction with little resistance.

A.12.3.3.5 For further information, see *NFPA 72®, National Fire Alarm Code®*.

A.12.4.1.1 A higher pressure reading on the system gauge is normal in variable pressure water supplies. Pressure over 12.1 bar (175 psi) can be caused by fire pump tests or thermal expansion and should be investigated and corrected.

A.12.4.1.2 The system should be drained for internal inspection of valve components as follows:

(1) Close the control valve
(2) Open the main drain valve
(3) Open the inspector's test valve
(4) Wait for the sound of draining water to cease and for all gauges to indicate 0 bar (0 psi) before removing the hand-hole cover or dismantling any component

A.12.4.3.2.1 High priming water levels can adversely affect the operation of supervisory air. Test the water level as follows:

(1) Open the priming level test valve
(2) If water flows, drain it
(3) Close the valve when water stops flowing and air discharges
(4) If air discharges when the valve is opened, the priming water level could be too low. To add priming water, refer to the manufacturer's instructions

A.12.4.3.2.2 Preaction and deluge valves in areas subject to freezing should be trip tested in the spring to allow time before the onset of cold weather for all water that has entered the system or condensation to drain to low points or back to the valve.

A.12.4.3.2.9 Methods of recording maintenance include tags attached at each riser, records retained at each building, and records retained at one building in a complex.

A.12.4.3.3.3 Suitable facilities should be provided to dispose of drained water. Low points equipped with a single valve should be drained as follows:

(1) Open the low point drain valve slowly
(2) Close the drain valve as soon as water ceases to discharge and allow time for additional accumulation above the valve
(3) Repeat this procedure until water ceases to discharge
(4) Replace plug or nipple and cap as necessary

Low points equipped with dual valves should be drained as follows:

(1) Close the upper valve
(2) Open the lower valve and drain the accumulated water
(3) Close the lower valve, open the upper valve, and allow time for additional water accumulation
(4) Repeat this procedure until water ceases to discharge
(5) Replace plug or nipple and cap in lower valve

A.12.4.4.1.2(C) A conflict in pressure readings could indicate an obstructed orifice or a leak in the isolated chamber of the quick-opening device, either of which could make the quick-opening device inoperative.

A.12.4.4.2.1 High priming water levels can affect the operation of supervisory air or nitrogen pressure maintenance devices. Test the water level as follows:

(1) Open the priming level test valve
(2) If water flows, drain it
(3) Close the valve when water stops flowing and air discharges
(4) If air discharges when the valve is opened, the priming water level could be too low. To add priming water, refer to the manufacturer's instructions

A.12.4.4.2.2 Dry pipe valves should be trip tested in the spring to allow time before the onset of cold weather for all water that

has entered the system or condensation to drain to low points or back to the valve.

A.12.4.4.2.2.2 A full flow trip test generally requires at least two individuals, one of whom is situated at the dry pipe valve while the other is at the inspector's test. If possible, they should be in communication with each other. A full flow trip test is conducted as follows:

(1) The main drain valve is fully opened to clean any accumulated scale or foreign material from the supply water piping. The main drain valve then is closed.
(2) The system air or nitrogen pressure and the supply water pressure is recorded.
(3) The system air or nitrogen pressure is relieved by opening the inspector's test valve completely. Concurrent with opening the valve, both testers start their stopwatches. If two-way communication is not available, the tester at the dry valve is to react to the start of downward movement on the air pressure gauge.
(4) Testers at the dry pipe valve note the air pressure at which the valve trips and note the tripping time.
(5) Testers at the inspector's test note the time at which water flows steadily from the test connection. This time is noted for comparison purposes to previous tests and is not meant to be a specific pass/fail criterion. Note that NFPA 13, *Standard for the Installation of Sprinkler Systems*, does not require water delivery in 60 seconds for all systems.
(6) When clean water flows, the test is terminated by closing the system control valve.
(7) The air or nitrogen pressure and the time elapsed are to be recorded as follows:
   (a) From the complete opening of the test valve to the tripping of the valve
   (b) From the complete opening of inspector's valve to the start of steady flow from the test connection
(8) All low point drains are opened and then closed when water ceases to flow.
(9) The dry pipe valve and quick-opening device are reset, if installed, in accordance with the manufacturer's instructions, and the system is returned to service.

A.12.4.4.2.2.3 A partial flow trip test is conducted in the following manner:

(1) Fully open the main drain valve to clean any accumulated scale or foreign material from the supply water piping
(2) Close the control valve to the point where additional closure cannot provide flow through the entire area of the drain outlet
(3) Close the valve controlling flow to the device if a quick-opening device is installed
(4) Record the system air or nitrogen pressure and the supply water pressure
(5) Relieve system air or nitrogen pressure by opening the priming level test valve
(6) Note and record the air or nitrogen pressure and supply water pressure when the dry pipe valve trips
(7) Immediately close the system control valve and open the main drain valve to minimize the amount of water entering the system piping
(8) Trip test the quick-opening device, if installed, in accordance with the manufacturer's instructions
(9) Open all low point drains; close when water ceases to flow

(10) Reset the dry pipe valve and quick-opening device, if installed, in accordance with the manufacturer's instructions and return the system to service

> **CAUTION:** A partial flow trip test does not provide a high enough rate of flow to latch the clappers of some model dry pipe valves in the open position. When resetting such valves, check that the latching equipment is operative.

A.12.4.4.2.4 Except when a full flow trip test is conducted in accordance with A.12.4.4.2.2.2, a quick-opening device should be tested in the following manner:

(1) Close the system control valve.
(2) Open the main drain valve and keep it in the open position.
(3) Verify that the quick-opening device control valve is open.
(4) Open the inspector's test valve. A burst of air from the device indicates that it has tripped.
(5) Close the device's control valve.
(6) Return the device to service in accordance with the manufacturer's instructions and return the system to service.

A.12.4.4.3.1 Leaks can be located by inspecting the system for damage or by applying leak detecting fluids to pipe joints and valve packing nuts or bonnets.

A.12.4.4.3.3 A quick-opening device, if installed, should be removed temporarily from service prior to draining low points.

A.12.5.1.2 The sectional drain valve should be opened to compare the results with the original installation or acceptance tests.

A.12.5.2.2 PRV devices can be bench tested in accordance with the manufacturer's instructions or tested in place. To test in place, a gauge is connected on both the inlet side and the outlet side of the device and flow readings are taken using a Pitot tube or a flowmeter. Water is discharged through a roof manifold, if available, or through hose to the exterior of the building. Another acceptable method for systems having at least two risers is to take one standpipe out of service and use it as a drain by removing PRV devices and attaching hoses at the outlets near the ground floor level. When testing in this manner, a flowmeter should be used and a hose line utilized to connect the riser being tested and the drain riser.

Readings are to be compared to the system's hydraulic demands at the test location. Field-adjustable valves are to be reset in accordance with manufacturer's instructions. Nonadjustable valves should be replaced. Extreme caution should be exercised because of the high pressure involved when testing.

A.12.5.5.2.1 Hose valves can be tested without a full flow if the cap is left on the hose threads. The purpose of this requirement is to exercise the valve so it can be operated easily.

A.12.5.5.2.2 See A.12.5.5.2.1.

A.12.6.1.2 Intermittent discharge from a differential-sensing valve relief port is normal. Continuous discharge is a sign of malfunction of either or both of the check valves, and maintenance is necessary.

A.12.6.2.1 The full flow test of the backflow prevention valve can be performed with a test header or other connections downstream of the valve. A bypass around the check valve in the fire department connection line with a control valve in the normally closed position can be an acceptable arrangement. When flow to a visible drain cannot be accomplished, closed loop flow can be acceptable if a flowmeter or sight glass is incorporated into the system to ensure flow.

A.12.6.2.2 The tests required by 12.6.2 typically test only for operation of the device under backflow conditions. Forward-flow test conditions are required by other portions of this standard.

A.13.2 For obstruction investigation and prevention, see Annex D.

A.13.2.2 For obstruction investigation procedures, see Section D.3.

A.13.2.3 For obstruction prevention program recommendations, see Section D.4.

A.13.2.4 For obstruction investigation flushing procedures, see Section D.5.

A.14.3.1 A clearly visible tag alerts building occupants and the fire department that all or part of the water-based fire protection system is out of service. The tag should be weather resistant, plainly visible, and of sufficient size [typically 100 mm × 150 mm (4 in. × 6 in.)]. The tag should identify which system is impaired, the date and time impairment began, and the person responsible. Figure A.14.3.1 illustrates a typical impairment tag.

FIGURE A.14.3.1 Sample Impairment Tag.

A.14.3.2 An impairment tag should be placed on the fire department connection to alert responding fire fighters of an abnormal condition. An impairment tag that is located on the system riser only could go unnoticed for an extended period if fire fighters encounter difficulty in gaining access to the building or sprinkler control room.

A.14.5 The need for temporary fire protection, termination of all hazardous operations, and frequency of inspections in the areas involved should be determined. All work possible should be done in advance to minimize the length of the impairment. Where possible, temporary feedlines should be used to maintain portions of systems while work is completed.

Water-based fire protection systems should not be removed from service when the building is not in use. Where a system that has been out of service for a prolonged period, such as in the case of idle or vacant properties, is returned to service, qualified personnel should be retained to inspect and test the systems.

A.14.5.2(3)(b) A fire watch should consist of trained personnel who continuously patrol the affected area. Ready access to fire extinguishers and the ability to promptly notify the fire department are important items to consider. During the patrol of the area, the person should not only be looking for fire, but making sure that the other fire protection features of the building such as egress routes and alarm systems are available and functioning properly.

A.14.5.2(3)(c) Temporary water supplies are possible from a number of sources including use of a large-diameter hose from a fire hydrant to a fire department connection, use of a portable tank and a portable pump, or use of a standby fire department pumper and/or tanker.

A.14.5.2(3)(d) Depending on the use and occupancy of the building, it could be enough in some circumstances to stop certain processes in the building or to cut off the flow of fuel to some machines. It is also helpful to implement "No Smoking" and "No Hot Work" (cutting, grinding, or welding) policies while the system is out of service because these activities are responsible for many fire ignitions.

Annex B Forms for Inspection, Testing, and Maintenance

This annex is not a part of the requirements of this NFPA document but is included for informational purposes only.

B.1 Forms [*see Figure B.1(a) through Figure B.1(p)*] need to be complete with respect to the requirements of NFPA 25 for the system being inspected, tested, or maintained, or any combination thereof. Because water-based fire protection systems are comprised of many components, it could be necessary to complete more than one form for each system.

Authorities having jurisdiction are legitimately concerned that the forms used are comprehensive. Therefore, they could develop their own forms or utilize those already developed and reviewed by their jurisdiction.

At least five formats can be used and are described as follows:

(1) All requirements for NFPA 25 are specified in one form having large sections of information that do not apply to most systems.
(2) Individual forms provide requirements corresponding to each chapter of NFPA 25. These forms address the following:
   (a) Sprinkler systems
   (b) Standpipe systems
   (c) Private fire service mains
   (d) Fire pumps
   (e) Storage tanks
   (f) Water spray systems
   (g) Foam-water sprinkler systems
(3) These forms include information from the specific system chapter: Chapter 1, Chapter 12, and Chapter 13.
(4) A series of forms similar to option (2) but with a more detailed breakdown of system types. For example, fire sprinkler systems are divided into five separate forms such as:
   (a) Wet pipe fire sprinkler systems
   (b) Dry pipe fire sprinkler systems
   (c) Preaction fire sprinkler systems
   (d) Deluge fire sprinkler systems
   (e) Foam-water sprinkler systems
(5) Separate forms for each individual component of each fire protection system.

Report of Inspection
of Water Based Fire Protection Systems

Information Section

Inspecting agency:	Inspector:	Inspection contract #
Date of this inspection:	Completed by:	
Occupant business name:		

Street address:

| City: | State: | Zip: |
| Phone: | Fax: | |

Contact person name:

| Position: | Authority to approve work? | Y | N/A | N |

Name of property owner:

Property owner's address:

| City: | State: | Zip: |
| Phone: | Fax: | |

| Responsible party name: | Position: |

| Name of supervisory alarm company: | Phone: |

| Date of last inspection: | Prior inspector's name: |

	Y	N/A	N
1. All prior inspection reports, logs and test data are available for review:			
2. Plans of systems on site for review?			
3. Modifications made to systems fully reviewed and documented?			
4. Reports of sprinkler action fully reviewed and documented?			
5. Copy of NFPA 25 on file?			
6. Weekly logs of inspections required by NFPA 25 on file?			
7. Is the occupancy and hazard the same reported on last inspection?			
8. All deficiencies reported at last inspection corrected?			
9. MS data sheets reviewed and hazards to inspector removed?			

(Use separate sheet for additional information as may be needed. All "NO" answers to be fully explained.)
Form 94-104A should be completed by the Inspecting Firm/Contractor and provided to the Owner.

Comments:

The owner and/or designated representative acknowledges the responsibility of the operating condition of the component parts at the time of this inspection. It is agreed that the inspection service provided by the contractor as prescribed herein is limited to performing a visual inspection and/or routine testing, and any investigation or unscheduled testing, modification, maintenance, repair etc., of the component parts is not included as part of the inspection work performed. It is further understood that all information contained herein is provided to the best of the knowledge of the party providing such information.

| Owner/designated representative: | Date: |

| Inspector's signature: | Date: |

(AFSA Form 94-103A)
Page 1 of 1

FIGURE B.1(a) AFSA Report of Inspection (Information Section) Form.

2002 Edition

Report of Inspection
of Water Based Fire Protection Systems

Inspector's Information Section

Inspecting firm: (contractor)   Inspection contract #

Street address:

City: State: Zip:

Phone: Fax:

Inspector name: Date:

Property name: (refer to Form 103A)

This report contains information resulting from a visual inspection of the following types of
Water Based Fire Protection Systems: (please check all that apply)

Form Description	Form #	
Report of inspection (Information section)	103A	Cover sheet
Report of inspection (Inspector's section)	104A	Cover sheet
Weekly report of inspection	105A	No. of systems
Wet pipe fire sprinkler system – inspection/testing/maintenance	106A	No. of systems
Dry pipe fire sprinkler system – inspection/testing/maintenance	107A	No. of systems
Wet standpipe system – inspection/testing/maintenance	108A	No. of risers
Dry pipe standpipe system – inspection/testing/maintenance	109A	No. of risers
Fire pump – inspection/testing/maintenance	110A	No. of pumps
Underground fire main – inspection/testing/maintenance	111A	--------------------
Water reservoir, tank, pond, etc. – inspection/testing/maintenance	112A	Reservoir cap
Preaction fire protection system – inspection/testing/maintenance	113A	No. of systems
Deluge fire protection system – inspection/testing/maintenance	114A	No. of systems
Water - foam fire protection system – inspection/testing/maintenance	115A	No. of systems
Foam fire protection system – inspection/testing/maintenance	116A	No. of systems
Other components description		

The scheduled visual inspection is to be performed as indicated below. The inspector is to complete all questions and review the
results of this inspection and any recommendations, corrections, testing, maintenance, etc., with the owner.
All "NO" answers are to be fully explained in detail.

Scheduled inspection: *(circle one)*   Weekly: Monthly: Quarterly: Annually:

Recommendations:

Note: There are scheduled periodic testing and maintenance tasks that must be conducted for the continuous reliability of the fire
protection system. These should be performed at the intervals indicated in NFPA 25 standard. This information is being provided as a matter of courtesy. These tasks should only be performed by properly trained personnel using proper equipment.

The owner's or designated representative's signature shall be obtained acknowledging receipt of this report.
(Each page shall be initialed and dated by the owner or designated representative and inspector.)

Owner/designated representative: Date:

Inspector's signature: Date:

(AFSA Form 94-104A)
Page 1 of 1

FIGURE B.1(b)   AFSA Report of Inspection (Inspector's Information Section) Form.

Weekly Report of Inspection
of Water Based Fire Protection Systems
ALL QUESTIONS ARE TO BE FULLY ANSWERED AND ALL BLANKS TO BE FILLED

This form is being offered to assist in the performance and recording of the results of Weekly Scheduled Inspection Tasks of the various types of Fire Sprinkler Systems and component parts as listed below.

Inspecting firm: _____

Name of property: _____

Inspector name: _____ Date: _____

Page ___ of ___

Wet Sprinkler and Standpipe Systems:

A-1.1 Spkr. supply gauge: ___ psi

A-1.2 Spkr. system gauge: ___ psi

A-1.3 Stpipe supply gauge: ___ psi

A-1.4 Stpipe system gauge: ___ psi

A-1.5 Stpipe (top flr) gauge: ___ psi

	Y	N/A	N
A-2.0 System in service on inspection:			
A-2.1 Spkr. control valves sealed open:			
A-2.2 Stpipe control valves sealed open:			
A-3.1 Trim piping leak tight:			
A-4.1 Backflow asmb. valves sealed open:			
A-5.1 Control valves accessible:			
A-8.1 Signage/identification tags in place:			
A-9.1 Alarm panel clear:			
A-9.2 Systems left in service:			
A-10.1 Comments:			

Dry Pipe Sprinkler System:

B-1.1 Air pressure gauge: ___ psi

B-1.2 Accelerator gauge: ___ psi

B-1.3 Water pressure gauge: ___ psi

	Y	N/A	N
B-2.0 System in service on inspection:			
B-2.1 Compressor operational:			
* B-2.2 Oil level full:			
B-3.1 Control valve sealed open:			
B-3.2 Control valves accessible:			
B-3.3 Alarm test valve closed:			
B-3.4 Alarm line valve open:			
B-4.1 Intermediate chamber leak tight:			
B-4.2 Low point drum drips drained: (as frequently as needed)			
B-5.1 Valve enclosure secured:			
* B-5.2 Low temperature alarm operational:			
B-5.3 Heater operational:			
B-8.1 Signage/identification tags in place:			
B-9.1 Alarm panel clear:			
B-9.2 System left in service:			
B-10.1 Comments:			

* The inspection tasks noted with an asterisk (*) are required to be performed on a monthly frequency schedule; however, due to varying conditions that may exist on any individual project, it is suggested that these tasks be performed on a weekly frequency schedule.

Fire Dept. Connection:

	Y	N/A	N
* C-1.1 Caps or plugs on FDC:			
* C-1.2 Swivel rotation nonbinding:			
* C-2.1 FDC location plainly visible:			
* C-2.2 FDC easily accessible:			
* C-2.3 FDC identification plate in place:			
* C-3.1 Ball drip drain leak tight:			
* C-4.1 Wall hydrant plainly visible:			
* C-4.2 Wall hydrant easily accessible:			
* C-4.3 Wall hydrant identification plate in place:			
* C-10.1 Comments:			

Sprinkler Heads:

	Y	N/A	N
* D-1.1 Extra heads in spare head cabinet:			
* D-1.2 Heads appear of proper temperature:			
* D-1.3 Head wrench for each type of head:			
* D-2.1 Head in cooler appears free of ice, corrosion:			
* D-2.2 Head appears free of leakage or damage:			
* D-2.3 Head appears free of paint:			
* D-2.4 Heads appear free of non-approved coverings:			
* D-3.1 Standard head less than 50 year:			
* D-3.2 Residential head less than 20 year:			
* D-3.3 Fast response heads 20 year:			
* D-3.4 High temperature heads 5 year:			
* D-10.1 Comments:			

(All "NO" answers to be fully explained.)

Inspector's initial _____ Owner/designated rep. initial _____ Date: _____

(AFSA Form 94-105A)
Page 1 of 2

FIGURE B.1(c) AFSA Weekly Report of Inspection of Water Based Fire Protection Systems.

Weekly Report of Inspection of Water Based Fire Protection Systems . . . *continued*

Preaction and Deluge System:

E-1.1   Air pressure gauge: psi

E-1.2   Water pressure gauge: psi

	Y	N/A	N
E-2.0 Systems in service on inspection:			
E-2.1 Control valves sealed open:			
E-2.2 Control valves accessible:			
E-3.1 Enclosure secured:			
E-3.2 Heater operational:			
E-3.3 Low temperature alarm operational:			
E-4.1 Trim valves normally open:			
E-4.2 Alarm test valve closed:			
E-4.3 Trim piping leak tight:			
E-5.1 Low point drum drips drained: (as frequently as needed)			
E-8.1 Signage/identification tags in place:			
E-9.1 Alarm panel clear:			
E-9.2 Systems left in service:			

E-10.1 Comments:

_____

_____

_____

Other:

_____

_____

_____

_____

_____

_____

_____

_____

_____

_____

_____

_____

_____

_____

_____

_____

_____

Fire Pump:

F-1.1   Suction pressure gauge: psi

F-1.2   Discharge pressure gauge: psi

	Y	N/A	N
F-2.0 Pump in service on inspection:			
F-2.1 Control valves sealed open:			
F-2.2 Control valves accessible:			
F-3.1 Pump enclosure secured:			
F-3.2 Pump enclosure heated (40° F):			
F-3.3 Adequately lighted:			
F-4.1 Weekly run test: (no water flow)			
F-4.2 Shaft seals dripping water properly:			
F-4.3 Casing relief valve free of damage:			
F-4.4 Pressure relief valve free of damage:			
F-5.1 Jockey pumps operational:			
F-6.1 Bearings and valves lubricated:			
F-6.2 Valves, fittings, pipe leak free:			
F-7.1 Controllers power "ON":			
F-7.2 Controllers set on "AUTO":			
F-8.1 Hose header control valve closed:			
F-9.1 Diesel tank ⅔ full:			
F-9.2 Oil level full:			
F-9.3 Water level full:			
F-9.4 Water hose condition good:			
F-9.5 Water jacket heater working:			
F-9.6 Antifreeze protect adequate:			
F-9.7 Cooling line strainer appears clear of debris:			
F-9.8 Water jacket piping leak tight:			
F-9.9 Batteries fully charged:			
F-9.10 Battery charger appears operating properly:			
F-9.11 Battery terminals clear:			
F-9.12 Battery state of charge checked:			
F-9.13 Solenoid valve appears operating correctly:			
F-10.1 Condensate drain cleaner:			
F-10.2 Louvers, intake duct clean:			
F-14.1 Signage/identification tags in place:			
F-15.1 Alarm panel clear:			
F-15.2 Systems left in service:			

F-16.1 Comments:

_____

_____

_____

_____

(All "NO" answers to be fully explained.)	(AFSA Form 94-105A)
Inspector's initial _____ Owner/designated rep. initial _____ Date: _____	Page 2 of 2

FIGURE B.1(c)   *Continued*

Report of Inspection & Testing

of Water Based Fire Protection Systems
Monthly Items to be Reviewed
ALL QUESTIONS ARE TO BE FULLY ANSWERED AND ALL BLANKS TO BE FILLED

(Weekly inspection tasks are included in this report.)

(There is not a scheduled monthly testing task requirement. See the quarterly schedule.)

Inspecting firm: (contractor) _____   Inspection contract # _____

Name of property: _____

Inspector name: _____   Date: _____

Page ____ of ____

Inspection frequency: ❏ Monthly   ❏ Quarterly   ❏ Annually   ❏ Other: _____

Wet Sprinkler System Inspection

A-1.1   Spkr. supply gauge: _____ psi

A-1.2   Spkr. system gauge: _____ psi

	Y	N/A	N
A-2.0 System in service on inspection:			
A-2.1 Spkr. control va. locked/tamper open:			
A-2.2 Stpipe control va. locked/tamper open:			
A-2.3 Backflow va. locked open/tamper:			
A-2.4 Anti-freeze system va. locked/tamper open:			
A-2.8 Tamper switches appear operational:			
A-3.1 Valve area accessible:			
A-3.2 Control valves accessible:			
A-4.1 Pressure regulating valve is open:			
A-4.2 Pressure regualting valve in good condition:			
A-4.3 Pressure reg. valve leak tight:			
A-4.4 Pressure reg. va. maintaining downstream pressure per design criteria:			
A-5.1 Pressure relief va. in closed position except when operational:			
A-5.2 Pressure relief va. in good condition:			
A-5.3 Pressure relief va. leak tight:			
A-5.4 Pressure relief va. maintaining upstream pressure per design criteria:			
A-6.1 Main check valve holding pressure:			
A-6.2 Alarm check va. exterior free of damage:			
A-6.3 Water flow switch operational:			
A-7.1 Trim piping leak tight:			
A-7.2 Retard chamber drip tight:			
A-7.3 Alarm drain drip tight when not operational:			
A-8.1 Trim valves in appropriate position:			
A-8.2 Alarm test line valve closed:			

	Y	N/A	N
A-9.1 FDC plainly visible:			
A-9.2 FDC easily accessible:			
A-9.5 FDC swivels non-binding rotation:			
A-9.6 FDC caps/plugs in place:			
A-9.7 FDC gaskets/signs in place:			
A-9.10 FDC check valve drip free:			
A-9.11 FDC ball drip drain drip free:			
A-10.1 Exterior alarms properly identified:			
A-10.2 Exterior alarms appear operational:			
A-10.5 Interior alarms appear operational:			
A-11.1 Extra heads in spare head cabinet:			
A-11.2 Heads appear of proper temperature:			
A-11.3 Head wrench for each type of head:			
A-11.6 Head in cooler appears free of ice, corrosion:			
A-11.7 Head appears free of leakage or damage:			
A-11.8 Head appears free of paint:			
A-11.9 Heads appear free of non-approved coverings:			
A-12.0 Standard head less than 50 year:			
A-13.0 Residential head less than 20 year:			
A-14.0 Watt hydrant plainly visible:			
A-14.1 Watt hydrant easily accessible:			
A-14.2 Watt hydrant identification plate in place:			
A-15.1 Hose/hydrant house free of damage:			
A-15.2 Hose/hydrant house fully equipped:			
A-15.3 Hose/hydrant house is accessible:			
A-16.1 Wet pipe areas appear properly heated:			
A-17.0 Alarm panel clear:			
A-18.0 System left in service:			

A-20.0   Comments: _____

_____

_____

_____

(All "NO" answers to be fully explained.)

Inspector's initial _____   Owner/designated rep. initial _____   Date: _____

(AFSA Form 94-106A)

Page 1 of 3

FIGURE B.1(d)   AFSA Report of Inspection and Testing of Water Based Fire Protection Systems.

Report of Inspection & Testing

of Water Based Fire Protection Systems
Quarterly and Annual Items to be Reviewed

ALL QUESTIONS ARE TO BE FULLY ANSWERED AND ALL BLANKS TO BE FILLED

Inspecting firm: (contractor) _____   Inspection contract # _____

Name of property: _____

Inspector name: _____   Date: _____

Page ____ of ____

Inspection frequency: ❏ Monthly   ❏ Quarterly   ❏ Annually   ❏ Other: _____

Quarterly Report of Inspection of Wet Sprinkler System

(For a quarterly inspection, complete all items listed on FORM 94-106A "Report of Inspection – Monthly Items to be Reviewed" **AND** the items listed below.)

	Y	N/A	N
B-1.1 Hydraulic nameplate attached:			
B-1.2 Strainers and filters cleaned:			
B-1.3 Exterior alarms properly identified:			
B-2.0 Alarm panel clear:			
B-3.0 System left in service:			

B-20.0 Comments:

_____
_____
_____
_____
_____
_____
_____
_____
_____
_____
_____
_____
_____
_____
_____
_____
_____

Quarterly Testing Requirements for Wet Sprinkler System

	Y	N/A	N
C-1.1 Main drain flow test with ____ in. valve full open:			

C-2.1 Spkr. supply gauge: ____ psi		
C-2.2 Spkr. supply gauge ____ main drain flow: ____ psi		
C-3.1 Spkr. system gauge: ____ psi		
C-3.2 Spkr. system gauge with main drain flow: ____ psi		

	Y	N/A	N
C-4.1 Water flow alarm devices activated:			
C-4.2 Interior bldg. alarms operating:			
C-4.3 Exterior alarms operating:			

C-5.1 Inspectors test flow: ____ psi		
C-6.1 Time to ring alarm from alarm check valve: ____ min ____ sec		
C-7.1 Time to ring alarm from flow switch: ____ min ____ sec		
C-8.1 Time to ring alarm from pressure switch: ____ min ____ sec		

	Y	N/A	N
C-9.1 Gauges appear operating properly:			
C-10.1 Did alarm supervisory company receive signal properly:			
C-10.2 Did alarm panel reset properly:			
C-11.0 Alarm panel clear:			
C-12.0 System left in service:			

C-20.0 Comments:

_____
_____
_____
_____
_____
_____

(All "NO" answers to be fully explained.)

Inspector's initial _____   Owner/designated rep. initial _____   Date: _____

(AFSA Form 94-106A)
Page 2 of 3

FIGURE B.1(d)   *Continued*

Report of Inspection & Testing of Water Based Fire Protection Systems (Quarterly & Annual Items to be Reviewed) . . . *continued*

Annual Report of Inspection of Wet Sprinkler System

(**Description of this form:** These tasks are in addition to the monthly and quarterly tasks. Complete the monthly and quarterly reports AND this report as required for a total annual report of inspection. Visual inspection is defined as what can be observed from the floor level by an inspector. The use of binoculars is recommended for visual inspections in high buildings.)

		Y	N/A	N
D-1.1	Prior to freezing season, owner is responsible for bldg. to be in secure condition and properly heated:			
D-2.1	Visual inspection: hanger/seismic bracing appear attached and secure:			
D-3.1	Visual inspection: "exposed" piping appear in good condition:			
D-3.2	Piping appears free of mechanical damage:			
D-3.3	Piping appears free of leakage:			
D-3.4	Piping appears free of corrosion:			
D-3.5	Piping appears properly aligned:			
D-3.6	Piping appears free of external loads:			
D-4.1	Sprinklers appear free of corrosion:			
D-4.2	Sprinklers appear properly positioned:			
D-4.3	Sprinklers appear properly spaced:			
D-4.4	Sprinklers appear free of foreign material:			
D-4.5	Sprinkler spray patterns appear free of obstructions:			
D-10.0	**Alarm panel clear:**			
D-11.0	**System in service:**			
D-20.0	**Comments:**			

_____

_____

_____

_____

_____

_____

_____

_____

*** Provide additional pages if necessary to record the:

Volume of flow _____ gpm,

Supply side pressure _____ psi,

System side pressure _____ psi.

Annual Testing & Maintenance Tasks that are in Addition to Other Frequency Tasks – For Wet Sprinkler System

		Y	N/A	N
E-1.1	Control valve lubricated:			
E-2.1	Control valve operated to closed position and returned to open position:			
F-1.1	Backflow assembly control valves lubricated:			
F-1.2	Backflow assemble valve operated and returned to open position:			
G-1.1	Post indicator valve operated with number of turns recorded: _____			
G-1.2	Post indicator valve returned to open position: (Valves left 1/4 turn from wide open)			
H-1.1	Antifreeze solution checked to provide adequate freeze protection: (protection temp: _____ F)			

Test Frequency Items of 5 Years or Greater

		Y	N/A	N
H-2.0	Internal inspection last date (5 years): _____			
H-2.1	Alarm check valve:			
H-2.15	Flow tested pressure regulating control valves: ***			
H-2.2	Make:			
H-2.3	Model:			
H-2.4	Size: Date:			
H-2.5	Check valve:			
H-2.6	Strainers:			
H-2.7	Filters:			
H-2.8	Trim orifices:			
H-2.9	Other:			
H-3.0	Gauge maintenance: date last tested (5 year):			
H-3.1	Replaced date:			
H-3.2	Calibrated date:			
J-1.0	Sprinkler maintenance test:			
	(5 year)			
J-1.1	High temp. date: _____			
	(20 year, then 10 year thereafter)			
J-1.2	Fast response date: _____			
J-1.3	Residential head 20 year:			
	(50 year, then 10 year thereafter)			
J-1.4	Standard sprinkler date: _____			
J-20.0	**Comments:**			

_____

(All "NO" answers to be fully explained.)	(AFSA Form 94-106A)
Inspector's initial _____ Owner/designated rep. initial _____ Date: _____	Page 3 of 3

FIGURE B.1(d) *Continued*

Report of Inspection & Testing

of Dry Pipe Fire Protection Systems
Monthly and/or Quarterly Items to be Reviewed
ALL QUESTIONS ARE TO BE FULLY ANSWERED AND ALL BLANKS TO BE FILLED

(Weekly inspection tasks are included in this report.)

(There is not a scheduled monthly testing task requirement. See the quarterly schedule.)

Inspecting firm: (contractor) _____   Inspection contract # _____

Name of property: _____

Inspector name: _____   Date: _____

Page ____ of ____

Inspection frequency: ❑ Monthly   ❑ Quarterly   ❑ Annually   ❑ Other: _____

Dry Pipe Sprinkler System Inspection

A-1.1 Air pressure gauge: ____ psi

A-1.2 Accelerate or quick
opening device gauge: ____ psi

A-1.3 Water pressure gauge: ____ psi

A-1.4 Water supply gauge: ____ psi

	Y	N/A	N
A-2.0 System in service on Inspection:			
A-2.1 Dry pipe valve appears free of damage:			
A-2.2 Trim valves in appropriate position:			
A-2.3 Alarm test valve closed:			
A-2.4 Intermediate chamber leak tight:			
A-3.1 Valve enclosure secured:			
A-3.2 Heater operational:			
A-3.3 Low temperature alarm operational:			
A-4.1 Compressor operational:			
A-4.2 Oil level full:			
A-4.3 High/low pressure switches operational:			
A-4.4 Auto. air maint. devices operational:			
A-5.1 Control va. locked/tamper open:			
A-5.2 Backflow va. locked open/tamper:			
A-5.3 Tamper switches appear operational:			
A-5.4 Valve area accessible:			
A-5.6 Control valves accessible:			
A-5.7 Main check valve holding pressure:			
A-6.1 FDC plainly visible:			
A-6.2 FDC easily accessible:			
A-6.3 FDC swivels non-binding rotation:			
A-6.4 FDC caps/plugs in place:			
A-6.5 FDC gaskets/signs in place			
A-6.6 FDC check valve drip free:			
A-6.7 FDC ball drip drain drip free:			

	Y	N/A	N
A-7.1 Exterior alarms properly identified:			
A-7.2 Exterior alarms appear operational:			
A-7.3 Interior alarms appear operational:			
A-8.1 Extra heads in spare head cabinet:			
A-8.2 Heads appear to be proper temperature:			
A-8.3 Head wrench for each type of head:			
A-8.6 Head in cooler appears free of ice, corrosion:			
A-8.7 Head appears free of leakage or damage:			
A-8.8 Head appears free of paint:			
A-8.9 Head appears free of non-approved coverings:			
A-9.0 Standard head less than 50 year:			
A-10.0 Residential head less than 20 year:			
A-11.1 Hose/hydrant house free of damage:			
A-11.2 Hose/hydrant house fully equipped:			
A-11.3 Hose/hydrant house is accessible:			
A-12.1 Wet pipe areas appear properly heated: (Wet SSP on dry pipe sys.?)			
A-13.1 Low point drum drips drained: (As frequently as needed)			
A-13.2 All low points drained:			
A-14.1 All valves identified with signage:			
A-14.2 Hydraulic nameplate attached:			
A-18.0 Alarm panel clear:			
A-19.0 System in service:			

A-20.0 Comments:

_____

_____

_____

_____

_____

(All "NO" answers to be fully explained.)

Inspector's initial _____   Owner/designated rep. initial _____   Date: _____

(AFSA Form 94-107A)
Page 1 of 4

FIGURE B.1(e)   AFSA Report of Inspection and Testing of Dry Pipe Fire Protection Systems.

Report of Inspection & Testing

of Dry Pipe Fire Protection Systems
Quarterly and Annual Items to be Reviewed
ALL QUESTIONS ARE TO BE FULLY ANSWERED AND ALL BLANKS TO BE FILLED

Inspecting firm: (contractor) _____   Inspection contract # _____

Name of property: _____

Inspector name: _____   Date: _____

Page ____ of ____

Inspection frequency: ❏ Monthly   ❏ Quarterly   ❏ Annually   ❏ Other: _____

Quarterly Testing Requirements for a Dry Pipe Sprinkler System

	Y	N/A	N
C-1.1 Quick opening devices tested during semi-annual inspections:			
C-1.2 Quick opening device test date: _____			
C-1.3 Priming water at proper level:			
C-2.1 Low air pressure alarm tested:			
C-3.1 Main drain flow test with _____ in. valve full open:			
C-3.2 Spkr. supply gauge: _____ psi			
C-3.3 Spkr. supply gauge with main drain flow: _____ psi			

	Y	N/A	N
C-3.4 Gauges operating:			
C-4.1 Water flow alarm devices activated:			
C-4.2 Interior bldg. alarms operate:			
C-4.3 Exterior alarms operate:			
C-4.6 Did alarm supervisory company receive signal:			
C-4.7 Did alarm panel reset:			
C-18.0 Alarm panel clear:			
C-19.0 System left in service:			
C-20.0 Comments:			

Annual Inspection of Dry Pipe Sprinkler System

	Y	N/A	N
D-1.1 Interior of dry pipe valve in good condition:			
D-1.2 Interior of quick opening device in good condition:			
D-1.3 Inspect interior of strainers, filters, restricted orifices every 5th year: Date:			
D-1.4 Inspect interior of main check valve every 5th year: Date: _____			
D-2.1 Visual inspection: hanger/seismic bracing appear attached and secure:			
D-3.1 Visual inspection: "exposed" piping appears in good condition:			
D-3.2 Piping appears free of mechanical damage:			
D-3.3 Piping appears free of leakage:			
D-3.4 Exterior of piping appears free of corrosion:			
D-3.6 Piping appears properly aligned:			
D-3.7 Piping appears free of external loads:			
D-4.1 Sprinklers appear free of corrosion:			
D-4.2 Sprinklers appear properly positioned:			
D-4.3 Sprinklers appear properly spaced:			
D-4.6 Sprinklers appear free of foreign material:			
D-4.7 Sprinkler spray patterns appear free of obstructions:			
D-18.0 Alarm panel clear:			
D-19.0 System left in service:			
D-20.0 Comments:			

(All "NO" answers to be fully explained.)   (AFSA Form 94-107A)

Inspector's initial _____   Owner/designated rep. initial _____   Date: _____   Page 2 of 4

FIGURE B.1(e) *Continued*

Annual Testing and Maintenance Tasks That Are in Addition to Other Frequency Tasks — For Dry Pipe System

	Y	N/A	N
E-1.1 Dry pipe valve: (annually)			
E-2.1 Quick opening devices: (semi-annually)			
E-3.1 Dry pipe valve trip tested with control valve partially open: Date: _____			
E-3.2 Trip test with control valve fully open when system is altered or every 3rd year: Date: _____			

(Exception: When protecting a cooler or freezer, DO NOT introduce moisture into system.)

	Y	N/A	N
E-4.1 Strainers and filters and restricted orifices cleaned after trip test or every 5 years:			
E-4.2 Information on last trip test recorded:			
E-5.1 Automatic air maintenance device tested and operating properly:			
E-6.1 Control valve lubricated:			
E-6.2 Control valve operated to closed position and returned to open position:			
E-6.3 Backflow assembly control valves lubricated:			
E-6.6 Backflow assembly control valves operated and returned to open position:			
E-6.7 Post indicator valve operated with _____ number of turns recorded:			
E-6.8 Post indicator valve returned to open position:			

(All above listed control valves to be left ¼ turn from wide open)

	Y	N/A	N
E-7.1 All low points drained:			
E-7.2 Internal pipe inspection recommended:			

F-10.0 Comments:

	Y	N/A	N
Test Frequency Items of 5 Years Unless noted			
F-1.1 Gauge maintenance test: (5 year) _____			
F-1.2 Replaced date:			
F-1.3 Calibrated date:			
F-2.1 Sprinkler maintenance test frequencies:			
F-2.2 (5 year) high temp. date: _____			
F-2.3 (20 year, then 10 year thereafter) Fast response date: _____			
F-2.4 (50 year, then 10 year thereafter) Standard sprinkler date: _____			
F3.1 Other:			

F-4.1 Supplemental Information on Dry Pipe Valve and System Condition Report (Annual)

	Y	N/A	N
F-4.2 Dry system controls sprinklers in: _____			
F-4.3 D.P.V. trip test satisfactory:			
F-4.4 Reason for failure/or partly satisfactory:			
F-4.5 Condition: interior of body in good condition			
F-4.6 Condition: water from test pipe in good condition			
F-4.7 Condition: moving parts in good condition			
F-4.8 Condition: seats in good condition			
F-4.9 Condition: rubber facing in good condition			
F-4.10 Q.O.D operation indicate satisfactory:			
F-4.11 Q.O.D operation indicate failed:			
F-4.12 Q.O.D operation indicate shut off:			

Trip Test Table

Dry pipe operating test	Dry Valve		Size	Year	Q.O.D.			Year		
	Make		Model	Serial no.	Make		Model	Serial no.		
		Time to trip thru test pipe		Water pressure	Air pressure	Trip point air pressure		Time water reached test outlet		Alarm operated
		Min	Sec	psi	psi	psi		Min	Sec	Yes	No
	Without Q.O.D.										
	With Q.O.D.										

If No, explain:

(All "NO" answers to be fully explained.)

Inspector's initial _____   Owner/designated rep. initial _____   Date: _____

(AFSA Form 94-107A)
Page 3 of 4

FIGURE B.1(e) *Continued*

Report of Inspection & Testing
of Fire Protection Systems
Report of Internal Condition of Sprinkler Piping (5 years and/or as required)
ALL QUESTIONS ARE TO BE FULLY ANSWERED AND ALL BLANKS TO BE FILLED

Inspecting firm: (contractor) _____ Inspection contract # _____

Name of property: _____

Inspector name: _____ Date: _____

Page ___ of ___ Date of previous internal pipe inspection: _____

Inspection frequency: ❑ Monthly ❑ Quarterly ❑ Annually ❑ Other: _____

Identify system(s) involved: ❑ Wet ❑ Dry ❑ Preaction ❑ Deluge ❑ Other: _____

An examination of representative sections of this sprinkler system has been made to determine internal conditions.

Initial Examination Data:

Number of branch lines examined: _____ % of total branch lines _____

Number of cross mains examined: _____ % of bulk lines _____

Other points examined (describe): _____

_____

_____

_____

Results of Initial Examination:
(Check box which applies)

❑ 1. The interior of the sprinkler piping appears in satisfactory condition.

❑ 2. The sprinkler systems are in need of internal cleaning. Some of the pipes were found to be partially full of foreign materials. (specify nature of internal stoppage, i.e., pipe scale, silt, mud, tuberculation)

_____

_____

_____

Examination Subsequent to Cleaning System:

Cleaning method used (describe): _____

Number of branch lines examined: _____ % of total branch lines _____

Number of cross mains examined: _____ % of bulk lines _____

Other points examined (describe): _____

_____

_____

_____

Results of Examination Subsequent to Cleaning:
(Check box which applies)

❑ 1. The interior of the sprinkler piping appears in satisfactory condition.

❑ 2. If interior of piping other than satisfactory, describe: _____

_____

_____

_____

Signature and title of person conducting cleaning _____ Date of cleaning _____

Witness (owner or lessee of the property) _____

(All "NO" answers to be fully explained.)	(AFSA Form 94-107A)
Inspector's initial _____ Owner/designated rep. initial _____ Date: _____	Page 4 of 4

FIGURE B.1(e) *Continued*

Report of Inspection & Testing
of Wet Standpipe Systems

ALL QUESTIONS ARE TO BE FULLY ANSWERED AND ALL BLANKS TO BE FILLED

Inspecting firm: (contractor) _____ Inspection contract # _____

Name of property: _____

Inspector name: _____ Date: _____

Page ____ of ____ **Date of previous internal pipe inspection:** _____

Inspection frequency: ❏ Monthly ❏ Quarterly ❏ Annually ❏ Other: _____

		Y	N/A	N
A-1.1 Supply water gauge: ____ psi	A-6.12 Roof manifold control valve closed:			
A-1.2 System water gauge: ____ psi	A-7.1 Tamper switches appear operational:			
A-1.3 Top floor gauge: ____ psi	A-7.2 Alarm devices appear operational:			
A-1.6 Class of service: I II III	A-7.5 Exterior of devices in good condition:			
A-2.1 Hose valve size: ____ in.	A-7.6 Exterior bells, gongs unobstructed:			
A-2.2 Hose valve with adapter size: ____ × ____ in.	A-7.7 Exterior fittings free of water leakage:			
A-2.3 Hose valve with ____ in. hose:	_____ Main drain:			
A-2.6 Type and size of nozzle:	_____ Alarm bell line:			
_____ Adjustable ____ in.	A-8.1 Hose valve free of physical damage:			
_____ Straight stream ____ in.	A-8.2 Hose valve outlets with cap:			
_____ Fog ____ in.	A-8.3 Hose valve outlet thread in good condition:			
_____ Non-adjustable ____ in.	A-8.6 System free of visible water leaks:			
A-3.1 Indicate the type and record the information for the TOP FLOOR hose valve:	A-8.8 Hose valve outlets equipped with reducing hose adapter:			
_____ Pressure reducing valves inlet pressure set ____ psi	A-9.1 Inspection of cabinet per NFPA 1962:			
_____ Pressure reducing valves outlet pressure set ____ psi	A-9.2 Inspection of hose per NFPA 1962:			
_____ Pressure restricting valve inlet pressure set ____ psi	A-9.3 Inspection of hose nozzle per NFPA 1962:			
_____ Pressure restricting valve outlet pressure set ____ psi	A-9.6 Wall penetrations caulked/sealed:			
_____ Pressure regulating valve inlet pressure set ____ psi	A-10.1 Roof manifold equipped with hose valves:			
_____ Pressure regulating valve outlet pressure set ____ psi	A-10.2 Roof manifold hose valve caps in place:			
(Attach supplemental sheet recording the gpm and pressure setting for EACH FLOOR hose valve.)	A-10.3 Roof manifold swivel rotation is nonbinding:			
	A-10.4 Roof manifold valves good condition:			

	Y	N/A	N		Y	N/A	N
A-4.1 System in service on inspection:				A-10.5 Roof manifold ball drip operational:			
A-4.2 System equipped with flow switch:				A-11.1 Caps or plugs on FDC:			
A-4.3 System equipped with alarm check valve:				A-11.2 FDC swivel rotation nonbinding:			
A-4.4 Trim piping leak tight:				A-11.3 FDC location plainly visible:			
A-5.1 Control valves sealed open:				A-11.4 FDC easily accessible:			
A-5.2 Control valves locked/tamper open:				A-11.5 FDC identification plate in place:			
A-5.6 Backflow asmb. valves sealed open:				A-12.1 Piping free of physical damage:			
A-5.7 Backflow asmb. valves locked/tamper open:				A-12.2 Piping (exterior) is free of corrosion:			
A-5.8 Backflow assembly operating OK:				A-12.3 Piping appears to be leak tight:			
A-6.1 Wall hydrant sealed open:				A-12.6 Ball drip drain drip tight:			
A-6.2 Wall hydrant locked/tamper open:				A-12.7 Main drain at supply ____ (in.): ____ psi			
A-6.6 Valve area clear of obstructions:				A-12.9 Signage/identification plates in place:			
A-6.7 Valve area accessible:				**A-15.1 Alarm panel clear:**			
A-6.9 Wall hydrant plainly visible:				**A-15.2 All systems in service:**			
A-6.10 Wall hydrant easily accessible:				**A-16.1 Comments:**			
A-6.11 Wall hydrant identification plate in place:							

(All "NO" answers to be fully explained.)

Inspector's initial _____ Owner/designated rep. initial _____ Date: _____

(AFSA Form 94-108A)
Page 1 of 2

FIGURE B.1(f) AFSA Report of Inspection and Testing of Wet Standpipe Systems.

Report of Inspection, Testing, & Maintenance of Wet Standpipe System . . . *continued*

Quarterly Testing of Wet Standpipe System

		Y	N/A	N
B-1.1	Main drain ____ (in.) flow at riser: ____ psi			
B-2.1	Alarm devices operated:			

Refer to NFPA 1962 for testing of standpipe system in addition to the task indicated herein.

Annual Testing

		Y	N/A	N
C-1.1	Test of hose per NFPA 1962:			
C-1.2	Test of hose nozzle per NFPA 1962:			

Five Year Inspection

		Y	N/A	N
D-1.1	Internal inspection of check valves: Date: _____			
D-1.1	Internal inspection of alarm check: Date: _____			

Five Year Testing

		Y	N/A	N
E-1.1	Pressure gauges calibrated: Date: _____			
E-1.2	Pressure gauges replaced: Date: _____			
E-2.1	Hydrostatic test performed: Date: _____			
E-2.2	Water supply test performed: Date: _____			
E-3.1	Pressure regulating type hose valves flow tested: Date: _____			

(Attach additional pages to record the results of the flow test information indicated below which shall be provided for each type of hose valve connection including the roof manifold, for each floor and for each standpipe riser. The authority having jurisdiction shall be consulted prior to conducting the flow test.)

		Y	N/A	N
E-4.1	Volume of flow: ____ gpm			
E-4.2	Supply side: ____ psi			
E-4.3	Hose connection side: ____ psi			

(All "NO" answers to be fully explained.)	(AFSA Form 94-108A)
Inspector's initial _____ Owner/designated rep. initial _____ Date: _____	Page 2 of 2

FIGURE B.1(f) *Continued*

Report of Inspection, Testing, & Maintenance
of Fire Pumps

The following inspection, testing, and maintenance tasks are to be performed at the indicated frequencies. The required weekly tasks are also included on this list.

ALL QUESTIONS ARE TO BE FULLY ANSWERED AND ALL BLANKS TO BE FILLED

Inspecting firm: (contractor) _____   Inspection contract # _____

Name of property: _____

Inspector name: _____   Date: _____

Page ____ of ____

Fire Pumps

	Y	N/A	N			Y	N/A	N
A-1.0 Inspection of Pump Enclosure:					**A-5.0 Diesel Pumps — Semiannual Inspection and Maintenance:**			
A-1.1 Pump enclosure secured:					A-5.1 Test antifreeze protection level:			
A-1.2 Pump enclosure heated (40° F if diesel engine equipped with engine heater):					A-5.2 Inspect flexible exhaust section:			
A-1.3 Pump enclosure heated (70° F if diesel engine is not equipped with engine heater):					A-5.3 Check and test operation of safeties and alarms:			
A-1.4 Vent louvers operate:					A-5.4 Clean boxes, panels and cabinets:			
A-1.5 Vent louvers intake duct clean:								
A-1.6 Pump enclosure adequately lighted:					**A-6.0 Maintenance to be Performed Annually or as Indicated:**			
					A-6.1 Lubrication of bearings performed:			
A-2.0 Electrical Pumps — Monthly Inspection and Maintenance:					A-6.2 Lubrication of coupling performed:			
					A-6.3 Lubrication of right angle gear performed:			
A-2.1 Isolating switch and circuit breaker exercised:					A-6.4 Lubrication of motor bearings performed:			
A-2.2 Inspect, check, clean, and test circuit breakers: (replace as needed) (replace date: _____)					A-7.1 Accuracy of pressure sensors checked:			
					A-7.2 Calibrate pressure switch settings:			
					A-8.1 Change oil (50 hours of operation):			
A-3.0 Diesel Pumps — Monthly Inspection and Maintenance:					A-8.2 Change oil filter (50 hours of operation):			
					A-17.0 Fire pump controller in service:			
A-3.1 Inspect and remove corrosion, battery case exterior clean and dry:					**A-18.0 Jockey pump controller in service:**			
A-3.2 Test specific or state of charge:					**A-19.0 Alarm panel clear:**			
A-3.3 Inspect charger and charger rate:					**A-20.0 System in service:**			
A-3.4 Check equalize charge:					**A-21.0 Comments:**			
					_____			
A-4.0 Diesel Pumps — Monthly Inspection and Maintenance:					_____			
					_____			
A-4.1 Service fuel strainer, filter and/or dirt leg:					_____			
A-4.2 Clean or replace crankcase breather:					_____			
A-4.3 Check and clean water strainer:					_____			
A-4.4 Inspect insulation and fire hazards:					_____			
A-4.5 Inspect and check wire chafing where subject to movement:					_____			

(All "NO" answers to be fully explained.)

Inspector's initial _____   Owner/designated rep. initial _____   Date: _____

(AFSA Form 94-110A)
Page 1 of 5

FIGURE B.1(g)   AFSA Report of Inspection, Testing, and Maintenance of Fire Pumps.

Report of Inspection, Testing, & Maintenance of Fire Pumps . . . *continued*

	Y	N/A	N
B-1.0 Annual Inspection of Hydrolic System:			
B-1.1 Suction pressure gauge: _____ psi			
B-1.2 Discharge pressure gauge: _____ psi			
B-1.3 Pump starting pressure: _____ psi			
B-1.4 Suction line control valves sealed open:			
B-1.5 Discharge line control valves sealed open:			
B-1.6 By-pass line valves sealed open:			
B-1.7 All control valves accessible:			
B-1.8 Suction reservoir full:			
B-1.9 Shaft seals dripping water properly: (1 drop per second)			
B-1.10 System free of vibration or unusual noise:			
B-1.11 Packing boxes, bearings, pump casing free of overheating:			

Comments:
_____
_____
_____
_____
_____
_____
_____

	Y	N/A	N
B-2.0 Annual Inspection of Electrical Pump System:			
B-2.6 Isolating switch closed-standby emergency source:			
B-2.7 Normal phase rotation pilot light "ON":			
B-2.8 Reverse phase alarm pilot light "OFF":			
B-2.9 Oil level in vertical motor sight glass is in the normal range:			

Comments:
_____
_____
_____
_____
_____
_____
_____
_____
_____

	Y	N/A	N
B-3.0 Annual Inspection of Diesel Engine System:			
B-3.1 Diesel tank ⅔ full:			
B-3.2 Batteries fully charged:			
B-3.3 Battery charger operating properly:			
B-3.4 Battery terminals clean:			
B-3.5 Battery state of charge checked:			
B-3.6 Battery pilot lights "ON":			
B-3.7 Battery failure pilot lights "OFF":			
B-3.8 Electrolyte level in batteries normal:			
B-3.9 All alarm pilot lights "OFF":			
B-3.10 Engine running time meter recording pump operation properly:			
B-3.11 Oil level in right angle gear drive normal:			
B-3.12 Diesel engine oil level full:			
B-3.13 Diesel engine water level full:			
B-3.14 Water jacket heater appears working properly:			
B-3.15 Water jacket piping drip tight:			
B-3.16 Diesel engine water hose good condition:			
B-3.17 Coolant antifreeze protection adequate:			
B-3.18 Cooling line strainer clean:			
B-3.19 Solenoid valve operating correctly:			
B-3.20 Bearings and valves lubricated:			

Comments:
_____
_____
_____
_____

	Y	N/A	N
B-4.0 Annual Inspection of Steam Pump Systems:			
B-4.1 Steam pressure gauge reading normal: _____ psi			
B-4.2 Record time required to reach running speed: _____ min _____ sec			
B-4.3 Weekly test conducted and results recorded:			

Comments:
_____
_____
_____
_____
_____
_____

(All "NO" answers to be fully explained.)

Inspector's initial _____   Owner/designated rep. initial _____   Date: _____

(AFSA Form 94-110A)
Page 2 of 5

FIGURE B.1(g) *Continued*

Report of Inspection, Testing, & Maintenance of Fire Pumps . . . *continued*

	Y	N/A	N
C-1.0 Annual Test of Electric Pump Systems:			
C-1.1 Electric pump weekly 10-min test run results recorded: (water flow not required)			
C-1.2 Time controller on first step for reduced voltage or reduced current starting: _____ min _____ sec			
C-1.3 Record time pump runs after starting (for automatic stop controllers): _____ min _____ sec			
C-1.4 Time required for motor to reach full speed: _____ min _____ sec			

Comments: _____

_____

_____

_____

_____

_____

	Y	N/A	N
C-2.0 Annual Test of Diesel Pump System:			
C-2.1 Weekly auto start/run 30 min and results recorded: (water flow not required)			
C-2.2 Auto. weekly test timer used for the starting procedure:			
C-2.3 Time required for engine to crank: _____ min _____ sec			
C-2.4 Time required to reach running speed: _____ min _____ sec			
C-2.5 Observations while engine operating:			
Oil pressure: _____ psi			
Speed indicator: _____ rpm			
Water temperature: _____ ° F			
Oil temperature: _____ ° F			
C-2.6 Pump operational without abnormalities:			
C-2.7 Heat exchanger cooling water flow normal:			
C-2.8 Alarm company notified of test run:			
C-2.9 Pump test run performed satisfactorily:			

Fire Pump Test

Pump:

Make:

Type:

Rated capacity:

Rated pressure:

Rated rpm:

Power:

Type:

Supervision:

Controller:

Make:

Listed:

Water Supply:

Source:

Electronic Characteristics:

Test Data:

Type of test (hydrant, drain or pump)	Static or suction pressure (psi)	Residual or discharge pressure (psi)	Net pump pressure (psi)	Pump speed (rpm/ amperes)	Pilot pressure	Dia. of nozzle openings flowed	No. of nozzle openings flowed	Flow at C=.90 C=.97 (gpm)	Opening coefficient C= ___	Actual flow (gpm)

Notes: _____

Remarks on test: _____

_____

Signature and title of person making test: _____ Company name and address: _____

Witness (owner or designated rep.): _____ Date of examination: _____

(All "NO" answers to be fully explained.)	(AFSA Form 94-110A)
Inspector's initial _____ Owner/designated rep. initial _____ Date: _____	Page 3 of 5

FIGURE B.1(g) *Continued*

Annual Inspection and Test of Fire Pump Components:
Conduct the Inspection and Test Tasks and Record Results as
Applicable to the Type of Pump System:

	Y	N/A	N
D-1.0 Annual Inspection of System Components:			
D-1.1 Pump in service on inspection:			
D-1.2 Pump identification no.: _____			
D-1.3 Casing relief valve free of damage:			
D-1.4 Pressure relief valve free of damage:			
D-1.5 ALL valves, fittings, pipe leak tight:			
D-1.6 Condensate drain trap clean:			
D-2.1 Fire pump controller power "ON":			
D-2.2 Transfer switch normal pilot light "ON":			
D-3.1 Jockey pump operational:			
D-3.2 Jockey pump controller power "ON":			
D-3.3 Jockey pump controller set on "AUTO":			
D-4.1 Fire pump shaft coupling appears properly aligned:			
D-4.2 Packing glands appear properly adjusted:			
D-5.1 Weekly test run records available:			
D-5.2 Date of last pump run test: _____			
D-5.3 Pump peak load at 150% capacity: ____			
D-6.1 Test header control valve closed:			
D-6.2 Test header in good condition:			
D-6.3 Test header valves and caps in good condition:			
D-6.4 Test header valve handles in good condition:			
D-6.5 Test header valve swivels rotation is nonbinding:			
D-7.1 By-pass control valves open:			
D-7.2 Control valves sealed/not tampered:			
D-7.3 Control valves locked/tampered:			
D-7.4 Control valves properly tagged and identified:			
D-7.5 Flow meter control valves closed:			
D-8.1 Relief valve and cone operational:			
D-8.2 Relief valve pressure appears properly adjusted:			
D-8.3 Suction gauge while flowing psi: _____			
D-8.4 Fire pump operating psi: _____			
D-8.5 Discharge gauge flowing psi: _____			

	Y	N/A	N
D-9.1 Automatic starts performed 10 times			
D-9.2 Automatic start function properly:			
D-9.3 Automatic stop function properly:			
D-9.4 Automatic start psi: _____			
D-9.5 Automatic stop psi: _____			
D-10.1 Manual starts performed 10 times			
D-10.2 Manual start function properly:			
D-10.3 Manual stop function properly:			
D-10.4 Manual start psi: _____			
D-10.5 Manual stop psi: _____			
D-11.1 Remote start function properly:			
D-11.2 Remote stop function properly:			
D-11.3 Remote start psi: _____			
D-11.4 Remote stop psi: _____			
D-12.1 Timer indicates total run time: ____ min			
D-12.2 Timer reset and graph paper changed:			
D-12.3 Test data and flow charts completed: (Attach all water flow charts, electrical power charts, performance curves, etc.)			
D-12.4 Fire pump electrical power readings recorded at each flow condition:			
D-12.5 Fire pump motor speed: _____ rpm			
D-12.6 Fire pump discharge flow: _____ gpm			
D-13.1 Jockey pump operational:			
D-13.2 Jockey pump appears properly aligned:			
D-13.3 Jockey pump valves open:			
D-13.4 Jockey pump "turn-on": _____ psi:			
D-13.5 Jockey pump "turn-off": _____ psi:			
D-20.0 Comments:			

D-20.0 Comments: _____
_____
_____
_____
_____
_____
_____
_____
_____
_____

Note: Pump performance curve should be plotted on page 5 of 5.

(All "NO" answers to be fully explained.)	(AFSA Form 94-110A)
Inspector's initial _____ Owner/designated rep. initial _____ Date: _____	Page 4 of 5

FIGURE B.1(g) *Continued*

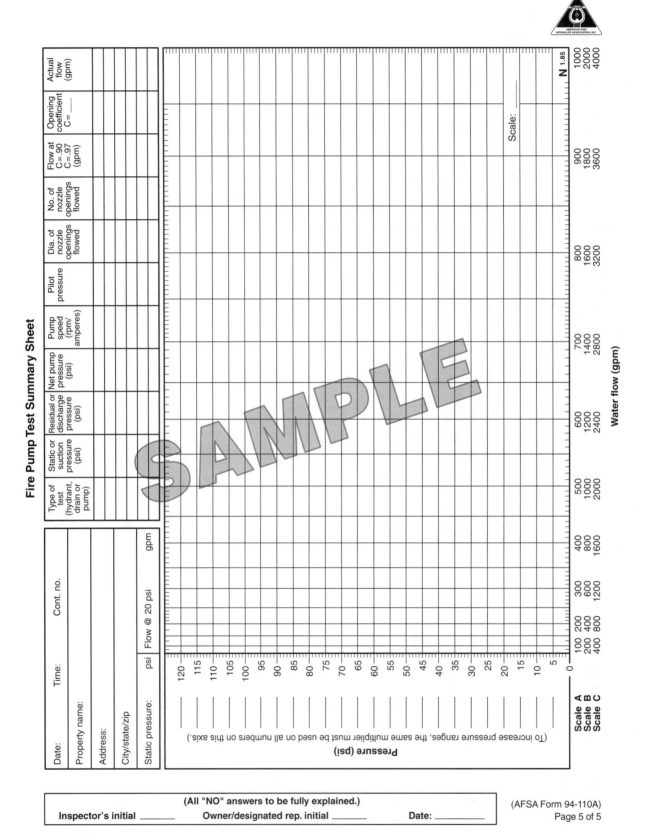

FIGURE B.1(g)   *Continued*

Form for Inspection, Testing and Maintenance of Dry-Pipe Fire Sprinkler Systems

NATIONAL FIRE SPRINKLER ASSOCIATION, INC.

Information on this form covers the minimum requirements of **NFPA 25-2002** for fire sprinkler systems connected to distribution systems without supplemental tanks or fire pumps. Separate forms are available to inspect, test and maintain fire pumps, water tanks and other fire protection systems. More frequent inspection, testing and maintenance may be necessary depending on the conditions of the occupancy and the water supply.

Owner: _____ Owner's Phone Number: _____

Owner's Address: _____

Property Being Evaluated: _____

Property Address: _____

Date of Work: _____ All responses refer to the current work (inspection, testing and maintenance) performed on this date.

This work is (*check one*): ❏ Monthly   ❏ Quarterly   ❏ Annual   ❏ Third Year   ❏ Fifth Year

Notes: 1) All questions are to be answered *Yes*, *No*, or *Not Applicable*. All *No* answers are to be explained in Part III of this form.
2) Inspection, Testing and Maintenance are to be performed with water supplies (including fire pumps) in service, unless the impairment procedures of Chapter 11 of NFPA 25 are followed.

Part I - Owner's Section

A. Is the building occupied? ❏ Yes ❏ No

B. Has the occupancy classification and hazard of contents remained the same since the last inspection? ❏ Yes ❏ No

C. Are all fire protection systems in service? ❏ Yes ❏ No

D. Has the system remained in service without modification since the last inspection? ❏ Yes ❏ No

E. Was the system free of actuation of devices or alarms since the last inspection? ❏ Yes ❏ No

_____   _____
Owner or representative (print name)   Signature and Date

Part II - Inspector's Section

A. Inspections

1. Daily and Weekly Items

A. Control valves supervised with seals in correct (open or closed) position? ❏ Yes ❏ No ❏ N/A

B. Dry-Pipe Valves: Enclosures around valves maintaining a minimum of 40° F and gauges in good condition showing normal air and water pressure? ❏ Yes ❏ No ❏ N/A

D. Backflow preventers:

1. Valves in correct (open or closed) position? ❏ Yes ❏ No ❏ N/A
2. Sealed, locked or supervised & accessible? ❏ Yes ❏ No ❏ N/A
3. Relief port on RPZ device not discharging? ❏ Yes ❏ No ❏ N/A

E. For freezer systems, is the gage near the compressor reading the same as the gage near the dry-pipe valve? ❏ Yes ❏ No ❏ N/A

4. Monthly Inspection Items (in addition to above items)

A. Control valves with locks or electrical supervision in correct (open or closed) position? ❏ Yes ❏ No ❏ N/A

B. Dry-Pipe Valves: Free from physical damage, trim valves in appropriate (open or closed) position, and no leakage from intermediate chamber? ❏ Yes ❏ No ❏ N/A

C. Sprinkler wrench with spare sprinklers? ❏ Yes ❏ No ❏ N/A

5. Quarterly Inspection Items (in addition to above items)

A. Pressure Reducing Valves: In open position, not leaking, maintaining downstream pressure per design criteria, and in good condition with handwheels not broken? ❏ Yes ❏ No ❏ N/A

B. Hydraulic nameplate (calculated systems) securely attached to riser and legible? ❏ Yes ❏ No ❏ N/A

C. Fire Department Connections: Visible, accessible, couplings and swivels not damaged and rotate smoothly, plugs or caps in place and undamaged, gaskets in place and in good condition, identification sign(s) in place, check valve is not leaking, clapper is in place and operating properly and automatic drain valve in place and operating properly? ❏ Yes ❏ No ❏ N/A

(If plugs or caps are not in place, inspect interior for obstructions.)

D. Alarm devices free from physical damage? ❏ Yes ❏ No ❏ N/A

6. Annual Inspection Items (in addition to above items)

A. Proper number and type of spare sprinklers? ❏ Yes ❏ No ❏ N/A

B. Visible sprinklers:

1. Free of corrosion and physical damage? ❏ Yes ❏ No ❏ N/A
2. Free of obstructions to spray patterns? ❏ Yes ❏ No ❏ N/A
3. Free of foreign materials including paint? ❏ Yes ❏ No ❏ N/A
4. Liquid in all glass bulb sprinklers? ❏ Yes ❏ No ❏ N/A

C. Visible pipe:

1. In good condition/no external corrosion? ❏ Yes ❏ No ❏ N/A
2. No mechanical damage and no leaks? ❏ Yes ❏ No ❏ N/A
3. Properly aligned and no external loads? ❏ Yes ❏ No ❏ N/A

D. Visible pipe hangers and seismic braces not damaged or loose? ❏ Yes ❏ No ❏ N/A

E. Dry-pipe valves passed internal inspection? ❏ Yes ❏ No ❏ N/A

F. Must be done before cold weather

1. Adequate heat in areas with wet piping? ❏ Yes ❏ No ❏ N/A
2. Low temperature alarms functioning? ❏ Yes ❏ No ❏ N/A
3. Interior of pipe that passes through freezers free of ice blockage? ❏ Yes ❏ No ❏ N/A

G. Has an internal inspection of the pipe been performed by removing the flushing connection and one sprinkler near the end of a branch line within the last 5 years? ❏ Yes ❏ No ❏ N/A

(If the answer was "No," conduct an internal inspection.)

8. Fifth Year Inspection Items (in addition to above items)

A. Check valves internally inspected and all parts operate properly, move freely and are in good condition? ❏ Yes ❏ No ❏ N/A

B. Strainers, filters, restricted orifices and diaphragm chambers on dry-pipe valves passed internal inspection? ❏ Yes ❏ No ❏ N/A

B. Testing

The following tests are to be performed at the noted intervals. Report any failures on Part III of this form.

1. Quarterly Tests

A. Mechanical waterflow alarm devices passed tests by opening the inspector's test connection or bypass connection with alarms actuating and flow observed? ❏ Yes ❏ No ❏ N/A

B. Post indicating valves opened until spring or torsion is felt in the rod, then closed back one-quarter turn? ❏ Yes ❏ No ❏ N/A

C. Is the priming level correct and has the low air pressure signal passed its test? ❏ Yes ❏ No ❏ N/A

D. Quick opening devices passed test? ❏ Yes ❏ No ❏ N/A

E. Main drain test for system downstream of backflow or pressure reducing valve:

1. Record Static Pressure _____ psi and Residual Pressure _____ psi.
2. Was flow observed? ❏ Yes ❏ No ❏ N/A
3. Are results comparable to previous test? ❏ Yes ❏ No ❏ N/A

FIGURE B.1(h) NFSA Form for Inspection, Testing, and Maintenance of Dry Pipe Fire Sprinkler Systems.

2. Semiannual Test (in addition to previous items)

A. Valve supervisory switches indicate movement? ❏ Yes ❏ No ❏ N/A

B. Electrical waterflow alarm devices passed tests by opening the inspector's test connection or bypass connection with alarms actuating and flow observed? ❏ Yes ❏ No ❏ N/A

3. Annual Tests (in addition to previous items)

A. Main drain test:

   1. Record Static Pressure_____ psi and Residual Pressure _____ psi.

   2. Was flow observed? ❏ Yes ❏ No ❏ N/A

   3. Are results comparable to previous test? ❏ Yes ❏ No ❏ N/A

B. Are all sprinklers dated 1920 or later? ❏ Yes ❏ No ❏ N/A

C. Fast response sprinklers 20 or more years old replaced or successfully sample tested within last 10 years? ❏ Yes ❏ No ❏ N/A

D. Standard response sprinklers 50 or more years old replaced or successfully sample tested within last 10 years? ❏ Yes ❏ No ❏ N/A

E. Standard response sprinklers 75 or more years old replaced or successfully sample tested within last 5 years? ❏ Yes ❏ No ❏ N/A

F. Dry-type sprinklers replaced or successfully sample tested within last 10 years? ❏ Yes ❏ No ❏ N/A

G. All control valves operated through full range and returned to normal position? ❏ Yes ❏ No ❏ N/A

H. Low temperature alarms passed test? ❏ Yes ❏ No ❏ N/A

I. Dry-pipe valve partial flow trip test:

   1. Record initial air pressure_____ psi and water pressure_____ psi.

   2. Record tripping air pressure_____ psi and tripping time_____ (sec.).

   3. Above results comparable to previous tests? ❏ Yes ❏ No ❏ N/A

J. Automatic air maintenance devices passed test? ❏ Yes ❏ No ❏ N/A

K. Backflow devices passed backflow test? ❏ Yes ❏ No ❏ N/A

L. Backflow devices passed full flow test? ❏ Yes ❏ No ❏ N/A

M. Pressure reducing valves passed partial flow test? ❏ Yes ❏ No ❏ N/A

4. Test to be done every third year:

Dry-pipe full flow trip test:

   1. Record initial air pressure _____ psi and water pressure_____ psi.

   2. Record tripping air pressure_____ psi and tripping time _____ (sec.).

   3. Record water delivery time _____ (min.) _____ (sec.).

   Water delivery time not required to be 60 sec. per NFPA 25

   4. Above results comparable to previous tests? ❏ Yes ❏ No ❏ N/A

5. Tests to be done every fifth year: A.

Sprinklers rated above High temperature tested? ❏ Yes ❏ No ❏ N/A

B. Gages checked by calibrated gage or replaced? ❏ Yes ❏ No ❏ N/A

C. Pressure reducing valves passed full flow test? ❏ Yes ❏ No ❏ N/A

C. Maintenance

1. Regular Maintenance Items

A. If sprinklers have been replaced, were they proper replacements? ❏ Yes ❏ No ❏ N/A

B. Air leaks in dry-pipe system resulting in air pressure loss more than 10 psi/week repaired? ❏ Yes ❏ No ❏ N/A

C. Dry-pipe systems maintained in dry condition? ❏ Yes ❏ No ❏ N/A

D. Have low point drains been emptied? ❏ Yes ❏ No ❏ N/A

1. Regular Maintenance Items (continued)

E. If any of the following were discovered, was an obstruction investigation conducted? ❏ Yes ❏ No ❏ N/A

Explain reason(s) and obstruction investigation findings in Part III.

   1. Defective intake screen on pump with suction from open sources.

   2. Obstructive material discharged during waterflow tests.

   3. Foreign materials found in dry-pipe valves, check valves or pumps.

   4. Foreign material in water during drain test or plugging of inspector's test connection.

   5. Plugging of pipe or sprinklers found during activation or alteration.

   6. Failure to flush yard piping or surrounding public mains following new installation or repairs.

   7. Record of broken mains in the vicinity.

   8. Abnormally frequent false-tripping of dry-pipe valves.

   9. System is returned to service after an extended period out of service (greater than one year).

   10. There is reason to believe the system contains sodium silicate or its derivatives or highly corrosive fluxes in copper pipe systems.

F. If conditions were found that required flushing, was flushing of system conducted? ❏ Yes ❏ No ❏ N/A

2. Annual Maintenance Items (in addition to previous items)

A. Operating stem of all OS&Y valves lubricated, completely closed, and reopened? ❏ Yes ❏ No ❏ N/A

B. Interior of dry-pipe valves cleaned? ❏ Yes ❏ No ❏ N/A

C. Low points drained prior to the onset of freezing weather? ❏ Yes ❏ No ❏ N/A

D. Sprinklers and spray nozzles protecting commercial cooking equipment and ventilating systems replaced except for bulb-type which show no signs of grease buildup? ❏ Yes ❏ No ❏ N/A

Part III - Comments *(Any "No" answers, test failures or other problems found with the sprinkler system must be explained here. Also, note here any products noticed on the system that have been the subject of a recall or a replacement program.*

_____

_____

_____

_____

_____

_____

_____

_____

_____

_____

_____

_____

Part IV - Inspector's Information

Inspector: _____   Company: _____   Signature of Inspector: _____

Company's Address: _____

I state that the information on this form is correct at the time and place of my inspection and that all equipment tested at this time was left in operational condition upon completion of this inspection except as noted in Part III above.

Date:_____

License or Certification Number (if applicable): _____

FIGURE B.1(h) *Continued*

Form for Inspection, Testing and Maintenance of Wet Pipe Fire Sprinkler Systems

Information on this form covers the minimum requirements of **NFPA 25-2002** for fire sprinkler systems connected to distribution systems without supplemental tanks or fire pumps. Separate forms are available to inspect, test and maintain fire pumps, water tanks and other fire protection systems. More frequent inspection, testing and maintenance may be necessary depending on the conditions of the occupancy and the water supply.

Owner: _____ Owner's Phone Number: _____

Owner's Address: _____

Property Being Evaluated: _____

Property Address: _____

Date of Work: _____ All responses refer to the current work (inspection, testing and maintenance) performed on this date.

This work is (*check one*): ❏ Monthly ❏ Quarterly ❏ Annual ❏ Third Year ❏ Fifth Year

Notes: 1) All questions are to be answered *Yes*, *No*, or *Not Applicable*. All *No* answers are to be explained in Part III of this form.

2) Inspection, Testing and Maintenance are to be performed with water supplies (including fire pumps) in service, unless the impairment procedures of Chapter 11 of NFPA 25 are followed.

Part I - Owner's Section

A. Is the building occupied?   ❏ Yes ❏ No

B. Has the occupancy classification and hazard of contents remained the same since the last inspection?   ❏ Yes ❏ No

C. Are all fire protection systems in service?   ❏ Yes ❏ No

D. Has the system remained in service without modification since the last inspection?   ❏ Yes ❏ No

E. Was the system free of actuation of devices or alarms since the last inspection?   ❏ Yes ❏ No

_____   _____

Owner or representative (print name)   Signature and Date

Part II - Inspector's Section

A. Inspections

1. Daily and Weekly Items

A. Control valves supervised with seals in correct (open or closed) position?   ❏ Yes ❏ No ❏ N/A

B. Backflow preventers:

1. Valves in correct (open or closed) position?   ❏ Yes ❏ No ❏ N/A

2. Sealed, locked or supervised & accessible?   ❏ Yes ❏ No ❏ N/A

3. Relief port on RPZ device not discharging?   ❏ Yes ❏ No ❏ N/A

4. Monthly Inspection Items (in addition to above items)

A. Control valves with locks or electrical supervision in correct (open or closed) position?   ❏ Yes ❏ No ❏ N/A

B. Sprinkler wrench with spare sprinklers?   ❏ Yes ❏ No ❏ N/A

C. Gauges on wet-pipe system in good condition and showing normal water supply pressure?   ❏ Yes ❏ No ❏ N/A

D. Alarm Valves:

Gauges show normal supply water pressure, free from physical damage, valves in correct (open or closed) position and no leakage from retarding chamber or drains?   ❏ Yes ❏ No ❏ N/A

5. Quarterly Inspection Items (in addition to above items)

A. Pressure Reducing Valves: In open position, not leaking, maintaining downstream pressure per design criteria, and in good condition with handwheels not broken?   ❏ Yes ❏ No ❏ N/A

B. Hydraulic nameplate (calculated systems) securely attached to riser and legible?   ❏ Yes ❏ No ❏ N/A

C. Fire Department Connections:

Visible, accessible, couplings and swivels not damaged and rotate smoothly, plugs or caps in place and undamaged, gaskets in place and in good condition, identification sign(s) in place, check valve is not leaking, clapper is in place and operating properly and automatic drain valve in place and operating properly?   ❏ Yes ❏ No ❏ N/A

(*If plugs or caps are not in place, inspect interior for obstructions.*)

D. Alarm devices free from physical damage?   ❏ Yes ❏ No ❏ N/A

6. Annual Inspection Items (in addition to above items)

A. Proper number and type of spare sprinklers?   ❏ Yes ❏ No ❏ N/A

B. Visible sprinklers:

1. Free of corrosion and physical damage?   ❏ Yes ❏ No ❏ N/A

2. Free of obstructions to spray patterns?   ❏ Yes ❏ No ❏ N/A

3. Free of foreign materials including paint?   ❏ Yes ❏ No ❏ N/A

4. Liquid in all glass bulb sprinklers?   ❏ Yes ❏ No ❏ N/A

C. Visible pipe:

1. In good condition/no external corrosion?   ❏ Yes ❏ No ❏ N/A

2. No mechanical damage and no leaks?   ❏ Yes ❏ No ❏ N/A

3. Properly aligned and no external loads?   ❏ Yes ❏ No ❏ N/A

D. Visible pipe hangers and seismic braces not damaged or loose?   ❏ Yes ❏ No ❏ N/A

E. Hose, hose couplings and nozzles on sprinkler system passed inspection in accordance with NFPA 1962?   ❏ Yes ❏ No ❏ N/A

F. Adequate heat in areas with wet piping?   ❏ Yes ❏ No ❏ N/A

G. Has an internal inspection of the pipe been performed by removing the flushing connection and one sprinkler near the end of a branch line within the last 5 years?   ❏ Yes ❏ No ❏ N/A

(*If the answer was "No," conduct an internal inspection.*)

8. Fifth Year Inspection Items (in addition to above items)

A. Alarm valves and their associated strainers, filters and restriction orifices passed internal inspection?   ❏ Yes ❏ No ❏ N/A

B. Check valves internally inspected and all parts operate properly, move freely and are in good condition?   ❏ Yes ❏ No ❏ N/A

B. Testing

The following tests are to be performed at the noted intervals. Report any failures on Part III of this form.

1. Quarterly Tests

A. Mechanical waterflow alarm devices passed tests by opening the inspector's test connection or bypass connection with alarms actuating and flow observed?   ❏ Yes ❏ No ❏ N/A

B. Post indicating valves opened until spring or torsion is felt in the rod, then closed back one-quarter turn?   ❏ Yes ❏ No ❏ N/A

C. Main drain test for system downstream of backflow or pressure reducing valve:

1. Record Static Pressure ____ psi and Residual Pressure ____ psi.

2. Was flow observed?   ❏ Yes ❏ No ❏ N/A

3. Are results comparable to previous test?   ❏ Yes ❏ No ❏ N/A

2. Semiannual Test (in addition to previous items)

A. Valve supervisory switches indicate movement?   ❏ Yes ❏ No ❏ N/A

B. Electrical waterflow alarm devices passed tests by opening the inspector's test connection or bypass connection with alarms actuating and flow observed?   ❏ Yes ❏ No ❏ N/A

FIGURE B.1(i)   NFSA Form for Inspection, Testing, and Maintenance of Wet Pipe Fire Sprinkler Systems.

3. Annual Tests (in addition to previous items)

A. Main drain test:

  1. Record Static Pressure _____ psi and Residual Pressure _____ psi.

  2. Was flow observed? ❏ Yes ❏ No ❏ N/A

  3. Are results comparable to previous test? ❏ Yes ❏ No ❏ N/A

B. Are all sprinklers dated 1920 or later? ❏ Yes ❏ No ❏ N/A

C. Fast response sprinklers 20 or more years old replaced or successfully sample tested within last 10 years? ❏ Yes ❏ No ❏ N/A

D. Standard response sprinklers 50 or more years old replaced or successfully sample tested within last 10 years? ❏ Yes ❏ No ❏ N/A

E. Standard response sprinklers 75 or more years old replaced or successfully sample tested within last 5 years? ❏ Yes ❏ No ❏ N/A

F. Dry-type sprinklers replaced or successfully sample tested within last 10 years? ❏ Yes ❏ No ❏ N/A

G. Specific gravity of antifreeze correct? ❏ Yes ❏ No ❏ N/A

H. All control valves operated through full range and returned to normal position? ❏ Yes ❏ No ❏ N/A

I. Backflow devices passed backflow test? ❏ Yes ❏ No ❏ N/A

J. Backflow devices passed full flow test? ❏ Yes ❏ No ❏ N/A

K. Pressure reducing valves passed partial flow test? ❏ Yes ❏ No ❏ N/A

4. Test to be done every third year:

Hose (more than 5 years old) connected to the system has been service tested in accordance with NFPA 1962. Water discharged and water flow alarms operated? ❏ Yes ❏ No ❏ N/A

5. Tests to be done every fifth year.

A. Sprinklers rated above High temperature tested? ❏ Yes ❏ No ❏ N/A

B. Gages checked by calibrated gage or replaced? ❏ Yes ❏ No ❏ N/A

C. Pressure reducing valves passed full flow test? ❏ Yes ❏ No ❏ N/A

C. Maintenance

1. Regular Maintenance Items

A. If sprinklers have been replaced, were they proper replacements? ❏ Yes ❏ No ❏ N/A

B. Used hose was cleaned, drained and dried before being placed back in service? Hose exposed to hazardous materials was disposed of or decontaminated in an approved manner? ❏ Yes ❏ No ❏ N/A

C. Systems normally filled with fresh water were drained and refilled twice if raw water got into the system? ❏ Yes ❏ No ❏ N/A

D. If any of the following were discovered, was an obstruction investigation conducted? ❏ Yes ❏ No ❏ N/A

Explain reason(s) and obstruction investigation findings in Part III.

1. Defective intake screen on pump with suction from open sources.

2. Obstructive material discharged during waterflow tests.

3. Foreign materials found in dry-pipe valves, check valves or pumps.

4. Foreign material in water during drain test or plugging of inspector's test connection.

5. Plugging of pipe or sprinklers found during activation or alteration.

6. Failure to flush yard piping or surrounding public mains following new installation or repairs.

7. Record of broken mains in the vicinity.

8. Abnormally frequent false-tripping of dry-pipe valves.

9. System is returned to service after an extended period out of service (greater than one year).

10. There is reason to believe the system contains sodium silicate or its derivatives or highly corrosive fluxes in copper pipe systems.

E. If conditions were found that required flushing, was flushing of system conducted? ❏ Yes ❏ No ❏ N/A

2. Annual Maintenance Items (in addition to previous items)

A. Operating stem of all OS&Y valves lubricated, completely closed, and reopened? ❏ Yes ❏ No ❏ N/A

D. Sprinklers and spray nozzles protecting commercial cooking equipment and ventilating systems replaced except for bulb-type which show no signs of grease buildup? ❏ Yes ❏ No ❏ N/A

Part III - Comments *(Any "No" answers, test failures or other problems found with the sprinkler system must be explained here. Also, note here any products noticed on the system that have been the subject of a recall or a replacement program.)*

_____

_____

_____

_____

_____

_____

_____

_____

_____

_____

_____

_____

_____

_____

_____

_____

_____

_____

_____

_____

_____

_____

_____

_____

_____

_____

_____

_____

_____

_____

Part IV - Inspector's Information

Inspector: _____

Company: _____

Company's Address: _____

I state that the information on this form is correct at the time and place of my inspection, and that all equipment tested at this time was left in operational condition upon completion of this inspection except as noted in Part III above.

Signature of Inspector: _____ Date: _____

License or Certification Number (if applicable): _____

FIGURE B.1(i) *Continued*

Form for Inspection, Testing and Maintenance of Preaction and Deluge Fire Sprinkler Systems

Information on this form covers the minimum requirements of **NFPA 25-2002** for fire sprinkler systems connected to distribution systems without supplemental tanks or fire pumps. Separate forms are available to inspect, test and maintain fire pumps, water tanks and other fire protection systems. More frequent inspection, testing and maintenance may be necessary depending on the conditions of the occupancy and the water supply.

Owner: _____   Owner's Phone Number: _____

Owner's Address: _____

Property Being Evaluated: _____

Property Address: _____

Date of Work: _____   All responses refer to the current work (inspection, testing and maintenance) performed on this date.

This work is *(check one)*: ❑ Monthly   ❑ Quarterly   ❑ Annual   ❑ Third Year   ❑ Fifth Year

Notes: 1) All questions are to be answered *Yes*, *No*, or *Not Applicable*. All *No* answers are to be explained in Part III of this form.

2) Inspection, Testing and Maintenance are to be performed with water supplies (including fire pumps) in service, unless the impairment procedures of Chapter 11 of NFPA 25 are followed.

Part I - Owner's Section

A. Is the building occupied?   ❑ Yes ❑ No

B. Has the occupancy classification and hazard of contents remained the same since the last inspection?   ❑ Yes ❑ No

C. Are all fire protection systems in service?   ❑ Yes ❑ No

D. Has the system remained in service without modification since the last inspection?   ❑ Yes ❑ No

E. Was the system free of actuation of devices or alarms since the last inspection?   ❑ Yes ❑ No

_____   _____
Owner or representative (print name)   Signature and Date

Part II - Inspector's Section

A. Inspections

1. Daily and Weekly Items

A. Control valves supervised with seals in correct (open or closed) position?   ❑ Yes ❑ No ❑ N/A

B. Valve enclosures maintaining at least 40°F?   ❑ Yes ❑ No ❑ N/A

C. Gauges in good condition and showing normal air and water pressure?   ❑ Yes ❑ No ❑ N/A

D. Backflow preventers:

1. In correct (open or closed) position?   ❑ Yes ❑ No ❑ N/A

2. Sealed, locked or supervised & accessible?   ❑ Yes ❑ No ❑ N/A

3. Relief port on RPZ device not discharging?   ❑ Yes ❑ No ❑ N/A

E. For freezer systems, is the gage near the compressor reading the same as the gage near the preaction valve?   ❑ Yes ❑ No ❑ N/A

4. Monthly Inspection Items (in addition to above items)

A. Control valves with locks or electrical supervision in correct (open or closed) position?   ❑ Yes ❑ No ❑ N/A

B. Valves free from physical damage, trim valves in appropriate (open or closed) position, no leakage from valve seat, and all electrical components in service?   ❑ Yes ❑ No ❑ N/A

C. Sprinkler wrench with spare sprinklers?   ❑ Yes ❑ No ❑ N/A

5. Quarterly Inspection Items (in addition to above items)

A. Pressure Reducing Valves: In open position, not leaking, maintaining downstream pressure per design criteria, and in good condition with handwheels not broken?   ❑ Yes ❑ No ❑ N/A

B. Hydraulic nameplate (calculated systems) securely attached to riser and legible?   ❑ Yes ❑ No ❑ N/A

C. Fire Department Connections:

Visible, accessible, couplings and swivels not damaged and rotate smoothly, plugs or caps in place and undamaged, gaskets in place and in good condition, identification sign(s) in place, check valve is not leaking, clapper is in place and operating properly and automatic drain valve in place and operating properly?   ❑ Yes ❑ No ❑ N/A

(If plugs or caps are not in place, inspect interior for obstructions.)

D. Alarm devices free from physical damage?   ❑ Yes ❑ No ❑ N/A

6. Annual Inspection Items (in addition to above items)

A. Proper number and type of spare sprinklers?   ❑ Yes ❑ No ❑ N/A

B. Visible sprinklers:

1. Free of corrosion and physical damage?   ❑ Yes ❑ No ❑ N/A

2. Free of obstructions to spray patterns?   ❑ Yes ❑ No ❑ N/A

3. Free of foreign materials including paint?   ❑ Yes ❑ No ❑ N/A

4. Liquid in all glass bulb sprinklers?   ❑ Yes ❑ No ❑ N/A

C. Visible pipe:

1. In good condition/no external corrosion?   ❑ Yes ❑ No ❑ N/A

2. No mechanical damage and no leaks?   ❑ Yes ❑ No ❑ N/A

3. Properly aligned and no external loads?   ❑ Yes ❑ No ❑ N/A

D. Visible pipe hangers and seismic braces not damaged or loose?   ❑ Yes ❑ No ❑ N/A

E. Preaction and deluge valves that need to be opened to be reset passed internal inspection?   ❑ Yes ❑ No ❑ N/A

F. Must be done before cold weather

1. Adequate heat in areas with wet piping?   ❑ Yes ❑ No ❑ N/A

2. Low temperature alarms functioning?   ❑ Yes ❑ No ❑ N/A

3. Pipe through freezers free of ice blockage?   ❑ Yes ❑ No ❑ N/A

G. Has an internal inspection of the pipe been performed by removing the flushing connection and one sprinkler near the end of a branch line within the last 5 years?   ❑ Yes ❑ No ❑ N/A

(If the answer was "No," conduct an internal inspection.)

8. Fifth Year Inspection Items (in addition to above items)

A. Check valves internally inspected and all parts operate properly, move freely and are in good condition?   ❑ Yes ❑ No ❑ N/A

B. Strainers, filters, restricted orifices and diaphragm chambers passed internal inspection?   ❑ Yes ❑ No ❑ N/A

C. Preaction and deluge valves that can be externally reset passed internal inspection?   ❑ Yes ❑ No ❑ N/A

B. Testing

The following tests are to be performed at the noted intervals. Report any failures on Part III of this form.

1. Quarterly Tests

A. Mechanical waterflow alarm devices passed tests by opening the inspector's test connection or bypass connection with alarms actuating and flow observed?   ❑ Yes ❑ No ❑ N/A

B. Post indicating valves opened until spring or torsion is felt in the rod, then closed back one-quarter turn?   ❑ Yes ❑ No ❑ N/A

C. Is the priming level correct and has the low air pressure signal passed its test?   ❑ Yes ❑ No ❑ N/A

D. Main drain test for system downstream of backflow or pressure reducing valve:

1. Record Static Pressure ____ psi and Residual Pressure ____ psi.

2. Was flow observed?   ❑ Yes ❑ No ❑ N/A

3. Are results comparable to previous test?   ❑ Yes ❑ No ❑ N/A

FIGURE B.1(j)   NFSA Form for Inspection, Testing, and Maintenance of Preaction and Deluge Fire Sprinkler Systems.

2. Semiannual Test (in addition to previous items)

A. Valve supervisory switches indicate movement? ❏ Yes ❏ No ❏ N/A

B. Electrical waterflow alarm devices passed tests by opening the inspector's test connection or bypass connection with alarms actuating and flow observed? ❏ Yes ❏ No ❏ N/A

3. Annual Tests (in addition to previous items)

A. Main drain test:

  1. Record Static Pressure _____ psi and Residual Pressure _____ psi.

  2. Was flow observed? ❏ Yes ❏ No ❏ N/A

  3. Are results comparable to previous test? ❏ Yes ❏ No ❏ N/A

B. Are all sprinklers dated 1920 or later? ❏ Yes ❏ No ❏ N/A

C. Fast response sprinklers 20 or more years old replaced or successfully sample tested within last 10 years? ❏ Yes ❏ No ❏ N/A

D. Standard response sprinklers 50 or more years old replaced or successfully sample tested within last 10 years? ❏ Yes ❏ No ❏ N/A

E. Standard response sprinklers 75 or more years old replaced or successfully sample tested within last 5 years? ❏ Yes ❏ No ❏ N/A

F. Dry-type sprinklers replaced or successfully sample tested within last 10 years? ❏ Yes ❏ No ❏ N/A

G. All control valves operated through full range and returned to normal position? ❏ Yes ❏ No ❏ N/A

H. Low temperature alarms passed test? ❏ Yes ❏ No ❏ N/A

I. Full flow trip test: *(Not required where water can't be discharged)*

(Test all systems together that will operate simultaneously.)

  1. Discharge from all nozzles unimpeded? ❏ Yes ❏ No ❏ N/A

  2. Pressure reading at hydraulically most remote nozzle _____ psi.

  3. Residual pressure reading at valve _____ psi.

  4. Above readings comparable to design values? ❏ Yes ❏ No ❏ N/A

  5. Manual activation devices passed test? ❏ Yes ❏ No ❏ N/A

J. Automatic air maintenance devices on dry-pipe and preaction systems passed test? ❏ Yes ❏ No ❏ N/A

K. Backflow devices passed backflow test? ❏ Yes ❏ No ❏ N/A

L. Backflow devices passed full flow test? ❏ Yes ❏ No ❏ N/A

M. Pressure reducing valves passed partial flow test? ❏ Yes ❏ No ❏ N/A

4. Tests to be done every fifth year.

A. Sprinklers rated above High temperature tested? ❏ Yes ❏ No ❏ N/A

B. Gages checked by calibrated gage or replaced? ❏ Yes ❏ No ❏ N/A

C. Pressure reducing valves passed full flow test? ❏ Yes ❏ No ❏ N/A

C. Maintenance

1. Regular Maintenance Items

A. If sprinklers have been replaced, were they proper replacements? ❏ Yes ❏ No ❏ N/A

B. Have low point drains been emptied? ❏ Yes ❏ No ❏ N/A

C. If any of the following were discovered, was an obstruction investigation conducted? ❏ Yes ❏ No ❏ N/A

Explain reason(s) and obstruction investigation findings in Part III.

  1. Defective intake screen on pump with suction from open sources.

  2. Obstructive material discharged during waterflow tests.

  3. Foreign materials found in dry-pipe valves, check valves or pumps.

  4. Foreign material in water during drain test or plugging of inspector's test connection.

  5. Plugging of pipe or sprinklers found during activation or alteration.

  6. Failure to flush yard piping or surrounding public mains following new installation or repairs.

  7. Record of broken mains in the vicinity.

  8. Abnormally frequent false-tripping of dry-pipe valves.

  9. System is returned to service after an extended period out of service (greater than one year).

  10. There is reason to believe the system contains sodium silicate or its derivatives or highly corrosive fluxes in copper pipe systems.

D. If conditions were found that required flushing, was flushing of system conducted? ❏ Yes ❏ No ❏ N/A

2. Annual Maintenance Items (in addition to previous items)

A. Operating stem of all OS&Y valves lubricated, completely closed, and reopened? ❏ Yes ❏ No ❏ N/A

B. Low points drained prior to the onset of freezing weather? ❏ Yes ❏ No ❏ N/A

C. Sprinklers and spray nozzles protecting commercial cooking equipment and ventilating systems replaced except for bulb-type which show no signs of grease buildup? ❏ Yes ❏ No ❏ N/A

Part III - Comments *(Any "No" answers, test failures or other problems found with the sprinkler system must be explained here. Also, note here any products noticed on the system that have been the subject of a recall or a replacement program.)*

_____

_____

_____

_____

_____

_____

_____

_____

_____

_____

_____

_____

_____

_____

_____

_____

_____

_____

_____

_____

_____

_____

_____

_____

Part IV - Inspector's Information

Inspector: _____

Company: _____

Company's Address: _____

I state that the information on this form is correct at the time and place of my inspection, and that all equipment tested at this time was left in operational condition upon completion of this inspection except as noted in Part III above.

Signature of Inspector: _____ Date: _____

License or Certification Number (if applicable): _____

FIGURE B.1(j) *Continued*

Form for Inspection, Testing and Maintenance of Standpipe and Hose Systems

NATIONAL FIRE SPRINKLER ASSOCIATION, INC.

Information on this form covers the minimum requirements of **NFPA 25-2002** for standpipe and hose systems.
Where the standpipe system includes a fire pump or water tank, an additional form must be completed for inspection, testing and maintenance of the pump or tank. Forms are also available for fire sprinkler systems, private fire service mains, water spray fixed systems and foam-water sprinkler systems. More frequent inspection, testing and maintenance may be necessary depending on the conditions of the occupancy and the water supply.

Owner: _____ Owner's Phone Number: _____

Owner's Address: _____

Property Being Evaluated: _____

Property Address: _____

Date of Work: _____ All responses refer to the current work (inspection, testing and maintenance) performed on this date.

This work is (check one): ❑ Monthly ❑ Quarterly ❑ Semiannual ❑ Annual ❑ Third Year ❑ Fifth Year

Notes: 1) All questions are to be answered *Yes, No*, or *Not Applicable*. All "No" answers are to be explained in the comments portion of this form.
2) Inspection, Testing and Maintenance are to be performed with water supplies (including fire pumps) in service, unless the impairment procedures of Chapter 11 of NFPA 25 are followed.

Part I - Owner's Section

A. Is the building occupied? ❑ Yes ❑ No

B. Has the occupancy classification and hazard of contents remained the same since the last inspection? ❑ Yes ❑ No

C. Are all fire protection systems in service? ❑ Yes ❑ No

D. Has the system remained in service without modification since the last inspection? ❑ Yes ❑ No

E. Was the system free of actuation of devices or alarms since the last inspection? ❑ Yes ❑ No

_____ _____
Owner or representative (print name) Signature and Date

Part II - Inspector's Section

A. Inspections

1. Daily and Weekly Inspection Items

A. Enclosures around dry-pipe valves (without low temperature alarms) maintaining a minimum of 40°F? ❑ Yes ❑ No ❑ N/A

B. Relief port on reduced pressure backflow prevention assemblies not continuously discharging? ❑ Yes ❑ No ❑ N/A

C. Gauges on dry system (no low pressure alarm) in good condition showing normal air and water pressure? ❑ Yes ❑ No ❑ N/A

D. Sealed control valves and valves on backflow assemblies in normal (open or closed) position, accessible, with seals in place, free from external leaks, and provided with appropriate identification? ❑ Yes ❑ No ❑ N/A

2. Monthly Inspection Items (in addition to above items)

A. Dry-Pipe Valves:
Enclosures around valves (with low temperature alarms) maintaining a minimum of 40°F, free from physical damage, trim valves in appropriate (open or closed) position, and no leakage from intermediate chamber? ❑ Yes ❑ No ❑ N/A

B. Pressure Reducing Valves (Hose Connection):
1. Handwheels in place and in good condition? ❑ Yes ❑ No ❑ N/A
2. Hose threads in good condition? ❑ Yes ❑ No ❑ N/A
3. Valves not leaking? ❑ Yes ❑ No ❑ N/A
4. Reducers and caps in place & in good condition? ❑ Yes ❑ No ❑ N/A

C. Pressure Reducing Valves (Hose Rack):
1. Handwheels in place and in good condition? ❑ Yes ❑ No ❑ N/A
2. Valves not leaking? ❑ Yes ❑ No ❑ N/A

D. Gauges (on dry system with low pressure alarm or on wet system) in good condition and showing normal air and water pressure? ❑ Yes ❑ No ❑ N/A

E. Control Valves and Valves on Backflow Assemblies (with locks or electric supervision) in normal (open or closed) position with locks or supervision in place, accessible, free from external leaks, provided with appropriate wrenches, and provided with appropriate identification? ❑ Yes ❑ No ❑ N/A

F. Alarm devices free from physical damage? ❑ Yes ❑ No ❑ N/A

G. Alarm Valves free from physical damage, valves in correct (open or closed) position, no leakage from retard chamber or drains, gauges indicating normal water pressure? ❑ Yes ❑ No ❑ N/A

4. Quarterly Inspection Items (in addition to above items)

A. Hose Valve Outlets:
Valves not leaking and no visible obstructions with caps, hose connections, valve handle, cap gasket, restricting devices in place, undamaged and in good condition? ❑ Yes ❑ No ❑ N/A

B. Visible pipe and supports in good condition? ❑ Yes ❑ No ❑ N/A

C. Alarm devices free from physical damage? ❑ Yes ❑ No ❑ N/A

D. Fire Department Connections:
Visible, accessible, couplings and swivels not damaged and rotate smoothly, plugs or caps in place and undamaged, gaskets in place and in good condition, identification sign(s) in place, check valve is not leaking, clapper is in place and operating properly and automatic drain valve in place and operating properly? ❑ Yes ❑ No ❑ N/A
(If plugs or caps are not in place, inspect interior for obstructions.)

5. Annual Inspection Items (in addition to above items)

A. Hose free from mildew, cuts and deterioration, couplings of compatible threads and undamaged, gaskets in place and in good condition, and hose connected? ❑ Yes ❑ No ❑ N/A

B. Hose Nozzles:
1. Nozzles and gaskets in place and good condition? ❑ Yes ❑ No ❑ N/A
2. No visible obstructions? ❑ Yes ❑ No ❑ N/A
3. Nozzles operate smoothly? ❑ Yes ❑ No ❑ N/A

C. Hose Storage Devices:
1. Hose properly racked or rolled? ❑ Yes ❑ No ❑ N/A
2. Nozzle clips in place and nozzles contained? ❑ Yes ❑ No ❑ N/A
3. Undamaged, unobstructed and operable? ❑ Yes ❑ No ❑ N/A
4. Will racks swing out of cabinet at least 90°? ❑ Yes ❑ No ❑ N/A

D. Storage Cabinets:
1. Cabinets have no corroded or damaged parts, are easy to fully open, and are accessible and identified? ❑ Yes ❑ No ❑ N/A
2. Door glazings in good condition? ❑ Yes ❑ No ❑ N/A
3. Locks functioning in break-glass type cabinets? ❑ Yes ❑ No ❑ N/A
4. All parts, valves, hoses and fire extinguishers accessible? ❑ Yes ❑ No ❑ N/A

E. Adequate heat available to areas where wet pipe is located? (Must be done before cold weather) ❑ Yes ❑ No ❑ N/A

F. Interior of dry-pipe valves (which must be open to be reset) passed internal inspection? ❑ Yes ❑ No ❑ N/A

6. Fifth Year Inspection Items (in addition to previous items)

A. Interior of dry-pipe valves (which can be reset without opening) passed internal inspection? ❑ Yes ❑ No ❑ N/A

B. Alarm valves and their associated strainers, filters and restriction orifices passed internal inspection? ❑ Yes ❑ No ❑ N/A

C. Check valves internally inspected and all parts operate properly, move freely and are in good condition? ❑ Yes ❑ No ❑ N/A

D. Strainers, filters, restricted orifices and diaphragm chambers on dry-pipe valves passed internal inspection? ❑ Yes ❑ No ❑ N/A

© 2002 National Fire Sprinkler Association, P.O. Box 1000, Patterson, NY 12563 (845) 878-4200 Used by Permission Form 25-14 Sheet 1 of 2

FIGURE B.1(k) NFSA Form for Inspection, Testing, and Maintenance of Standpipe and Hose Systems.

B. Testing

The following tests are to be performed at the noted intervals. Report any failures on Part III of this form.

1. Quarterly Tests

A. Mechanical waterflow alarm devices passed tests by opening the inspector's test connection or bypass connection with alarms actuating and flow observed? ❑ Yes ❑ No ❑ N/A

B. Post indicator valves opened until spring or torsion is felt in the rod, then closed back one quarter turn? ❑ Yes ❑ No ❑ N/A

C. Priming water level (dry-pipe) passed test? ❑ Yes ❑ No ❑ N/A

D. Low air pressure signal (dry-pipe) passed test? ❑ Yes ❑ No ❑ N/A

E. Quick opening device passed test? ❑ Yes ❑ No ❑ N/A

F. Main Drain Test for system downstream of backflow or pressure reducing valve (automatic water supply):

  1. Record static pressure _____ psi and residual pressure _____ psi.
  2. Was flow observed? ❑ Yes ❑ No ❑ N/A
  3. Are results comparable to previous test? ❑ Yes ❑ No ❑ N/A

2. Semiannual Test (in addition to above items)

A. Electrical waterflow alarm devices passed tests by opening the inspector's test connection or bypass connection with alarms actuating and flow observed? ❑ Yes ❑ No ❑ N/A

B. Valve supervisory devices indicate movement? ❑ Yes ❑ No ❑ N/A

3. Annual Tests (in addition to above items)

A. System Main Drain Test (automatic water supply)

  1. Record static pressure _____ psi and residual pressure _____ psi.
  2. Was flow observed? ❑ Yes ❑ No ❑ N/A
  3. Are results comparable to previous test? ❑ Yes ❑ No ❑ N/A

B. Specific gravity of antifreeze correct? ❑ Yes ❑ No ❑ N/A

C. All control valves operated through full range and returned to normal position? ❑ Yes ❑ No ❑ N/A

D. Low temperature alarms in dry pipe enclosures passed test? ❑ Yes ❑ No ❑ N/A

E. Dry-pipe valve partial flow trip test:

  1. Record initial air pressure _____ psi and water pressure _____ psi.
  2. Record tripping air pressure _____ psi and time _____ (sec).
  3. Above results comparable to previous tests? ❑ Yes ❑ No ❑ N/A

F. Automatic air maintenance devices on dry-pipe system passed test? ❑ Yes ❑ No ❑ N/A

G. Backflow devices passed backflow test? ❑ Yes ❑ No ❑ N/A

H. Backflow devices passed full flow test? ❑ Yes ❑ No ❑ N/A

I. Pressure reducing valves passed partial flow test? ❑ Yes ❑ No ❑ N/A

4. Third Year Tests (in addition to above items)

A. Dry-Pipe Valve Full Flow Trip Test:

  1. Record initial air pressure _____ psi and water pressure _____ psi.
  2. Record tripping air pressure _____ psi and tripping time _____ (sec).
  3. Was water delivered to inspectors test connection? ❑ Yes ❑ No ❑ N/A
  4. Above results comparable to previous tests? ❑ Yes ❑ No ❑ N/A

B. Is hose less than five years old? ❑ Yes ❑ No ❑ N/A

If "no," has hose been tested within three years? ❑ Yes ❑ No ❑ N/A

If "no," test hose now and every three years.

5. Fifth Year Tests

A. Gauges tested against calibrated one or replaced? ❑ Yes ❑ No ❑ N/A

B. Automatic standpipe systems tested at required flows:

  1. Record static pressure _____ psi and residual pressure _____ psi.
  2. Record total flow _____ gpm.
  3. Above flows and pressures acceptable? ❑ Yes ❑ No ❑ N/A

C. Manual systems not a part of a sprinkler/standpipe system passed hydrostatic test? ❑ Yes ❑ No ❑ N/A

D. All hose connection and hose rack assembly pressure reducing and valves passed full flow test? ❑ Yes ❑ No ❑ N/A

C. Maintenance

1. Regular Maintenance Items

A. Items found missing or in disrepair during inspection or testing repaired or replaced? ❑ Yes ❑ No ❑ N/A

B. Air leaks in dry-pipe systems resulting in air pressure loss more than 10 psi/week repaired? ❑ Yes ❑ No ❑ N/A

C. Dry systems being maintained in dry condition? ❑ Yes ❑ No ❑ N/A

D. If any of the following were discovered, was an obstruction investigation conducted? ❑ Yes ❑ No ❑ N/A

Explain reason(s) and obstruction investigation findings in Part III.

1. Defective intake screen for pumps taking suction from open sources.
2. Obstructive material discharged during waterflow test.
3. Foreign materials found in dry-pipe valves, check valves or pumps.
4. Heavy discoloration of water during drain test or plugging of inspector's test connection.
5. Plugging found in piping dismantled during alterations.
6. Failure to flush yard piping or surrounding public mains following new installation or repairs.
7. Record of broken mains in the vicinity.
8. Abnormally frequent false tripping of dry-pipe valves.
9. System is returned to service after an extended period out of service (greater than one year).
10. There is reason to believe the system contains sodium silicate or its derivatives.

E. If conditions were found that required flushing, was flushing of system conducted? ❑ Yes ❑ No ❑ N/A

2. Annual Maintenance Items (in addition to above items)

A. Operating stem of all OS&Y valves lubricated, completely closed, and reopened? ❑ Yes ❑ No ❑ N/A

B. Hose reracked or rerolled so folds do not occur in same position? ❑ Yes ❑ No ❑ N/A

C. Interior of dry-pipe valves cleaned? ❑ Yes ❑ No ❑ N/A

D. Low points drained in dry systems prior to onset of freezing weather? ❑ Yes ❑ No ❑ N/A

Part III - Comments *(Any "No" answers, test failures or other problems found with the standpipe and hose system must be explained here.)*

_____
_____
_____
_____
_____
_____
_____
_____
_____
_____
_____
_____

Part IV - Inspector's Information

Inspector: _____

Company: _____

Company's Address: _____

I state that the information on this form is correct at the time and place of my inspection, and that all equipment tested at this time was left in operational condition upon completion of this inspection except as noted in Part III above.

Signature of Inspector: _____ Date: _____

License or Certification Number (if applicable): _____

FIGURE B.1(k) *Continued*

Form for Inspection, Testing and Maintenance of Private Fire Service Mains

NATIONAL
FIRE
SPRINKLER
ASSOCIATION, INC.

Information on this form covers the minimum requirements of **NFPA 25-2002** for Private Fire Service Mains.
Separate forms are available to inspect, test and maintain other portions of the fire protection system of which the private fire service main is a part.
More frequent inspection, testing and maintenance may be necessary depending on conditions of the occupancy and water supply.

Owner: _____   Owner's Phone Number: _____

Owner's Address: _____

Property Being Evaluated: _____

Property Address: _____

Date of Work: _____   All responses refer to the current work (inspection, te sting and maintenance) performed on this date.

This inspection is (check one):   ❏ Monthly   ❏ Quarterly   ❏ Semiannual   ❏ Annual   ❏ Fifth Year

Notes: 1) All questions are to be answered Yes, No or Not Applicable. All No answers are to be explained in the comments portion of this form.
2) Inspection, Testing and Maintenance are to be performed with water supplies (including fire pumps) in service, unless the impairment procedures of Chapter 11 of NFPA 25 are followed.

Part I - Owner's Section

A. Is the private fire service main in service?   ❏ Yes ❏ No

B. Remained in service since the last inspection?   ❏ Yes ❏ No

C. Were the systems supplied by the fire main free from actuation of devices or alarms since the last inspection?   ❏ Yes ❏ No

_____   _____
Owner or representative (print name)   Signature and Date

Part II - Inspector's Section

A. Inspection

1. Weekly Inspection Items

a. Relief port on reduced pressure backflow prevention assemblies free of continuous discharge?   ❏ Yes ❏ No ❏ N/A

b. Sealed control valves & valves on backflow assemblies:

1. In normal (open or closed) position?   ❏ Yes ❏ No ❏ N/A

2. Accessible with seals in place?   ❏ Yes ❏ No ❏ N/A

3. Free from external leaks?   ❏ Yes ❏ No ❏ N/A

4. Provided with appropriate identification?   ❏ Yes ❏ No ❏ N/A

2. Monthly Inspection Item (in addition to above items)

Control valves and valves on backflow assemblies (with locks or electric supervision):

In normal (open or closed) position, lock or electric supervision in place, accessible and free from external leaks, provided with appropriate wrenches, and provided with appropriate identification?   ❏ Yes ❏ No ❏ N/A

3. Quarterly Inspection Item (in addition to above items)

Hose/hydrant houses accessible, free from physical damage and fully equipped?   ❏ Yes ❏ No ❏ N/A

4. Semiannual Inspection Item (in addition to above items)

Monitor nozzles free of leaks, damage & corrosion?   ❏ Yes ❏ No ❏ N/A

5. Annual Inspection Items (in addition to above items)

a. Dry Barrel and Wall Hydrants:

1. Accessible and operating wrench available?   ❏ Yes ❏ No ❏ N/A

2. Outlets lubricated?   ❏ Yes ❏ No ❏ N/A

3. Free from ice or water in barrel?   ❏ Yes ❏ No ❏ N/A

4. Free from leaks and cracks?   ❏ Yes ❏ No ❏ N/A

5. Threads in good condition?   ❏ Yes ❏ No ❏ N/A

6. Operating nut in good condition?   ❏ Yes ❏ No ❏ N/A

b. Wet Barrel Hydrants:

1. Accessible and operating wrench available?   ❏ Yes ❏ No ❏ N/A

2. Free from leaks at outlets and top of hydrant?   ❏ Yes ❏ No ❏ N/A

3. Free from cracks in hydrant barrel?   ❏ Yes ❏ No ❏ N/A

4. Outlets lubricated?   ❏ Yes ❏ No ❏ N/A

5. Threads in good condition?   ❏ Yes ❏ No ❏ N/A

6. Operating nut in good condition?   ❏ Yes ❏ No ❏ N/A

c. Mainline strainers free from plugging and corrosion?   ❏ Yes ❏ No ❏ N/A

d. Exposed piping is free from leaks, physical damage and corrosion?   ❏ Yes ❏ No ❏ N/A

e. Exposed piping is properly restrained?   ❏ Yes ❏ No ❏ N/A

6. Fifth Year Inspection Item (in addition to above items)

Check valves internally inspected and all parts operate properly, move freely and are in good condition?   ❏ Yes ❏ No ❏ N/A

B. Testing

1. Quarterly Test

Post indicator valves opened until spring or torsion is felt in rod, then closed back one quarter turn?   ❏ Yes ❏ No ❏ N/A

2. Semiannual Test (in addition to the above items)

Valve supervisory devices indicate movement?   ❏ Yes ❏ No ❏ N/A

3. Annual Tests (in addition to the above items)

a. Monitor nozzles move through full range?   ❏ Yes ❏ No ❏ N/A

b. Monitor nozzles flowed an acceptable amount of water?   ❏ Yes ❏ No ❏ N/A

c. Hydrants flowed until clear (at least 1 minute)?   ❏ Yes ❏ No ❏ N/A

d. Dry barrel hydrants drain in at least one hour?   ❏ Yes ❏ No ❏ N/A

e. Dry barrel hydrants requiring pumping are identified?   ❏ Yes ❏ No ❏ N/A

f. All control valves operated through full range and returned to normal position?   ❏ Yes ❏ No ❏ N/A

g. Backflow devices passed backflow test?   ❏ Yes ❏ No ❏ N/A

h. Backflow devices passed full flow test?   ❏ Yes ❏ No ❏ N/A

4. Fifth Year Test — Exposed and underground piping passed flow test at expected flows?   ❏ Yes ❏ No ❏ N/A

C. Maintenance

1. Annual Maintenance Items

a. Mainline strainers cleaned?   ❏ Yes ❏ No ❏ N/A

b. Hose/hydrant houses and equipment in usable condition?   ❏ Yes ❏ No ❏ N/A

c. Hydrant caps, stems, plugs, and threads lubricated?   ❏ Yes ❏ No ❏ N/A

d. Hydrants free of ice, snow and damage?   ❏ Yes ❏ No ❏ N/A

e. Monitor nozzles are lubricated?   ❏ Yes ❏ No ❏ N/A

Part III - Comments (any "No" answers, test failures or other problems found with the system must be explained here)

_____

_____

_____

_____

_____

_____

_____

Part IV - Inspector's Information

I state that the information on this form is correct at the time and place of my inspection and that all equipment tested at this time was left in operational condition upon completion of this inspection except as noted in Part III above.

Inspector: _____

Company: _____

Company Address: _____

Signature of Inspector: _____   Date: _____

License or Certification Number (if applicable): _____

© 2002 National Fire Sprinkler Association, P.O. Box 1000, Patterson, NY 12563   (845) 878-4200   Used by Permission   Form 25-24   Sheet 1 of 1

FIGURE B.1(1)   NFSA Form for Inspection, Testing, and Maintenance of Private Fire Service Mains.

Form for Inspection, Testing and Maintenance of Fire Pumps

NATIONAL FIRE SPRINKLER ASSOCIATION, INC.

Information on this form covers the minimum requirements of **NFPA 25-2002** for centrifugal fire pumps.

Separate forms are available to inspect, test and maintain the rest of the fire protection system of which the fire pump is a part. More frequent inspection, testing and maintenance may be necessary depending on the conditions of the occupancy and water supply.

Owner: _____   Owner's Phone Number: _____

Owner's Address: _____

Property Being Evaluated: _____

Property Address: _____

Date of Work: _____ All responses refer to the current work (inspection, testing and maintenance) performed on this date.

This inspection is (*check one*): ❑ Weekly ❑ Monthly ❑ Quarterly ❑ Semiannual ❑ Annual

Notes: 1) All questions are to be answered *Yes, No,* or *Not Applicable*. All *No* answers are to be explained in the comments portion of this form.

   2) Inspection, Testing and Maintenance are to be performed with water supplies (including fire pumps) in service, unless the impairment procedures of Chapter 11 of NFPA 25 are followed.

Part I - Owner's Section

A. Is the fire pump in service? ❑ Yes ❑ No ❑ N/A

B. Has the fire pump remained in service since the last inspection? ❑ Yes ❑ No ❑ N/A

C. Was the system (of which the fire pump is a part) free from actuation of devices or alarms since the last inspection? ❑ Yes ❑ No ❑ N/A

Note to owner: Periodic tests of transfer switches and emergency generators are to be performed in accordance with NFPA 110 by a qualified electrical contractor.

_____   _____
Owner or representative (print name)   Signature and Date

Part II - Inspector's Section

A. Inspections - All to be performed weekly.

1. Pump house/room proper temperature (at least 70° F for diesels without engine heaters or 40° F for others)? ❑ Yes ❑ No ❑ N/A

2. Ventilating louvers free to operate? ❑ Yes ❑ No ❑ N/A

3. Suction, discharge and bypass valves open? ❑ Yes ❑ No ❑ N/A

4. Piping free from leaks? ❑ Yes ❑ No ❑ N/A

5. Suction and system pressure gauges normal? ❑ Yes ❑ No ❑ N/A

6. Suction reservoir, if provided, full? ❑ Yes ❑ No ❑ N/A

7. Electric Motor Driven Pumps

   a. Controller indicating power on, transfer switch indicating normal situation and isolation switch closed? ❑ Yes ❑ No ❑ N/A

   b. Reverse phase alarm indicator off or normal phase rotation indicator on? ❑ Yes ❑ No ❑ N/A

   c. Oil level in vertical motor sight normal? ❑ Yes ❑ No ❑ N/A

8. Diesel Engine Driven Pumps

   a. Fuel tank at least two thirds full? ❑ Yes ❑ No ❑ N/A

   b. Controller selector switch in Auto position? ❑ Yes ❑ No ❑ N/A

   c. Battery voltage and charger readings normal? ❑ Yes ❑ No ❑ N/A

   d. Battery indicators on or failure indicators off? ❑ Yes ❑ No ❑ N/A

   e. All alarm indicators off? ❑ Yes ❑ No ❑ N/A

   f. Record engine running time meter reading. _____ Is this appropriately higher than previous reading? ❑ Yes ❑ No ❑ N/A

   g. Oil level in right angle gear drive normal? ❑ Yes ❑ No ❑ N/A

   h. Crankcase oil level normal? ❑ Yes ❑ No ❑ N/A

   i. Cooling water level normal? ❑ Yes ❑ No ❑ N/A

   j. Electrolyte level in batteries normal? ❑ Yes ❑ No ❑ N/A

   k. Battery terminals free from corrosion? ❑ Yes ❑ No ❑ N/A

   l. Water-jacket heater operating? ❑ Yes ❑ No ❑ N/A

9. Steam pressure gauge for steam driven pump reading normal? ❑ Yes ❑ No ❑ N/A

10. Circulation relief valve flowing water while pump churns? ❑ Yes ❑ No ❑ N/A

11. Pressure relief valves operating with proper pressure downstream while pump is operational? ❑ Yes ❑ No ❑ N/A

B. Tests

1. Weekly Test Items

A. Electric Motor-Driven Pumps

   1. Pump started automatically? ❑ Yes ❑ No ❑ N/A

      Record starting pressure. _____ psi.

   2. Pump run for at least 10 minutes? ❑ Yes ❑ No ❑ N/A

      Record suction _____ and discharge _____ pressure while running.

   3. Pump packing gland showing slight discharge? *Adjust if necessary.* ❑ Yes ❑ No ❑ N/A

   4. Free from unusual noises or vibrations? ❑ Yes ❑ No ❑ N/A

   5. Packing boxes, bearings and pump casing free from overheating? ❑ Yes ❑ No ❑ N/A

   6. Record time for motor to accelerate to full speed. _____

   7. For reduced voltage or reduced current starting, record time controller is on first step. _____

   8. For automatic stop controllers, record time pump runs after starting. _____

   9. All times and pressures in Part A acceptable? ❑ Yes ❑ No ❑ N/A

B. Diesel Engine-Driven Pumps

   1. Pump started automatically? ❑ Yes ❑ No ❑ N/A

      Record starting pressure. _____ psi.

   2. Pump run for at least 30 minutes? ❑ Yes ❑ No ❑ N/A

      Record suction _____ and discharge _____ pressure while running.

   3. Pump packing gland showing slight discharge? ❑ Yes ❑ No ❑ N/A *Adjust if necessary.*

   4. Free from unusual noises or vibrations? ❑ Yes ❑ No ❑ N/A

   5. Packing boxes, bearings and pump casing free from overheating? ❑ Yes ❑ No ❑ N/A

   6. Record time for engine to crank. _____

   7. Record time for engine to reach running speed. _____

   8. Engine oil pressure gauge, speed indicator, water and oil temperature indicators all reading normal? ❑ Yes ❑ No ❑ N/A

   9. Cooling water flowing from heat exchanger? ❑ Yes ❑ No ❑ N/A

   10. All times and pressures in Part B acceptable? ❑ Yes ❑ No ❑ N/A

C. Steam Turbine-driven Pumps

   1. Record pump starting pressure _____ , suction _____ and discharge _____ pressures while running.

   3. Pump packing gland showing slight discharge? ❑ Yes ❑ No ❑ N/A *Adjust if necessary.*

   4. Free from unusual noises or vibrations? ❑ Yes ❑ No ❑ N/A

   5. Packing boxes, bearings and pump casing free from overheating? ❑ Yes ❑ No ❑ N/A

   6. Record steam pressure gauge reading. _____

   7. Record time for turbine to reach running speed. _____

   8. All times and pressures in Part C acceptable? ❑ Yes ❑ No ❑ N/A

FIGURE B.1(m)   NFSA Form for Inspection, Testing, and Maintenance of Fire Pumps.

2. Annual Tests

Annual pump test was run using the following method: (check one)

❏ Method A. Discharge of flow through hose streams. Flow readings taken at each hose stream.

❏ Method B. Discharge through by-pass flow meter to drain or suction reservoir. Flow readings taken by flow meter.

❏ Method C. Discharge through by-pass flow meter directly returned to pump suction. Flow readings taken by flow meter.

Note: At least once every three years method A or B must be used.

Pump Test Results

	No Flow	Rated Flow	Peak Flow
Suction Pressure			
Discharge Pressure			
Flow	N/A		
Electric Voltage and Current	N/A		
Pump Speed			

A. Are the values in the above table acceptable? ❏ Yes ❏ No ❏ N/A

B. No-flow (churn) test run for 30 min? ❏ Yes ❏ No ❏ N/A

C. Circulation relief valve and pressure relief valve operated properly during all flow tests? ❏ Yes ❏ No ❏ N/A

D. No alarm indicators or other visible abnormalities observed during no flow test? ❏ Yes ❏ No ❏ N/A

E. Suction screens cleaned after flow? ❏ Yes ❏ No ❏ N/A

F. Low Suction Throttling Device Test

  1. Low suction pressure simulated? ❏ Yes ❏ No ❏ N/A

  Free from abnormalities in throttling action? ❏ Yes ❏ No ❏ N/A

  2. Free from abnormalities in return to full flow? ❏ Yes ❏ No ❏ N/A

G. Automatic Transfer Switch Test

  1. Power failure simulated during peak flow? ❏ Yes ❏ No ❏ N/A

  Connection made to alternate power source? ❏ Yes ❏ No ❏ N/A

  2. After termination of simulated power failure did motor reconnect to the normal power source? ❏ Yes ❏ No ❏ N/A

H. All alarm conditions simulated? ❏ Yes ❏ No ❏ N/A

  All alarms operated? ❏ Yes ❏ No ❏ N/A

C. Maintenance

A maintenance schedule must be established in accordance with the manufacturer's instructions. In the absence of such a schedule, the following must be used:

1. Weekly Maintenance Items for Diesel Engine Systems:

A. Fuel tank level, tank float switch, and solenoid valve operation acceptable? ❏ Yes ❏ No ❏ N/A

B. Diesel fuel system free of water? ❏ Yes ❏ No ❏ N/A

C. Flexible hoses and connectors in fuel and coolant systems acceptable? ❏ Yes ❏ No ❏ N/A

D. Oil level and lube oil heater acceptable? ❏ Yes ❏ No ❏ N/A

E. Coolant level acceptable? ❏ Yes ❏ No ❏ N/A

F. Water pump for coolant system operating? ❏ Yes ❏ No ❏ N/A

G. Jacket water heater for coolant system acceptable? ❏ Yes ❏ No ❏ N/A

H. Exhaust system free of leakage? ❏ Yes ❏ No ❏ N/A

I. Drain condensate trap on exhaust system operational? ❏ Yes ❏ No ❏ N/A

J. Electrolyte level in batteries acceptable? ❏ Yes ❏ No ❏ N/A

K. Connections to electrical system acceptable? ❏ Yes ❏ No ❏ N/A

2. Monthly Maintenance Items

A. Isolation switch and circuit breaker exercised? ❏ Yes ❏ No ❏ N/A

B. Battery case clean, dry and free of corrosion and battery's specific gravity or state of charge passed test? ❏ Yes ❏ No ❏ N/A

C. Charger and charge rate passed visual inspection and battery charge being equalized? ❏ Yes ❏ No ❏ N/A

D. Circuit breakers appear clean? ❏ Yes ❏ No ❏ N/A

3. Quarterly Maintenance Items

A. Cleaned strainer, filter or dirt leg in diesel fuel system? ❏ Yes ❏ No ❏ N/A

B. Cleaned or replaced crank case breather in lubrication system? ❏ Yes ❏ No ❏ N/A

C. Cleaned water strainer in coolant system? ❏ Yes ❏ No ❏ N/A

D. Insulation acceptable and fire hazards eliminated from exhaust system? ❏ Yes ❏ No ❏ N/A

E. Battery terminals clean and tight? ❏ Yes ❏ No ❏ N/A

F. Electrical system free of wire chafing? ❏ Yes ❏ No ❏ N/A

4. Semiannual Maintenance Items

A. Manual starting means on electrical systems operated and boxes, panels and cabinets cleaned? ❏ Yes ❏ No ❏ N/A

B. Antifreeze tested in coolant system? ❏ Yes ❏ No ❏ N/A

C. Flexible exhaust section acceptable? ❏ Yes ❏ No ❏ N/A

D. Alarms operated on electrical portions of diesel engine systems? ❏ Yes ❏ No ❏ N/A

5. Annual Maintenance Items

A. Changed pump bearing lubrication? ❏ Yes ❏ No ❏ N/A

B. Shaft end play acceptable? ❏ Yes ❏ No ❏ N/A

C. Transmission coupling, right angle gear drive and mechanical moving parts lubricated? ❏ Yes ❏ No ❏ N/A

D. Circuit breakers passed trip test? ❏ Yes ❏ No ❏ N/A

E. Emergency manual starting means operated without power? ❏ Yes ❏ No ❏ N/A

F. Electrical connections secure? ❏ Yes ❏ No ❏ N/A

G. Pressure switch settings calibrated? ❏ Yes ❏ No ❏ N/A

H. Motor bearings greased? ❏ Yes ❏ No ❏ N/A

I. Fuel tank free of water and foreign material, tank vents and overflow pipes free of obstructions, fuel piping acceptable, and oil and filters changed in diesel systems? ❏ Yes ❏ No ❏ N/A

J. Antifreeze changed in coolant system? ❏ Yes ❏ No ❏ N/A

K. Heater exchanger cleaned out? ❏ Yes ❏ No ❏ N/A

L. Duct work and louvers (combustion air) acceptable? ❏ Yes ❏ No ❏ N/A

M. Exhaust system free of back pressure? ❏ Yes ❏ No ❏ N/A

N. Exhaust system hangers and supports acceptable? ❏ Yes ❏ No ❏ N/A

O. Control and power wiring tight? ❏ Yes ❏ No ❏ N/A

Part III - Comments *(Any "No" answers, test failure or other problems found with the fire pump must be explained here.)*

_____

_____

_____

_____

Part IV - Inspector's Information

Inspector: _____

Company: _____

Company's Address: _____

I state that the information on this form is correct at the time and place of my inspection, and that all equipment tested at this time was left in operational condition upon completion of this inspection except as noted in Part III above.

Signature of Inspector: _____ Date: _____

License or Certification Number (if applicable): _____

FIGURE B.1(m) *Continued*

Form for Inspection, Testing and Maintenance of Water Storage Tanks

NATIONAL FIRE SPRINKLER ASSOCIATION, INC.

Information on this form covers the minimum requirements of **NFPA 25-2002** for water storage tanks. Separate forms are available to inspect, test and maintain the rest of the fire protection system of which the water tank is a part. More frequent inspection, testing, and maintenance may be necessary depending on the conditions of the occupancy and water supply.

Owner: _____ Owner's Phone Number: _____

Owner's Address: _____

Property Being Evaluated: _____

Property Address: _____

Date of Work: _____ All responses refer to the current work (inspection, testing and maintenance) performed on the date shown above.

This inspection is (*check one*): ❏ Daily   ❏ Monthly   ❏ Semiannual   ❏ Annual   ❏ Two Years   ❏ Third Year   ❏ Fifth Year

Notes: 1) All questions are to be answered *Yes, No* or *Not Applicable*. All *No* answers are to be explained in the comments portion of this form.
    2) Inspection, Testing and Maintenance are to be performed with water supplies (including fire pumps) in service, unless the impairment procedures of Chapter 11 of NFPA 25 are followed.

Part I - Owner's Section

A. Is the water storage tank in service?   ❏ Yes ❏ No

B. Has the tank remained in service since the last inspection?   ❏ Yes ❏ No

C. Was the system (of which the tank is a part) free from actuation of devices or alarms since the last inspection?   ❏ Yes ❏ No

_____   _____
Owner or representative (print name)   Signature and Date

Part II - Inspector's Section

A. Inspection

1. **Daily items during cold weather where tank is subject to freezing which can be weekly if tank is electronically supervised**

   a. Heating system operational?   ❏ Yes ❏ No ❏ N/A

   b. Record water temperature. _____ Acceptable? ❏ Yes ❏ No ❏ N/A

2. **Weekly Inspection Item (in addition to above items)**
   Sealed valves in proper (open or closed) position? ❏ Yes ❏ No ❏ N/A

3. **Monthly Inspection Items (in addition to above items)**

   a. Embankment-Supported Rubberized-Fabric tanks free from erosion along exterior sides? ❏ Yes ❏ No ❏ N/A

   b. Locked and supervised valves in proper (open or closed) position? ❏ Yes ❏ No ❏ N/A

   c. Gages in good condition, showing normal pressure? ❏ Yes ❏ No ❏ N/A

4. **Monthly items which can be done quarterly when tank is electronically supervised (in addition to above items)**

   a. Water level and condition correct? ❏ Yes ❏ No ❏ N/A

   b. Air pressure in pressure tanks correct? ❏ Yes ❏ No ❏ N/A

5. Quarterly Inspection Items (in addition to above items)

   a. Exterior of tank, support structure, foundation, condition of water in tank, catwalks and ladders strong and free from obvious damage? ❏ Yes ❏ No ❏ N/A

   b. Area surrounding tank free from combustibles, materials which could accelerate corrosion and ice? ❏ Yes ❏ No ❏ N/A

   c. Tank vents clean? ❏ Yes ❏ No ❏ N/A

6. **Annual Inspection Items (in addition to above items)**

   a. Exterior coated and insulated surfaces of tank and supporting structure free from degradation? ❏ Yes ❏ No ❏ N/A

   b. Expansion joints not leaking or cracking? ❏ Yes ❏ No ❏ N/A

   c. Hoops and grills on wooden tanks in acceptable condition? ❏ Yes ❏ No ❏ N/A

7. **Interior Inspection to be performed once every three years on pressure tanks and steel tanks without corrosion protection and once every five years on all other tanks**

   Interior coating in good condition, center columns of tubular design not holding water, center columns not permanently attached to the floor, tanks on ring type foundations with sand in the middle have no voids beneath the floor, heating system components and piping in good condition, and anti-vortex plates in good condition? ❏ Yes ❏ No ❏ N/A

B. Testing

1. **Monthly Tests**

   a. Low water temperature alarms passed test? ❏ Yes ❏ No ❏ N/A

   b. High temperature limit switches on tank heating system passed test? *Only test when heating system is on.* ❏ Yes ❏ No ❏ N/A

2. **Quarterly Test (in addition to above items)**

   b. High water level alarm passed test? ❏ Yes ❏ No ❏ N/A

   c. Low water level alarm passed test? ❏ Yes ❏ No ❏ N/A

3. **Semiannual Test (in addition to above items)**
   Valve supervisory devices indicate movement? ❏ Yes ❏ No ❏ N/A

4. **Annual Test – Before Freezing Weather (in addition to above)**
   Tank heating system in proper working order? ❏ Yes ❏ No ❏ N/A

5. **Interior tests to be performed every third or fifth year with the Internal Inspection of Part II A 7 of this form**

   a. Tank coating passed adhesion, coating thickness, and wet sponge tests? ❏ Yes ❏ No ❏ N/A

   b. Tank walls and bottoms passed ultrasonic test if evidence of pitting or corrosion? ❏ Yes ❏ No ❏ N/A

   c. Flat bottom tanks passed vacuum box test? ❏ Yes ❏ No ❏ N/A

6. **Every Fifth Year Tests**

   a. Level indicators accurate and free to move? ❏ Yes ❏ No ❏ N/A

   b. Gages compared to calibrated gage or replaced? ❏ Yes ❏ No ❏ N/A

C. Maintenance

1. **Semiannual Maintenance**
   Sediment drained or flushed from the tank? ❏ Yes ❏ No ❏ N/A

2. **Annual Maintenance (in addition to above items)**
   Cathodic protection maintained in accordance with manufacturer's instructions, all tank drains fully opened then closed, and tank vents cleaned? ❏ Yes ❏ No ❏ N/A

Part III - Comments *(Any "No" answers, test failures or other problems found with the water storage tank must be explained here).*

_____

_____

_____

_____

_____

_____

Part IV - Inspector's Information

Inspector: _____

Company: _____

Company Address: _____

I state that the information on this form is correct at the time and place of my inspection, and that all equipment tested at this time was left in operational condition upon completion of this inspection except as noted in Part III above.

Signature of Inspector: _____ Date: _____

License or Certification Number (if applicable): _____

© 2002 National Fire Sprinkler Association, P.O. Box 1000, Patterson, NY 12563   (845) 878-4200   Used by Permission   Form 25-22   Sheet 1 of 1

FIGURE B.1(n)   NFSA Form for Inspection, Testing, and Maintenance of Water Storage Tanks.

Form for Inspection, Testing and Maintenance of Water Spray Fixed Systems

NATIONAL
FIRE
SPRINKLER
ASSOCIATION, INC.

Information on this form covers the minimum requirements of **NFPA 25-2002** for water spray fixed systems.
Where the spray system includes a fire pump or water tank, an additional form must be completed for inspection, testing and maintenance of the pump or tank. Forms are also available for fire sprinkler systems, standpipe and hose systems, private fire service mains, and foam-water sprinkler systems.
More frequent inspection, testing and maintenance may be necessary depending on the conditions of the occupancy and the water supply.

Owner: _____ Owner's Phone Number: _____

Owner's Address: _____

Property Being Evaluated: _____

Property Address: _____

Date of Work: _____ All responses refer to the current work (inspection, testing and maintenance) performed on this date.

This inspection is (*check one*): ❏ Daily ❏ Weekly ❏ Monthly ❏ Quarterly ❏ Annual ❏ Fifth Year

Notes: 1) All questions are to be answered *Yes, No,* or *Not Applicable.* All *No* answers are to be explained in the comments portion of this form.
2) Inspection, Testing and Maintenance are to be performed with water supplies (including fire pumps) in service, unless the impairment procedures of Chapter 11 of NFPA 25 are followed.

Part I - Owner's Section

Note: Periodic inspection and testing of detection systems must be performed in accordance with NFPA 72E by a qualified alarm contractor.

A. Has the hazard being protected remained the same since the last inspection?   ❏ Yes ❏ No ❏ N/A

B. Are all fire protection systems in service?   ❏ Yes ❏ No ❏ N/A

C. Has the system remained in service without modification since the last inspection?   ❏ Yes ❏ No ❏ N/A

D. Was the system free of actuations of devices or alarms since the last inspection?   ❏ Yes ❏ No ❏ N/A

_____
Owner or representative (print name)   Signature and Date

Part II - Inspector's Section

A. Inspections

1. Daily Inspection Item

Deluge valve enclosures (without low temperature alarms) maintained at 40°F?   ❏ Yes ❏ No ❏ N/A

2. Weekly Items (in addition to above item)

A. Sealed control valves and valves on backflow assemblies

In normal (open or closed) position, seals in place, accessible and free from external leaks and provided with appropriate identification?   ❏ Yes ❏ No ❏ N/A

B. Relief port on reduced pressure backflow prevention assemblies free of continuous discharge?   ❏ Yes ❏ No ❏ N/A

C. Gages on system in good condition and showing normal water pressure?   ❏ Yes ❏ No ❏ N/A

3. Monthly Items (in addition to above items)

A. Deluge Valves:

Enclosures (with low temperature alarms) maintained at 40°F, free from physical damage, trim valves in appropriate condition, and electrical components in service?   ❏ Yes ❏ No ❏ N/A

B. Low point drains are in good condition?   ❏ Yes ❏ No ❏ N/A

C. Rubber gasketed fittings are in proper location? ❏ Yes ❏ No ❏ N/A

D. Water Spray Nozzles:

1. In proper location?   ❏ Yes ❏ No ❏ N/A
2. Aimed in proper direction?   ❏ Yes ❏ No ❏ N/A
3. Free from external loading and corrosion?   ❏ Yes ❏ No ❏ N/A
4. Capped or plugged (when required)?   ❏ Yes ❏ No ❏ N/A

E. Control valves and valves on backflow assemblies (with locks or electronic supervision):

1. In normal (open or closed) position?   ❏ Yes ❏ No ❏ N/A
2. Lock or supervision in place?   ❏ Yes ❏ No ❏ N/A
3. Accessible and free from external leaks?   ❏ Yes ❏ No ❏ N/A
4. Provided with appropriate wrenches?   ❏ Yes ❏ No ❏ N/A
5. Provided with appropriate identification?   ❏ Yes ❏ No ❏ N/A

F. Gages in good condition and showing normal pressure?   ❏ Yes ❏ No ❏ N/A

4. Quarterly Items (in addition to above items)

A. Hangers and supports in good condition, secured to structural supports and in proper location?   ❏ Yes ❏ No ❏ N/A

B. Drainage system in good condition?   ❏ Yes ❏ No ❏ N/A

C. Piping and fittings free from mechanical damage, corrosion, and misalignment?   ❏ Yes ❏ No ❏ N/A

B. Testing

1. Quarterly Tests

A. Post indicator valves opened until spring or torsion is felt in the rod, then closed back one-quarter turn?   ❏ Yes ❏ No ❏ N/A

B. Mechanical Water Flow Alarm Test: Bypass connection opened, alarms actuated and flow observed?   ❏ Yes ❏ No ❏ N/A

C. Main drain test for system downstream of backflow or pressure reducing valve:

1. Record static _____ psi and residual _____ psi pressures.
2. Was flow observed?   ❏ Yes ❏ No ❏ N/A
3. Pressures comparable to those from last test? ❏ Yes ❏ No ❏ N/A

2. Semiannual Tests (in addition to above items)

A. Valve supervisory devices indicate movement?   ❏ Yes ❏ No ❏ N/A

B. Electrical Water Flow Alarm Test: Bypass connection opened, alarms actuated and flow observed?   ❏ Yes ❏ No ❏ N/A

3. Annual Tests (in addition to above items)

A. System Main Drain Test:

1. Record static _____ psi and residual _____ psi pressures.
2. Was flow observed?   ❏ Yes ❏ No ❏ N/A
3. Pressures comparable to those from last test?   ❏ Yes ❏ No ❏ N/A

B. Operational Test: (Test all systems together which will operate simultaneously)

1. Record response time _____ and discharge time _____ .
2. Record pressure at most remote nozzle _____ psi.
3. Record pressure at deluge valve _____ psi.
4. Nozzle discharge was not impeded, area of operation was totally covered, and strainers were cleaned after the test?   ❏ Yes ❏ No ❏ N/A
5. Are above pressures and times acceptable?   ❏ Yes ❏ No ❏ N/A
6. Connection to riser flushed?   ❏ Yes ❏ No ❏ N/A

C. Manual actuation devices operated properly?   ❏ Yes ❏ No ❏ N/A

D. Control valves operated through full range and returned to normal position?   ❏ Yes ❏ No ❏ N/A

E. Backflow devices passed backflow test?   ❏ Yes ❏ No ❏ N/A

F. Backflow devices passed full flow test?   ❏ Yes ❏ No ❏ N/A

G. Pressure reducing valves passed partial flow test? ❏ Yes ❏ No ❏ N/A

4. Fifth Year Tests (in addition to above items)

A. Gages tested against calibrated one or replaced? ❏ Yes ❏ No ❏ N/A

B. Pressure reducing valves passed full flow test? ❏ Yes ❏ No ❏ N/A

SAMPLE

© 2002 National Fire Sprinkler Association, P.O. Box 1000, Patterson, NY 12563   (845) 878-4200   Used by Permission   Form 25-15   Sheet 1 of 2

FIGURE B.1(o)   NFSA Form for Inspection, Testing, and Maintenance of Water Spray Fixed Systems.

C. Maintenance

1. Regular Maintenance Items

A. Mainline strainers flushed after each flow
   or test?   ❏ Yes ❏ No ❏ N/A

B. If any of the following were discovered, was an
   obstruction investigation conducted?   ❏ Yes ❏ No ❏ N/A

   1. Defective intake screen for pumps taking suction from open sources.

   2. Obstructive material discharged during waterflow tests.

   3. Foreign materials found in check valves or pumps.

   4. Heavy discoloration of water during drain test or plugging of
      inspector's test connection or pipe dismantled during alterations.

   5. Failure to flush yard piping or surrounding public mains
      following new installation or repairs.

   6. Record of broken mains in the vicinity.

   7. System is returned to service after an extended period out of
      service (greater than one year).

   8. There is reason to believe the system contains sodium silicate
      or its derivatives.

2. Annual Maintenance Items (in addition to above items)

A. Operating stems of OS&Y valves lubricated,
   completely closed and reopened?   ❏ Yes ❏ No ❏ N/A
B. Interior of deluge valves thoroughly cleaned? ❏ Yes ❏ No ❏ N/A

3. Fifth Year Maintenance Item (in addition to above items)

Mainline strainers removed and cleaned?   ❏ Yes ❏ No ❏ N/A

D. Fire Department Connections:

   Visible, accessible, couplings and swivels not damaged and
   rotate smoothly, plugs or caps in place and undamaged,
   gaskets in place and in good condition, identification sign(s)
   in place, check valve is not leaking, clapper is in place and
   operating properly and automatic drain valve in place and
   operating properly?   ❏ Yes ❏ No ❏ N/A

   (If plugs or caps are not in place, inspect interior for obstructions.)

5. Annual Item

Interior of deluge valves (which must be open to be reset)
in good condition?   ❏ Yes ❏ No ❏ N/A

6. Fifth Year Items

A. Interior of deluge valves (which can be reset
   without opening) in good condition?   ❏ Yes ❏ No ❏ N/A
B. Strainers, filters and orifices in good condition? ❏ Yes ❏ No ❏ N/A
C. All check valve interiors in good condition? ❏ Yes ❏ No ❏ N/A

Part III - Comments *(Any "No" answers, test failures or other
problems found with the system must be explained here.)*

_____

_____

_____

_____

_____

_____

_____

_____

_____

_____

_____

_____

_____

_____

_____

_____

_____

_____

Part IV - Inspector's Information

Inspector: _____

Company: _____

Company Address: _____

I state that the information on this form is correct at the time and place
of my inspection, and that all equipment tested at this time was left in
operational condition upon completion of this inspection except as noted
in Part III above.

Signature of Inspector: _____ Date: _____

License or Certification Number (if applicable): _____

FIGURE B.1(o) *Continued*

Annex C   Possible Causes of Pump Troubles

*This annex is not a part of the requirements of this NFPA document
but is included for informational purposes only.*

This annex is extracted from NFPA 20, *Standard for the Installation of Stationary Pumps for Fire Protection.*

C.1 Causes of Pump Troubles. This annex contains a partial
guide for locating pump troubles and their possible causes *(see
Figure C.1).* It also contains a partial list of suggested remedies.
*(For other information on this subject, see Hydraulic Institute Stan-
dard for Centrifugal, Rotary and Reciprocating Pumps.)* The causes
listed here are in addition to possible mechanical breakage
that would be obvious on visual inspection. In case of trouble
it is suggested that those troubles that can be checked easily
should be corrected first or eliminated as possibilities.

C.1.1 Air Drawn into Suction Connection Through Leak(s).
Air drawn into suction line through leaks causes a pump to
lose suction or fail to maintain its discharge pressure. Uncover
suction pipe and locate and repair leak(s).

C.1.2 Suction Connection Obstructed. Examine suction intake, screen, and suction pipe and remove obstruction. Repair
or provide screens to prevent recurrence.

C.1.3 Air Pocket in Suction Pipe. Air pockets cause a reduction in delivery and pressure similar to an obstructed pipe.
Uncover suction pipe and rearrange to eliminate pocket.

C.1.4 Well Collapsed or Serious Misalignment. Consult a reliable well drilling company and the pump manufacturer regarding recommended repairs.

**C.1.5 Stuffing Box Too Tight or Packing Improperly In-
stalled, Worn, Defective, Too Tight, or of Incorrect Type.**
Loosen gland swing bolts and remove stuffing box gland
halves. Replace packing.

C.1.6 Water Seal or Pipe to Seal Obstructed. Loosen gland
swing bolt and remove stuffing box gland halves along with
the water seal ring and packing. Clean the water passage to
and in the water seal ring. Replace water seal ring, packing

Backflow Prevention Assembly Test and Maintenance Record

I. General information

Address:

Location of assembly	Date of installation	Incoming line pressure
Manufacturer	Model no.	Serial number
Size	Assembly type ☐ RP ☐ RP detector ☐ DC detector ☐ PVB	

II. Tests and repairs information

	Check valve no. 1	Check valve no. 2	Differential pressure relief valve
Initial test	☐ Leaked ☐ Closed tight Pressure drop across the first check valve is _____ psid	☐ Leaked ☐ Closed tight Pressure drop across the second check valve is _____ psid	☐ Opened at _____ psid ☐ Did not open
Repairs	List repairs and corrections	List repairs and corrections	List repairs and corrections
Final test	☐ Closed tight	☐ Closed tight	☐ Opened at _____ psid

Condition of no. 2 control valve: ☐ Closed tight   ☐ Leaked

Remarks: ☐ Assembly failed   ☐ Assembly passed

III. Approvals

"I hearby certify that this data is accurate and reflects the proper operation and maintenance of the assembly and that all control valves were left in the full open position."

Name of certified technician	Technician phone	Name of witness to test	
Signature of certified technician	Technician certification #	Date	Witness phone #

FIGURE B.1(p)   Backflow Prevention Assembly Test and Maintenance Record.

gland, and packing in accordance with manufacturer's instructions.

C.1.7 Air Leak into Pump Through Stuffing Boxes. Same as possible cause C.1.6.

C.1.8 Impeller Obstructed. Does not show on any one instrument, but pressures fall off rapidly when an attempt is made to draw a large amount of water.

For horizontal split-case pumps, remove upper case of pump and remove obstruction from impeller. Repair or provide screens on suction intake to prevent recurrence.

For vertical shaft turbine-type pumps, lift out column pipe and pump bowls from wet pit or well and disassemble pump bowl to remove obstruction from impeller.

For close-coupled, vertical in-line pumps, lift motor on top pull-out design and remove obstruction from impeller.

C.1.9 Wearing Rings Worn. Remove upper case and insert feeler gauge between case wearing ring and impeller wearing ring. Clearance when new is 0.19 mm (0.0075 in.). Clearances of more than 0.38 mm (0.015 in.) are excessive.

C.1.10 Impeller Damaged. Make minor repairs or return to manufacturer for replacement. If defect is not too serious, order new impeller and use damaged one until replacement arrives.

C.1.11 Wrong Diameter Impeller. Replace with impeller of proper diameter.

Fire pump troubles	Suction				Pump																Driver and/or Pump					Driver						
	Air drawn into suction connection through leak(s)	Suction connection obstructed	Air pocket in suction pipe	Well collapsed or serious misalignment	Stuffing box too tight or packing improperly installed, worn, defective, too tight, or incorrect type	Water seal or pipe to seal obstructed	Air leak into pump through stuffing boxes	Impeller obstructed	Wearing rings worn	Impeller damaged	Wrong diameter impeller	Actual net head lower than rated	Casing gasket defective permitting internal leakage (single-stage and multistage pumps)	Pressure gauge is on top of pump casing	Incorrect impeller adjustment (vertical shaft turbine-type pump only)	Impellers locked	Pump is frozen	Pump shaft or shaft sleeve scored, bent, or worn	Pump not primed	Seal ring improperly located in stuffing box, preventing water from entering space to form seal	Excess bearing friction due to lack of lubrication, wear, dirt, rusting, failure, or improper installation	Rotating element binds against stationary element	Pump and driver misaligned	Foundation not rigid	Engine-cooling system obstructed	Faulty driver	Lack of lubrication	Speed too low	Wrong direction of rotation	Speed too high	Rated motor voltage different from line voltage	Faulty electric circuit, obstructed fuel system, obstructed steam pipe, or dead battery
	1	2	3	4	5	6	7	8	9	10	11	12	13	14	15	16	17	18	19	20	21	22	23	24	25	26	27	28	29	30	31	32
Excessive leakage at stuffing box					X													X					X									
Pump or driver overheats				X	X	X		X			X				X			X	X	X	X	X	X	X	X	X			X	X	X	
Pump unit will not start				X	X										X	X	X				X					X	X					X
No water discharge	X	X	X					X									X															
Pump is noisy or vibrates				X	X			X		X								X			X	X	X	X		X						
Too much power required				X	X			X	X		X		X		X			X			X	X	X	X		X			X	X	X	
Discharge pressure not constant for same gpm	X				X	X	X																									
Pump loses suction after starting	X	X	X			X	X													X												
Insufficient water discharge	X	X	X					X	X	X	X	X	X	X	X														X	X		X
Discharge pressure too low for gpm discharge	X	X	X		X	X	X	X	X	X	X	X	X	X															X	X		X

FIGURE C.1 Possible Causes of Fire Pump Troubles.

C.1.12 Actual Net Head Lower than Rated. Check impeller diameter and number and pump model number to make sure correct head curve is being used.

C.1.13 Casing Gasket Defective Permitting Internal Leakage (Single-Stage and Multistage Pumps). Replace defective gasket. Check manufacturer's drawing to see whether gasket is required.

C.1.14 Pressure Gauge Is on Top of Pump Casing. Place gauges in correct location.

C.1.15 Incorrect Impeller Adjustment (Vertical Shaft Turbine-Type Pump Only). Adjust impellers according to manufacturer's instructions.

C.1.16 Impellers Locked. For vertical shaft turbine-type pumps, raise and lower impellers by the top shaft adjusting nut. If this adjustment is not successful, follow the manufacturer's instructions.

For horizontal split-case pumps, remove upper case and locate and eliminate obstruction.

C.1.17 Pump Is Frozen. Provide heat in the pump room. Disassemble pump and remove ice as necessary. Examine parts carefully for damage.

C.1.18 Pump Shaft or Shaft Sleeve Scored, Bent, or Worn. Replace shaft or shaft sleeve.

C.1.19 Pump Not Primed. If a pump is operated without water in its casing, the wearing rings are likely to seize. The first warning is a change in pitch of the sound of the driver. Shut down the pump.

For vertical shaft turbine-type pumps, check water level to determine whether pump bowls have proper submergence.

C.1.20 Seal Ring Improperly Located in Stuffing Box, Preventing Water from Entering Space to Form Seal. Loosen gland swing bolt and remove stuffing box gland halves along with the water-seal ring and packing. Replace, putting seal ring in proper location.

C.1.21 Excess Bearing Friction Due to Lack of Lubrication, Wear, Dirt, Rusting, Failure, or Improper Installation. Remove bearings and clean, lubricate, or replace as necessary.

C.1.22 Rotating Element Binds Against Stationary Element. Check clearances and lubrication and replace or repair the defective part.

C.1.23 Pump and Driver Misaligned. Shaft running off center because of worn bearings or misalignment. Align pump and driver according to manufacturer's instructions. Replace bearings according to manufacturer's instructions.

C.1.24 Foundation Not Rigid. Tighten foundation bolts or replace foundation if necessary.

C.1.25 Engine-Cooling System Obstructed. Heat exchanger or cooling water systems too small. Cooling pump faulty. Remove thermostats. Open bypass around regulator valve and strainer. Check regulator valve operation. Check strainer. Clean and repair if necessary. Disconnect sections of cooling system to locate and remove possible obstruction. Adjust engine-cooling water-circulating pump belt to obtain proper speed without binding. Lubricate bearings of this pump.

If overheating still occurs at loads up to 150 percent of rated capacity, contact pump or engine manufacturer so that necessary steps can be taken to eliminate overheating.

C.1.26 Faulty Driver. Check electric motor, internal combustion engine, or steam turbine, in accordance with manufacturer's instructions, to locate reason for failure to start.

C.1.27 Lack of Lubrication. If parts have seized, replace damaged parts and provide proper lubrication. If not, stop pump and provide proper lubrication.

C.1.28 Speed Too Low. For electric motor drive, check that rated motor speed corresponds to rated speed of pump, voltage is correct, and starting equipment is operating properly.

Low frequency and low voltage in the electric power supply prevent a motor from running at rated speed. Low voltage can be due to excessive loads and inadequate feeder capacity or (with private generating plants) low generator voltage. The generator voltage of private generating plants can be corrected by changing the field excitation. When low voltage is from the other causes mentioned, it can be necessary to change transformer taps or increase feeder capacity.

Low frequency usually occurs with a private generating plant and should be corrected at the source. Low speed can result in older type squirrel-cage-type motors if fastenings of copper bars to end rings become loose. The remedy is to weld or braze these joints.

For steam turbine drive, check that valves in steam supply pipe are wide open; boiler steam pressure is adequate; steam pressure is adequate at the turbine; strainer in the steam supply pipe is not plugged; steam supply pipe is of adequate size; condensate is removed from steam supply pipe, trap, and turbine; turbine nozzles are not plugged; and setting of speed and emergency governor is correct.

For internal combustion engine drive, check that setting of speed governor is correct; hand throttle is opened wide; and there are no mechanical defects such as sticking valves, timing off, or spark plugs fouled, and so forth. The latter can require the services of a trained mechanic.

C.1.29 Wrong Direction of Rotation. Instances of an impeller turning backward are rare but are clearly recognizable by the extreme deficiency of pump delivery. Wrong direction of rotation can be determined by comparing the direction in which the flexible coupling is turning with the directional arrow on the pump casing.

With polyphase electric motor drive, two wires must be reversed; with dc driver, the armature connections must be reversed with respect to the field connections. Where two sources of electrical current are available, the direction of rotation produced by each should be checked.

C.1.30 Speed Too High. See that pump- and driver-rated speed correspond. Replace electric motor with one of correct rated speed. Set governors of variable-speed drivers for correct speed. Frequency at private generating stations can be too high.

C.1.31 Rated Motor Voltage Different from Line Voltage. For example, a 220- or 440-V motor on 208- or 416-V line. Obtain motor of correct rated voltage or larger size motor.

C.1.32 Faulty Electric Circuit, Obstructed Fuel System, Obstructed Steam Pipe, or Dead Battery. Check for break in wiring open switch, open circuit breaker, or dead battery. If circuit breaker in controller trips for no apparent reason, make sure oil is in dash pots in accordance with manufacturer's specifications. Make sure fuel pipe is clear, strainers are clean, and control valves open in fuel system to internal combustion engine. Make sure all valves are open and strainer is clean in steam line to turbine.

C.2 Warning. Chapters 6 and 7 of NFPA 20, *Standard for the Installation of Stationary Pumps for Fire Protection*, include electrical requirements that discourage the installation of disconnect means in the power supply to electric motor–driven fire pumps. This requirement is intended to ensure the availability of power to the fire pumps. When equipment connected to those circuits is serviced or maintained, the employee can have unusual exposure to electrical and other hazards. It can be necessary to require special safe work practices and special safeguards, personal protective clothing, or both.

C.3 Maintenance of Fire Pump Controllers After a Fault Condition.

C.3.1 Introduction. In a fire pump motor circuit that has been properly installed, coordinated, and in service prior to the fault, tripping of the circuit breaker or the isolating switch indicates a fault condition in excess of operating overload.

It is recommended that the following general procedures be observed by qualified personnel in the inspection and repair of the controller involved in the fault. These procedures are not intended to cover other elements of the circuit, such as wiring and motor, which can also require attention.

C.3.2 Caution. All inspections and tests are to be made on controllers that are de-energized at the line terminal, disconnected, locked out, and tagged so that accidental contact cannot be made with live parts and so that all plant safety procedures will be observed.

C.3.2.1 Enclosure. Where substantial damage to the enclosure, such as deformation, displacement of parts, or burning has occurred, replace the entire controller.

C.3.2.2 Circuit Breaker and Isolating Switch. Examine the enclosure interior, circuit breaker, and isolating switch for evidence of possible damage. If evidence of damage is not apparent, the circuit breaker and isolating switch can continue to be used after closing the door.

If there is any indication that the circuit breaker has opened several short-circuit faults, or if signs of possible deterioration appear within either the enclosure, circuit breaker, or isolating switch (e.g., deposits on surface, surface discoloration, insulation cracking, or unusual toggle operation), replace the components. Verify that the external operating handle is capable of opening and closing the circuit breaker and isolating switch. If the handle fails to operate the device, this would also indicate the need for adjustment or replacement.

C.3.2.3 Terminals and Internal Conductors. Where there are indications of arcing damage, overheating, or both, such as discoloration and melting of insulation, replace the damaged parts.

C.3.2.4 Contactor. Replace contacts showing heat damage, displacement of metal, or loss of adequate wear allowance of the contacts. Replace the contact springs where applicable. If deterioration extends beyond the contacts, such as binding in the guides or evidence of insulation damage, replace the damaged parts or the entire contactor.

C.3.2.5 Return to Service. Before returning the controller to service, check for the tightness of electrical connections and for the absence of short circuits, ground faults, and leakage current.

Close and secure the enclosure before the controller circuit breaker and isolating switch are energized. Follow operating procedures on the controller to bring it into standby condition.

Annex D   Obstruction Investigation

This annex is not a part of the requirements of this NFPA document but is included for informational purposes only.

D.1 For effective control and extinguishment of fire, automatic sprinklers should receive an unobstructed flow of water. Although the overall performance record of automatic sprinklers has been very satisfactory, there have been numerous instances of impaired efficiency because sprinkler piping or sprinklers were plugged with pipe scale, corrosion products, including those produced by microbiologically influenced corrosion, mud, stones, or other foreign material. If the first sprinklers to open in a fire are plugged, the fire in that area cannot be extinguished or controlled by prewetting of adjacent combustibles. In such a situation, the fire can grow to an uncontrollable size, resulting in greater fire damage and excessive sprinkler operation and even threatening the structural integrity of the building, depending on the number of plugged sprinklers and fire severity.

Keeping the inside of sprinkler system piping free of scale, silt, or other obstructing material is an integral part of an effective loss prevention program.

D.2 Obstruction Sources.

D.2.1 Pipe Scale. Loss studies have shown that dry pipe sprinkler systems are involved in the majority of obstructed sprinkler fire losses. Pipe scale was found to be the most frequent obstructing material (it is likely that some of the scale was composed of corrosion products, including those produced by microbiologically influenced corrosion). Dry pipe systems that have been maintained wet and then dry alternately over a period of years are particularly susceptible to the accumulation of scale. Also, in systems that are continuously dry, condensation of moisture in the air supply can result in the formation of a hard scale, microbiological materials, and corrosion products along the bottom of the piping. When sprinklers open, the scale is broken loose and carried along the pipe, plugging some of the sprinklers or forming obstructions at the fittings.

D.2.2 Careless Installation or Repair. Many obstructions are caused by careless workers during installation or repair of yard or public mains and sprinkler systems. Wood, paint brushes, buckets, gravel, sand, and gloves have been found as obstructions. In some instances, with welded sprinkler systems and systems with holes for quick-connect fittings, the cutout discs or coupons have been left within the piping, obstructing flow to sprinklers.

D.2.3 Raw Water Sources. Materials can be sucked up from the bottoms of rivers, ponds, or open reservoirs by fire pumps with poorly arranged or inadequately screened intakes and then forced into the system. Sometimes floods damage intakes. Obstructions include fine, compacted materials such as rust, mud, and sand. Coarse materials, such as stones, cinders, cast-iron tubercles, chips of wood, and sticks, also are common.

D.2.4 Biological Growth. Biological growth has been known to cause obstructions in sprinkler piping. The Asiatic clam has been found in fire protection systems supplied by raw river or lake water. With an available food supply and sunlight, these clams grow to approximately 9 mm to 11 mm (⅜ in. to ⁷⁄₁₆ in.) across the shell in 1 year and up to 54 mm (2⅛ in.) and larger by the sixth year. However, once in fire mains and sprinkler piping, the growth rate is much slower. The clams get into the fire protection systems in the larval stage or while still small clams. They then attach themselves to the pipe and feed on bacteria or algae that pass through.

Originally brought to Washington state from Asia in the 1930s, the clams have spread throughout at least 33 states and possibly are present in every state. River areas reported to be highly infested include the Ohio River, Tennessee River Valley, Savannah River (S. Carolina), Altamaha River (Georgia), Columbia River (Washington), and Delta-Mendota Canal (California).

D.2.5 Sprinkler Calcium Carbonate Deposits. Natural fresh waters contain dissolved calcium and magnesium salts in varying concentrations, depending on the sources and location of the water. If the concentration of these salts is high, the water is considered hard. A thin film composed largely of calcium carbonate, $CaCO_3$, affords some protection against corrosion where hard water flows through the pipes. However, hardness is not the only factor to determine whether a film forms. The ability of $CaCO_3$ to precipitate on the metal pipe surface also depends on the water's total acidity or alkalinity, the concentration of dissolved solids in the water, and its pH. In soft water, no such film can form.

In automatic sprinkler systems, the calcium carbonate scale formation tends to occur on the more noble metal in the electrochemical series, which is copper, just as corrosion affects the less noble metal, iron. Consequently, scale formation naturally forms on sprinklers, often plugging the orifice. The piping itself could be relatively clear. This type of sprinkler obstruction cannot be detected or corrected by normal flushing procedures. It can only be found by inspection of sprinklers in suspected areas and then removed.

Most public water utilities in very hard water areas soften their water to reduce consumer complaints of scale buildup in water heaters. Thus, the most likely locations for deposits in sprinkler systems are where sprinklers are not connected to public water but supplied without treatment directly from wells or surface water in areas that have very hard water. These areas generally include the Mississippi basin west of the Mississippi River and north of the Ohio River, the rivers of Texas and the Colorado basin, and other white areas in Figure D.2.5(a). (The water of the Great Lakes is only moderately hard.)

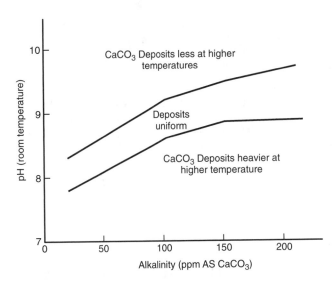

FIGURE D.2.5(b)   Scale Deposition as a Function of the Alkalinity/pH Ratio.

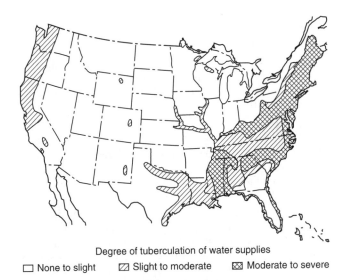

Degree of tuberculation of water supplies

☐ None to slight   ▨ Slight to moderate   ⊠ Moderate to severe

FIGURE D.2.5(a)   Map of Hard Water Areas. *(Courtesy of Cast Iron Pipe Research Association.)*

Within individual plants, the sprinklers most likely to have deposits are located as follows:

(1) In wet systems only.
(2) In high temperature areas, except where water has unusually high pH *[see Figure D.2.5(b)]*. High temperature areas include those near dryers, ovens, and skylights or at roof peaks.
(3) In old sprinkler systems that are frequently drained and refilled.
(4) In pendent sprinklers that are located away from air pockets and near convection currents.

D.2.6 Microbiologically Influenced Corrosion (MIC). The most common biological growths in sprinkler system piping are those formed by microorganisms, including bacteria and fungi. These microbes produce colonies (also called biofilms, slimes) containing a variety of types of microbes. Colonies form on the surface of wetted pipe in both wet and dry systems. Microbes also deposit iron, manganese, and various salts onto the pipe surface, forming discrete deposits (also termed

nodules, tubercles, and carbuncles). These deposits can cause obstruction to flow and dislodge causing plugging of fire sprinkler components. Subsequent under-deposit pitting can also result in pinhole leaks.

Microbiologically influenced corrosion (MIC) is corrosion influenced by the presence and activities of microorganisms. MIC almost always occurs with other forms of corrosion (oxygen corrosion, crevice corrosion, and under-deposit corrosion). MIC starts as microbial communities (also called biofilms, slimes) growing on the interior surface of the wetted sprinkler piping components in both wet and dry systems. The microbial communities contain many types of microbes, including slime formers, acid-producing bacteria, iron-depositing bacteria, and sulfate-reducing bacteria, and are most often introduced into the sprinkler system from the water source. The microbes deposit iron, manganese, and various salts onto the pipe surface, forming discrete deposits (also termed nodules, tubercles, and carbuncles). These deposits can cause obstruction to flow and dislodge, causing plugging of fire sprinkler components. MIC is most often seen as severe pitting corrosion occurring under deposits. Pitting is due to microbial activities such as acid production, oxygen consumption, and accumulation of salts. Oxygen and salts, especially chloride, can greatly increase the severity of MIC and other forms of corrosion.

In steel pipe, MIC is most often seen as deposits on the interior surface of the pipes. The deposits may be orange, red, brown, black, and white (or combinations thereof), depending on local conditions and water chemistry. The brown, orange, and red forms are most common in oxygenated portions of the system and often contain oxidized forms of iron and other materials on the outside, with reduced (blacker) corrosion products on the inside. Black deposits are most often in smaller diameter piping farther from the water source and contain reduced forms (those with less oxygen) of corrosion products. White deposits often contain carbonate scales.

MIC of copper and copper alloys occurs as discrete deposits of smaller size, which are green to blue in color. Blue slimes may also be produced in copper piping or copper components (e.g., brass heads).

MIC is often first noticed as a result of pinhole leaks after only months to a few years of service. Initial tests for the presence of MIC should involve on-site testing for microbes and chemical species (iron, pH, oxygen) important in MIC. This information is also very important in choosing treatment methods. These tests can be done on water samples from source waters and various locations in the sprinkler system (e.g., main drain, inspector's test valve). Confirmation of MIC can be made by examination of interior of pipes for deposits and under-deposit corrosion with pit morphology consistent with MIC (cup-like pits within pits and striations).

The occurrence and severity of MIC is enhanced by the following:

(1) Using untreated water to test and fill sprinkler piping. This is made worse by leaving the water in the system for long periods of time.
(2) Introduction of new and untreated water containing oxygen, microbes, salts, and nutrients into the system on a frequent basis (during repair, renovation, and/or frequent flow tests).
(3) Leaving dirt, debris, and especially oils, pipe joint compound, and so forth in the piping. These provide nutrients and protection for the microbes, often preventing biocides and corrosion inhibitors from reaching the microbes and corrosion sites.

Once the presence of MIC has been confirmed, the system should be assessed to determine the extent and severity of MIC. Severely affected portions should be replaced or cleaned to remove obstructions and pipe not meeting minimal mechanical specifications.

D.3 Investigation Procedures. If unsatisfactory conditions are observed as outlined in Section 13.2, investigations should be made to determine the extent and severity of the obstructing material. From the fire protection system plan, determine the water supply sources, age of underground mains and sprinkler systems, types of systems, and general piping arrangement. Consider the possible sources of obstruction material.

Examine the fire pump suction supply and screening arrangements. If necessary, have the suction cleaned before using the pump in tests and flushing operations. Gravity tanks should be inspected internally with the exception of steel tanks that have been recently cleaned and painted. If possible, have the tank drained and determine whether loose scale is on the shell or if sludge or other obstructions are on the tank bottom. Cleaning and repainting could be in order, particularly if it has not been done within the previous 5 years.

Investigate yard mains first, then sprinkler systems.

Where fire protection control valves are closed during investigation procedures, the fire protection impairment precautions outlined in Chapter 14 should be followed.

Large quantities of water are needed for investigation and for flushing. It is important to plan the safest means of disposal in advance. Cover stock and machinery susceptible to water damage and keep equipment on hand for mopping up any accidental discharge of water.

D.3.1 Investigating Yard Mains. Flow water through yard hydrants, preferably near the extremes of selected mains, to determine whether mains contain obstructive material. It is preferable to connect two lengths of 65-mm (2½-in.) hose to the hydrant. Attach burlap bags to the free ends of the hose from which the nozzles have been removed to collect any material flushed out, and flow water long enough to determine the condition of the main being investigated. If there are several water supply sources, investigate each independently, avoiding any unnecessary interruptions to sprinkler protection. In extensive yard layouts, repeat the tests at several locations, if necessary, to determine general conditions.

If obstructive material is found, all mains should be flushed thoroughly before investigating the sprinkler systems. *(See D.5.)*

D.3.2 Investigating Sprinkler Systems. Investigate dry systems first. Tests on several carefully selected, representative systems usually are sufficient to indicate general conditions throughout the plant. If, however, preliminary investigations indicate the presence of obstructing material, this justifies investigating all systems (both wet and dry) before outlining needed flushing operations. Generally, the system can be considered reasonably free of obstructing material, provided the following conditions apply:

(1) Less than ½ cup of scale is washed from the cross mains.
(2) Scale fragments are not large enough to plug a sprinkler orifice.
(3) A full, unobstructed flow is obtained from each branch line checked.

Where other types of foreign material are found, judgment should be used before considering the system unobstructed. Obstruction potential is based on the physical characteristics and source of the foreign material.

In selecting specific systems or branch lines for investigation, the following should be considered:

(1) Lines found obstructed during a fire or during maintenance work
(2) Systems adjacent to points of recent repair to yard mains, particularly if hydrant flow shows material in the main

Tests should include flows through 65-mm (2½-in.) fire hose directly from cross mains *[see Figure D.3.2(a) and Figure D.3.2(b)]* and flows through 40-mm (1½-in.) hose from representative branch lines. Two or three branch lines per system is a representative number of branch lines where investigating for scale accumulation. If significant scale is found, investigation of additional branch lines is warranted. Where investigating for foreign material (other than scale), the number of branch lines needed for representative sampling is dependent on the source and characteristic of the foreign material.

If provided, fire pumps should be operated for the large line flows, since maximum flow is desirable. Burlap bags should be used to collect dislodged material as is done in the investigation of yard mains. Each flow should be continued until the water clears (i.e., a minimum of 2 to 3 minutes at full flow for sprinkler mains). This is likely to be sufficient to indicate the condition of the piping interior.

D.3.3 Investigating Dry Pipe Systems. Flood dry pipe systems one or two days before obstruction investigations to soften pipe scale and deposits. After selecting the test points of a dry pipe system, close the main control valve and drain the system. Check the piping visually with a flashlight while it is being dismantled. Attach hose valves and 40-mm (1½-in.) hose to the ends of the lines to be tested, shut the valves, have air pressure restored on the system, and reopen the control valve. Open the hose valve on the end branch line, allowing the system to trip in simulation of normal action. Any obstructions should be cleared from the branch line before proceeding with further tests.

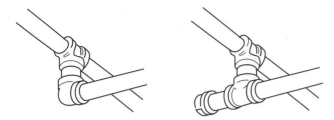

FIGURE D.3.2(a)   Replacement of Elbow at End of Cross Main with a Flushing Connection Consisting of a 50-mm (2-in.) Nipple and Cap.

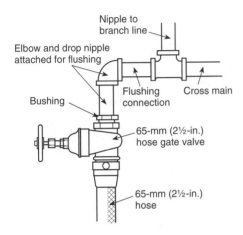

FIGURE D.3.2(b)   Connection of 65-mm (2½-in.) Hose Gate Valve with a 50-mm (2-in.) Bushing and Nipple and Elbow to 50-mm (2-in.) Cross Main.

After flowing the small end line, shut its hose valve and test the feed or cross main by discharging water through a 65-mm (2½-in.) fire hose, collecting any foreign material in a burlap bag.

After the test, the dry pipe valve should be cleaned internally and reset. Its control valve should be locked open and a drain test performed.

D.3.4   Investigating Wet Pipe Systems. Testing of wet systems is similar to that of dry systems, except that the system should be drained after closing the control valve to permit installation of hose valves for the test. Slowly reopen the control valve and make a small hose flow as specified for the branch line, followed by the 65-mm (2½-in.) hose flow for the cross main.

In any case, if lines become plugged during the tests, piping should be dismantled and cleaned, the extent of plugging noted, and a clear flow obtained from the branch line before proceeding further.

Perform similar tests on representative systems to indicate the general condition of the wet systems throughout the plant, keeping a detailed record of the procedures performed.

D.3.5   Other Obstruction Investigation Methods. Other obstruction investigation methods, such as technically proven ultrasonic and X-ray examination, have been evaluated and if applied correctly, are successful at detecting obstructions.

The sources of the obstructing material should be determined and steps taken to prevent further entrance of such material. This entails work such as inspection and cleaning of pump suction screening facilities or cleaning of private reservoirs. If recently laid public mains appear to be the source of the obstructing material, waterworks authorities should be requested to flush their system.

D.4   Obstruction Prevention Program.

D.4.1   Dry Pipe and Preaction Systems — Scale.

(1) Dry pipe and preaction systems using noncoated ferrous piping should be thoroughly investigated for obstruction from corrosion after they have been in service for 15 years, 25 years, and every 5 years thereafter.
(2) Dry pipe systems with noncoated ferrous piping should be kept on air year-round, rather than on air and water alternately, to inhibit formation of rust and scale.
(3) Piping that has been galvanized internally for new dry pipe and preaction sprinkler system installations should be used. Fittings, couplings, hangers, and other appurtenances are not required to be galvanized. Copper or stainless steel piping also is permitted.

D.4.2   Flushing Connections. Sprinkler systems installed in accordance with recent editions of NFPA 13, *Standard for the Installation of Sprinkler Systems*, should have provisions for flushing each cross main. Similarly, branch lines on gridded systems should be capable of being readily "broken" at a simple union or flexible joint. Owners of systems installed without these provisions should be encouraged to provide them when replacement or repair work is being done.

D.4.3   Suction Supplies.

(1) Screen pump suction supplies and screens should be maintained. Connections from penstocks should be equipped with strainers or grids, unless the penstock inlets themselves are so equipped. Pump suction screens of copper or brass wire tend to promote less aquatic growth.
(2) Extreme care should be used to prevent material from entering the suction piping when cleaning tanks and open reservoirs. Materials removed from the interior of gravity tanks during cleaning should not be allowed to enter the discharge pipe.
(3) Small mill ponds could need periodic dredging where weeds and other aquatic growth are inherent.

D.4.4   Asian Clams. Effective screening of larvae and small-size, juvenile Asian clams from fire protection systems is very difficult. To date, no effective method of total control has been found. Such controls can be difficult to achieve in fire protection systems.

D.4.5   Calcium Carbonate. For localities suspected of having hard water, sample sprinklers should be removed and inspected yearly. Section D.2.5 outlines sprinkler locations prone to the accumulation of deposits where hard water is a problem. Sprinklers found with deposits should be replaced and adjacent sprinklers should be checked.

D.4.6   Zebra Mussels. Several means of controlling the zebra mussel are being studied, including molluscides, chlorines, ozone, shell strainers, manual removal, robotic cleaning, water jetting, line pigging, sonic pulses, high-voltage electrical fields, and thermal backwashing. It is believed that these controls might need to be applied only during spawning periods when water temperatures are 14°C to 16°C (57°F to 61°F) and veligers are present. Several silicon grease-based coatings also are being investigated for use within piping systems.

While it appears that the use of molluscides could provide the most effective means of controlling the mussel, these chemicals are costly. It is believed that chlorination is the best available short-term treatment, but there are problems associated with the use of chlorine, including strict Environmental Protection Agency regulations on the release of chlorine into lakes and streams. The use of nonselective poison, such as chlorine, in the amounts necessary to kill the mussels in large bodies of water could be devastating to entire ecosystems.

To provide an effective means of control against zebra mussels in fire protection systems, control measures should be applied at the water source, instead of within the piping system. Effective controls for growth of the zebra mussel within fire protection systems include the following:

(1) Selecting a water source that is not subject to infestation. This could include well water or potable or pretreated water.
(2) Implementing a water treatment program that includes biocides or elevated pH, or both.
(3) Implementing a water treatment program to remove oxygen, which ensures control of biological growth within piping.
(4) Relying on a tight system approach to deny oxygen and nutrients that are necessary to support growth.

D.5 Flushing Procedures.

D.5.1 Yard Mains. Yard mains should be flushed thoroughly before flushing any interior piping. Flush yard piping through hydrants at dead ends of the system or through blow-off valves, allowing the water to run until clear. If the water is supplied from more than one direction or from a looped system, close divisional valves to produce a high-velocity flow through each single line. A velocity of at least 3 m/sec (10 ft/sec) is necessary for scouring the pipe and for lifting foreign material to an aboveground flushing outlet. Use the flow specified in Table D.5.1 or the maximum flow available for the size of the yard main being flushed.

Connections from the yard piping to the sprinkler riser should be flushed. These are usually 6-in. (150-mm) mains. Although flow through a short, open-ended 2-in. (50-mm) drain can create sufficient velocity in a 6-in. (150-mm) main to move small obstructing material, the restricted waterway of the globe valve usually found on a sprinkler drain might not allow stones and other large objects to pass. If the presence of large size material is suspected, a larger outlet is needed to pass such material and to create the flow necessary to move it. Fire department connections on sprinkler risers can be used as flushing outlets by removing the clappers. Yard mains also can be flushed through a temporary Siamese fitting attached to the riser connection before the sprinkler system is installed. *[See Figure D.5.1.]*

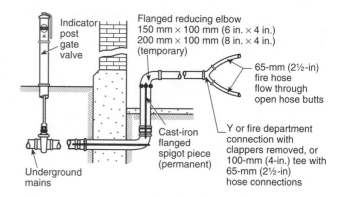

FIGURE D.5.1 Arrangement for Flushing Branches from Underground Mains to Sprinkler Risers.

D.5.2 Sprinkler Piping. Two methods commonly are used for flushing sprinkler piping:

(1) The hydraulic method
(2) The hydropneumatic method

The hydraulic method consists of flowing water from the yard mains, sprinkler risers, feed mains, cross mains, and branch lines, respectively, in the same direction in which water would flow during a fire.

The hydropneumatic method uses special equipment and compressed air to blow a charge of about 114 dm³ (30 gal) of water from the ends of branch lines back into feed mains and down the riser, washing the foreign material out of an opening at the base of the riser.

Table D.5.1 Flushing Rates to Accomplish Flow of 10 ft/sec (3 m/sec)

| Pipe Size | Steel | | | Copper | | | CPVC (gpm) | Polybutylene | |
	SCH 10 (gpm)	SCH 40 (gpm)	XL (gpm)	K (gpm)	L (gpm)	M (gpm)		CTS (gpm)	IPS (gpm)
¾	—	—	—	14	15	16	19	12	17
1	29	24	30	24	26	27	30	20	27
1¼	51	47	52	38	39	41	48	30	43
1½	69	63	70	54	55	57	63	42	57
2	114	105	114	94	96	99	98	72	90
2½	170	149	163	145	149	152	144	—	—
3	260	230	251	207	212	217	213	—	—
4	449	396	—	364	373	379	—	—	—
5	686	623	—	565	582	589	—	—	—
6	989	880	—	807	836	846	—	—	—
8	1665	1560	—	1407	1460	1483	—	—	—
10	2632	2440	—	2185	2267	2303	—	—	—
12	—	3520	—	—	—	—	—	—	—

For SI units: 1 gpm = 3.785 L/min.

The choice of method depends on conditions at the individual plant and the type of material installed. If examination indicates the presence of loose sand, mud, or moderate amounts of pipe scale, the piping generally can be flushed satisfactorily by the hydraulic method. Where the material is more difficult to remove and available water pressures are too low for effective scouring action, the hydropneumatic method generally is more satisfactory. The hydropneumatic method should not be used with listed CPVC sprinkler piping.

In some cases, where obstructive material is solidly packed or adheres tightly to the walls of the piping, the pipe needs to be dismantled and cleaned by rodding or other means.

Dry pipe systems should be flooded one or two days before flushing to soften pipe scale and deposits.

Successful flushing by either the hydraulic or hydropneumatic method is dependent on establishing sufficient velocity of flow in the pipes to remove silt, scale, and other obstructive material. With the hydraulic method, water should be moved through the pipe at least at the rate of flow indicated in Table D.5.1.

Where flushing a branch line through the end pipe, sufficient water should be discharged to scour the largest pipe in the branch line. Lower rates of flow can reduce the efficiency of the flushing operation. To establish the recommended flow, remove the small end piping and connect the hose to a larger section, if necessary.

Where pipe conditions indicate internal or external corrosion, a section of the pipe affected should be cleaned thoroughly to determine whether the walls of the pipe have seriously weakened. Hydrostatic testing should be performed as outlined in NFPA 13, *Standard for the Installation of Sprinkler Systems.*

Pendent sprinklers should be removed and inspected until it is reasonably certain that all are free of obstruction material.

Painting the ends of branch lines and cross mains is a convenient method for keeping a record of those pipes that have been flushed.

D.5.3 Hydraulic Method. After the yard mains have been thoroughly cleaned, flush risers, feed mains, cross mains, and finally the branch lines. In multistory buildings, systems should be flushed by starting at the lowest story and working up. Branch line flushing in any story can immediately follow the flushing of feed and cross mains in that story, allowing one story to be completed at a time. Following this sequence prevents drawing obstructing material into the interior piping.

To flush risers, feed mains, and cross mains, attach 65-mm (2½-in.) hose gate valves to the extreme ends of these lines [*see Figure D.5.3*]. Such valves usually can be procured from the manifold of fire pumps or hose standpipes. As an alternative, an adapter with 65-mm (2½-in.) hose thread and standard pipe thread can be used with a regular gate valve. A length of fire hose without a nozzle should be attached to the flushing connection. To prevent kinking of the hose and to obtain maximum flow, an elbow usually should be installed between the end of the sprinkler pipe and the hose gate valve. Attach the valve and hose so that no excessive strain will be placed on the threaded pipe and fittings. Support hose lines properly.

Where feed and cross mains and risers contain pipe 100 mm, 125 mm, and 150 mm (4 in., 5 in., and 6 in.) in diameter, it could be necessary to use a Siamese with two hose connections to obtain sufficient flow to scour this larger pipe.

Flush branch lines after feed and cross mains have been thoroughly cleared. Equip the ends of several branch lines with gate valves, and flush individual lines of the group con-

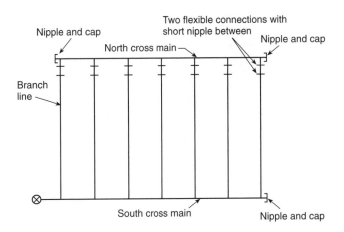

FIGURE D.5.3 Gridded Sprinkler System Piping.

secutively. This eliminates the need for shutting off and draining the sprinkler system to change a single hose line. The hose should be 40 mm (1½ in.) in diameter and as short as practicable. Branch lines can be permitted to be flushed in any order that expedites the work.

Branch lines also may be permitted to be flushed through pipe 40 mm (1½ in.) in diameter or larger while extended through a convenient window. If pipe is used, 45-degree fittings should be provided at the ends of branch lines. Where flushing branch lines, hammering the pipes is an effective method of moving obstructions.

Figure D.5.3 shows a typical gridded piping arrangement prior to flushing. The flushing procedure is as follows:

(1) Disconnect all branch lines and cap all open ends.
(2) Remove the cap from the east end of the south cross main, flush the main, and replace the cap.
(3) Remove the cap from branch line 1, flush the line, and replace the cap.
(4) Repeat step (3) for the remaining branch lines.
(5) Reconnect enough branch lines at the west end of the system so that the aggregate cross-sectional area of the branch lines approximately equals the area of the north cross main. For example, three 32-mm (1¼-in.) branch lines approximately equal a 65-mm (2½-in.) cross main. Remove the cap from the east end of the north cross main, flush the main, and replace the cap.
(6) Disconnect and recap the branch lines. Repeat step (5), but reconnect branch lines at the east end of the system and flush the north cross main through its west end.
(7) Reconnect all branch lines and recap the cross main. Verify that the sprinkler control valve is left in the open and locked position.

D.5.4 Hydropneumatic Method. The apparatus used for hydropneumatic flushing consists of a hydropneumatic machine, a source of water, a source of compressed air, 25-mm (1-in.) rubber hose for connecting to branch lines, and 65-mm (2½-in.) hose for connecting to cross mains.

The hydropneumatic machine [*see Figure D.5.4(a)*] consists of a 114-dm³ (4-ft³) (30-gal) water tank mounted over a 700-dm³ (25-ft³) (185-gal) compressed air tank. The compressed air tank is connected to the top of the water tank through a 50-mm (2-in.) lubricated plug cock. The bottom of the water tank is connected through hose to a suitable water supply. The compressed air tank is connected through suitable air hose to either the plant air system or a separate air compressor.

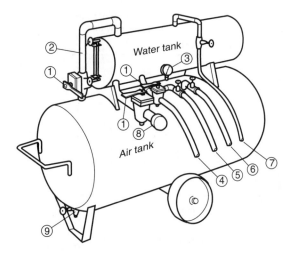

1 Lubricated plug cocks
2 Pipe connection between air and water tanks (This connection is open when flushing sprinkler system.)
3 Air pressure gauge
4 25-mm (1-in.) rubber hose (air type) (Used to flush sprinkler branch lines.)
5 Hose connected to source of water (Used to fill water tank.)
6 Hose connected to ample source of compressed air (Used to supply air tank.)
7 Water tank overflow hose
8 65-mm (2½-in.) pipe connection [Where flushing large interior piping, connect woven jacket fire hose here and close 25-mm (1-in.) plug cock hose connection (4) used for flushing sprinkler branch lines.]
9 Air tank drain valve

FIGURE D.5.4(a) Hydropneumatic Machine.

To flush the sprinkler piping, the water tank is filled with water, the pressure is raised to 6.9 bar (100 psi) in the compressed air tank, and the plug cock between tanks is opened to put air pressure on the water. The water tank is connected by hose to the sprinkler pipe to be flushed. The lubricated plug cock on the discharge outlet at the bottom of the water tank then is snapped open, allowing the water to be "blown" through the hose and sprinkler pipe by the compressed air. The water tank and air tank should be recharged after each blow.

Outlets for discharging water and obstructing material from the sprinkler system should be arranged. With the clappers of dry pipe valves and alarm check valves on their seats and cover plates removed, sheet metal fittings can be used for connection to 65-mm (2½-in.) hose lines or for discharge into a drum [maximum capacity per blow is approximately 114 dm³ (30 gal)]. If the 50-mm (2-in.) riser drain is to be used, the drain valve should be removed and a direct hose connection made. For wet pipe systems with no alarm check valves, the riser should be taken apart just below the drain opening and a plate inserted to prevent foreign material from dropping to the base of the riser. Where dismantling of a section of the riser for this purpose is impractical, the hydropneumatic method should not be used.

Before starting a flushing job, each sprinkler system to be cleaned should be studied and a schematic plan prepared showing the order of the blows.

To determine that the piping is clear after it has been flushed, representative branch lines and cross mains should be investigated, using both visual examination and sample flushings.

(1) *Branch Lines.* With the yard mains already flushed or known to be clear, the sprinkler branch lines should be flushed next. The order of cleaning individual branch lines should be laid out carefully if an effective job is to be done. In general, the branch lines should be flushed starting with the branch closest to the riser and working toward the dead end of the cross main. *[See Figure D.5.4(b).]* The order for flushing the branch lines is shown by the circled numerals. In this example, the southeast quadrant is flushed first, then the southwest, followed by the northeast, and, finally, the northwest. Air hose 25 mm (1 in.) in diameter is used to connect the machine with the end of the branch line being flushed. This hose air pressure should be allowed to drop to 5.9 bar (85 psi) before the valve is closed. The resulting short slug of water experiences less friction loss and a higher velocity and, therefore, cleans more effectively than if the full 114 dm³ (30 gal) of water were to be used. One blow is made for each branch line.

(2) *Large Piping.* Where flushing cross mains, fill the water tank completely and raise the pressure in the air receiver to 6.9 bar (690 kPa) (100 psi). Connect the machine to the end of the cross main to be flushed with no more than 15.2 m (50 ft) of 65-mm (2½-in.) hose. After opening the valve, allow air pressure in the machine to drop to zero (0). Two to six blows are necessary at each location, depending on the size and length of the main. In Figure D.5.4(b), the numerals in squares indicate the location and order of the cross main blows. Since the last branch line blows performed were located west of the riser, clean the cross main located east of the riser first. Where large cross mains are to be cleaned, it is best, if practical, to make one blow at 38, one at 39, the next again at 38, then again at 39, alternating in this manner until the required number of blows has been made at each location.

(3) Where flushing cross mains and feed mains, arrange the work so that the water passes through a minimum of right-angle bends. In Figure D.5.4(b), blows at 38 should be adequate to flush the cross mains back to the riser. Do not attempt to clean the cross main from location A to the riser by backing out branch line 16 and connecting the hose to the open side of the tee. If this were to be done, a considerable portion of the blow would pass northward up the 76-mm (3-in.) line supplying branches 34 to 37, and the portion passing eastward to the riser could be ineffective. Where the size, length, and condition of cross mains necessitate blowing from a location corresponding to location A, the connection should be made directly to the cross main corresponding to the 90-mm (3½-in.) pipe so that the entire flow travels to the riser. Where flushing through a tee, always flush the run of the tee after flushing the branch. Note the location of blows 35, 36, and 37 in Figure D.5.4(b). Gridded systems can be flushed in a similar fashion. With branch lines disconnected and capped, begin flushing the branch line closest to the riser (branch line 1 in Figure D.5.3), working toward the most remote line. Then flush the south cross main in Figure D.5.3 by connecting the hose to the east end. Flushing the north cross main involves connecting the hose to one end while discharging to a safe location from the other end.

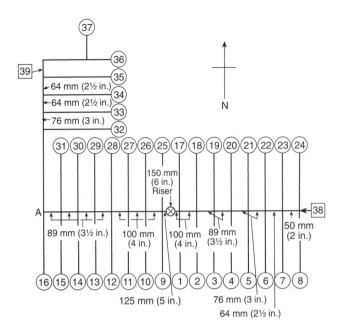

FIGURE D.5.4(b) Schematic Diagram of Sprinkler System Showing Sequence to Be Followed Where Hydropneumatic Method Is to Be Utilized.

Annex E Informational References

E.1 Referenced Publications. The following documents or portions thereof are referenced within this standard for informational purposes only and are thus not part of the requirements of this document unless also listed in Chapter 2.

E.1.1 NFPA Publications. National Fire Protection Association, 1 Batterymarch Park, P.O. Box 9101, Quincy, MA 02269-9101.

NFPA 13, *Standard for the Installation of Sprinkler Systems*, 1999 edition.

NFPA 20, *Standard for the Installation of Stationary Pumps for Fire Protection*, 1999 edition.

NFPA 72®, National Fire Alarm Code®, 1999 edition.

NFPA 780, *Standard for the Installation of Lightning Protection Systems*, 2000 edition.

E.1.2 Other Publications.

E.1.2.1 ASTM Publication. American Society for Testing and Materials, 100 Barr Harbor Drive, West Conshohocken, PA 19428-2959.

ASTM E 380, *Standard for Metric Practice*, 1993.

E.1.2.2 AWWA Publications. American Water Works Association, 6666 West Quincy Avenue, Denver, CO 80235.

AWWA D102, *Standard for Coating Steel Water-Storage Tanks*, 1997.

AWWA, *Manual of Water Supply Practices — M42 Steel Water-Storage Tanks*, 1998.

E.1.2.3 Hydraulic Institute Publication. Hydraulic Institute, 1230 Keith Building, Cleveland, OH 44115.

Hydraulic Institute Standards for Centrifugal, Rotary and Reciprocating Pumps, 14th edition, 1983.

E.1.2.4 SSPC Publication. Society of Protective Coatings, 40 24th Street, Pittsburgh, PA 15222.

Systems and Specifications, Steel Structures Painting Manual, 1999.

E.2 Informational References. The following documents or portions thereof are listed here as informational resources only. They are not a part of the requirements of this document.

E.2.1 NFPA Publication. National Fire Protection Association, 1 Batterymarch Park, P.O. Box 9101, Quincy, MA 02269-9101.

NFPA 230, *Standard for the Fire Protection of Storage*, 1999 edition.

E.2.2 Other Publications.

E.2.2.1 AWWA Publication. American Water Works Association, 6666 West Quincy Avenue, Denver, CO 80235.

AWWA D101, *Inspecting and Repairing Steel Water Tanks, Standpipes, Reservoirs, and Elevated Tanks, for Water Storage*, 1986.

E.2.2.2 SSPC Publications. Society of Protective Coatings, 40 24th Street, Pittsburgh, PA 15222.

SSPC Chapter 3, "Special Pre-Paint Treatments," 1993.

SSPC-PA 1, *Shop, Field, and Maintenance Painting*, 1991.

SSPC Paint 8, *Aluminum Vinyl Paint*, 1991.

SSPC Paint 9, *White (or Colored) Vinyl Paint*, 1995.

SSPC-SP 6, *Commercial Blast Cleaning*, 1994.

SSPC-SP 8, *Pickling*, 1991.

SSPC-SP 10, *Near-White Blast Cleaning*, 1994.

E.2.2.3 U.S. Government Publications. U.S. Government Printing Office, Washington, DC 20402.

Bureau of Reclamation Specification VR-3.

Federal Specification TT- P-86, *Specifications for Vinyl Resin Paint*, M-54, 1995.

E.3 References for Extracts. The following documents are listed here to provide reference information, including title and edition, for extracts given throughout this standard as indicated by a reference in brackets [ ] following a section or paragraph. These documents are not a part of the requirements of this document unless also listed in Chapter 2 for other reasons.

NFPA 13, *Standard for the Installation of Sprinkler Systems*, 1999 edition.

NFPA 14, *Standard for the Installation of Standpipe, Private Hydrant, and Hose Systems*, 2000 edition.

NFPA 16, *Standard for the Installation of Foam-Water Sprinkler and Foam-Water Spray Systems*, 1999 edition.

NFPA 20, *Standard for the Installation of Stationary Pumps for Fire Protection*, 1999 edition.

NFPA 820, *Standard for Fire Protection in Wastewater Treatment and Collection Facilities*, 1999 edition.

NFPA 1141, *Standard for Fire Protection in Planned Building Groups*, 1998 edition.

Index

Sequence of Events Leading to Publication of an NFPA Committee Document

Call goes out for proposals to amend existing document or for recommendations on new document.

Committee meets to act on proposals, to develop its own proposals, and to prepare its report.

Committee votes on proposals by letter ballot. If two-thirds approve, report goes forward. Lacking two-thirds approval, report returns to committee.

Report — *Report on Proposals* (ROP) — is published for public review and comment.

Committee meets to act on each public comment received.

Committee votes on comments by letter ballot. If two-thirds approve, supplementary report goes forward.
Lacking two-thirds approval, supplementary report returns to committee.

Supplementary report — *Report on Comments* (ROC) — is published for public review.

▼

NFPA membership meets (Annual or Fall Meeting) and acts on committee report (ROP or ROC).

▼

Committee votes on any amendments to report approved at NFPA Annual or Fall Meeting.

▼

Appeals to Standards Council on Association action must be filed within 20 days of the NFPA Annual or Fall Meeting.

▼

Standards Council decides, based on all evidence, whether or not to issue standard or to take other action, including upholding any appeals.

Committee Membership Classifications

The following classifications apply to Technical Committee members and represent their principal interest in the activity of a committee.

M   *Manufacturer:* A representative of a maker or marketer of a product, assembly, or system, or portion thereof, that is affected by the standard.

U   *User:* A representative of an entity that is subject to the provisions of the standard or that voluntarily uses the standard.

I/M   *Installer/Maintainer:* A representative of an entity that is in the business of installing or maintaining a product, assembly, or system affected by the standard.

L   *Labor:* A labor representative or employee concerned with safety in the workplace.

R/T   *Applied Research/Testing Laboratory:* A representative of an independent testing laboratory or independent applied research organization that promulgates and/or enforces standards.

E   *Enforcing Authority:* A representative of an agency or an organization that promulgates and/or enforces standards.

I   *Insurance:* A representative of an insurance company, broker, agent, bureau, or inspection agency.

C   *Consumer:* A person who is, or represents, the ultimate purchaser of a product, system, or service affected by the standard, but who is not included in the *User* classification.

SE   *Special Expert:* A person not representing any of the previous classifications, but who has special expertise in the scope of the standard or portion thereof.

NOTE 1: "Standard" connotes code, standard, recommended practice, or guide.

NOTE 2: A representative includes an employee.

NOTE 3: While these classifications will be used by the Standards Council to achieve a balance for Technical Committees, the Standards Council may determine that new classifications of members or unique interests need representation in order to foster the best possible committee deliberations on any project. In this connection, the Standards Council may make such appointments as it deems appropriate in the public interest, such as the classification of "Utilities" in the National Electrical Code Committee.

NOTE 4: Representatives of subsidiaries of any group are generally considered to have the same classification as the parent organization.

FORM FOR PROPOSALS ON NFPA TECHNICAL COMMITTEE DOCUMENTS

Mail to: Secretary, Standards Council
    National Fire Protection Association, 1 Batterymarch Park, Quincy, Massachusetts 02269-9101
    Fax No. 617-770-3500

Note: All proposals must be received by 5:00 p.m. EST/EDST on the published proposal-closing date.

> **If you need further information on the standards-making process, please contact the**
> **Standards Administration Department at 617-984-7249.**
> **For technical assistance, please call NFPA at 617-770-3000**

Please indicate in which format you wish to receive your ROP/ROC: ☐ paper ☐ electronic ☐ download
(Note: In choosing the download option you intend to view the ROP/ROC from our website; no copy will be sent to you.)

Date _9/18/93_   **Name** _John B. Smith_   **Tel. No.** _617-555-1212_

Company _____

Street Address _9 Seattle St., Seattle, WA 02255_

Please Indicate Organization Represented (if any) _Fire Marshals Assn. of North America_

1. a) NFPA Document Title _National Fire Alarm Code_   **NFPA No. & Year** _NFPA 72, 1993 ed._

  b) Section/Paragraph _1-5.8.1 (Exception No.1)_

2. Proposal Recommends: (Check one)
  ☐ new text
  ☐ revised text
  ☒ deleted text

FOR OFFICE USE ONLY

Log # _____

Date Rec'd _____

---

3. Proposal (include proposed new or revised wording, or identification of wording to be deleted): (Note: Proposed text should be in legislative format: i.e., use underscore to denote wording to be inserted (inserted wording) and strike-through to denote wording to be deleted (deleted wording).

    Delete exception.

4. Statement of Problem and Substantiation for Proposal: (Note: State the problem that will be resolved by your recommendation; give the specific reason for your proposal including copies of tests, research papers, fire experience, etc. If more than 200 words, it may be abstracted for publication.)

A properly installed and maintained system should be free of ground faults. The occurrence of one or more ground faults should be required to cause a "trouble" signal because it indicates a condition that could contribute to future malfunction of the system. Ground fault protection has been widely available on these systems for years and its cost is negligible. Requiring it on all systems will promote better installations, maintenance and reliability.

5. ☒ This Proposal is original material. (Note: Original material is considered to be the submitter's own idea based on or as a result of his/her own experience, thought, or research and, to the best of his/her knowledge, is not copied from another source.)

☐ **This Proposal is not original material; its source (if known) is as follows:** _____

Note 1: Type or print legibly in black ink.
Note 2: If supplementary material (photographs, diagrams, reports, etc.) is included, you may be required to submit sufficient copies for all members and alternates of the technical committee.

I hereby grant the NFPA all and full rights in copyright, in this proposal, and I understand that I acquire no rights in any publication of NFPA in which this proposal in this or another similar or analogous form is used.

John B. Smith
Signature (Required)

9/99B

FORM FOR PROPOSALS ON NFPA TECHNICAL COMMITTEE DOCUMENTS

Mail to: Secretary, Standards Council
       National Fire Protection Association, 1 Batterymarch Park, Quincy, Massachusetts 02269-9101
       Fax No. 617-770-3500
Note: All proposals must be received by 5:00 p.m. EST/EDST on the published proposal-closing date.

**If you need further information on the standards-making process, please contact the
Standards Administration Department at 617-984-7249.
For technical assistance, please call NFPA at 617-770-3000**

Please indicate in which format you wish to receive your ROP/ROC: ☐ paper ☐ electronic ☐ download
(Note: In choosing the download option you intend to view the ROP/ROC from our website; no copy will be sent to you.)

Date _____**Name** _____ **Tel. No.** _____

Company _____

Street Address _____

Please Indicate Organization Represented (if any) _____

1. a) NFPA Document Title _____**NFPA No. & Year** _____

  b) Section/Paragraph _____

2. Proposal Recommends: (Check one)   ☐ **new text**
                                    ☐ **revised text**
                                    ☐ **deleted text**

FOR OFFICE USE ONLY
Log # _____
Date Rec'd_____

3. Proposal (include proposed new or revised wording, or identification of wording to be deleted): (Note: Proposed text should be in legislative format: i.e., use underscore to denote wording to be inserted (inserted wording) and strike-through to denote wording to be deleted (~~deleted wording~~).

4. Statement of Problem and Substantiation for Proposal: (Note: State the problem that will be resolved by your recommendation; give the specific reason for your proposal including copies of tests, research papers, fire experience, etc. If more than 200 words, it may be abstracted for publication.)

5. ☐ This Proposal is original material. (Note: Original material is considered to be the submitter's own idea based on or as a result of his/her own experience, thought, or research and, to the best of his/her knowledge, is not copied from another source.)

☐ This Proposal is not original material; its source (if known) is as follows: _____

Note 1: Type or print legibly in black ink.
Note 2: If supplementary material (photographs, diagrams, reports, etc.) is included, you may be required to submit sufficient copies for all members and alternates of the technical committee.

    I hereby grant the NFPA all and full rights in copyright, in this proposal, and I understand that I acquire no rights in any publication of NFPA in which this proposal in this or another similar or analogous form is used.

_____
Signature (Required)

PLEASE USE SEPARATE FORM FOR EACH PROPOSAL   9/99C